WITHDRAWN

American Scene: New Voices

American Scene: New Voices

EDITED BY DON M. WOLFE

ALFRED * ASHLOCK * E. BARTLETT * P. BARTLETT
BORDAN * BRYAN * BURRESS * COHEN * CONRAD
CRAZ * DOHERTY * DRURY * DYLLER * EARNSHAW
FIELDS * GRECO * GREVER * GROBIN * HUDSON
JEFFREY * JENKINS * A. JOHNSON * D. J. JOHNSON
KHAN * KING * KOCH * KOTSOGEAN * KRUM
MAGAZINE * McGOVERN * McMAHON * MONT-
GOMERY * NEWBOLD * O'CONNOR * PATRICK
PFEIFFER * PORITZ * POSNER * ROBINSON * ROWE
SAUNDERS * SHEPPARD * SILVERBERG * SUMMERS
TENNEY * THOMPSON * WALDO * WALLANT
WEINBERG * WEINRAUB * WINNER * WOLFSON
ZELDIS

LYLE STUART INC. • NEW YORK

Queries regarding rights and permissions should be addressed to
Lyle Stuart, Inc.
at 239 Park Avenue South, New York 3, N.Y.

Typography by The Polyglot Press

Editorial supervision by Edward Sagarin

Printed in the United States of America

Contents

4. Scars That Vanish and Scars That Stay

5. Sons and Daughters

6. Fathers Look Homeward

7. Orange Blossoms in the Dust

8. The Good Die First

CONTENTS

9. Symmetry in Fire and Ice

Appendix I: Art in a Small Compass

Preface

THIS is a book of stories, sketches, poems, and excerpts from novels by writers new or unknown in American literature. The present authors have their roots in twenty-seven states and countries; their average age is thirty-eight. Some of them, like John Burress, Edward Wallant, Paul Bartlett, Ismith Khan, and Octavia Waldo, have written novels of substantial talent in the past few years; others, like Maurice Posner, Dora Johnson, Amanda Rowe, Peter Kotsogean, and Gwynneth Grobin, are until now unpublished and unknown. The purpose of this volume is to provide for these new voices the hearing they deserve from thoughtful critics. Such a hearing requires a mature critic, one who can see, as Maxwell Perkins saw in Thomas Wolfe, that a unique budding is at hand. Only the seasoned critic can evaluate accurately the first and middle stages of a long apprenticeship still spasmodic and unpredictable.

Many manuscripts in this volume have undergone a long process of revision carried on in conference with the editor or his colleagues. Such a process, described with striking instances by Maxwell Perkins in *From Editor to Writer,* explodes again the illusion of the unwary critic that genius has no inception, no embryo, no childhood, only a sudden miraculous birth of a grown man or woman, like that of Minerva from the head of Zeus. When William Styron's first professional story appeared in *American Vanguard 1948,* no one except the critics and teachers of the New School, particularly Hiram Haydn, and Styron himself, could have hoped that *Lie Down in Darkness* would appear a few years later. In *American Vanguard 1948* also appeared the nucleus of Sigrid de Lima's distinguished novel, *Captain's Beach,* and an excerpt from John Burress' *Little Mule,* which was to receive unanimous critical praise upon its publication in 1952, after five years of rejections by the publishing world. Similarly, in *American Vanguard 1950*, edited by Dr. Charles Glicksberg, appeared Leonard Bishop, whose novel, *Down All Your Streets,* was the culmination of long creative labor and training at the New School; Helen Upshaw, who later was to write *Day of the Harvest;* Bernice Kavinoky, then laboring on *All the Young Summer Days*; Nancy Hallinan, whose creative growth was to bear fruit years later in *Rough Winds of May.* Of the writers in *American Vanguard 1950* Mario Puzo was in some ways most remarkable in his gradual mastery of style and structure that were to make a great theme memorable in *The Dark Arena.* In *New Voices 2* (1955) appeared Edward Wallant's first professional story, "I Held Back My Hand"; it was unheralded and unnoticed. Five years later appeared Wallant's distinguished novel, *The Human Season,* unanimously praised by the critics.

The present volume has been initiated through the cooperation of Lyle Stuart (himself a novelist and former New School student), who believes that such a book would provide a hearing for some dozens of talented writers rooted in many states in the Union but now working for the most part in and around New York. The editor wishes to thank his colleagues at the New School, especially Dr. Charles Glicksberg, without whose tireless encouragement and comradeship this volume could not have gone forward. This volume is also indebted to Clara Mayer, formerly Dean of the New School, whose encouragement of young writers, like that of our perennial youth, Dr. Alvin Johnson, has been continuing and persistent.

D. M. W.

Princeton, New Jersey
November 17, 1962

Introduction:

The Growth of Talent

IT IS IMPOSSIBLE to believe that the number of talented writers emerging on the American scene represents its true potential. Every age produces talent that represents only a fragment of its resources. The Western world has known only a few eras in which genius flourished in that abundance which apparently nature makes possible. It cannot be imagined, wrote Alfred Kroeber, that nature turns the production of genius on and off again, "like a playful faucet." Francis Galton estimated that between 530 B.C. and 430 B.C., one in 4,032 born in Attica became a genius as measured by standards of later ages.

The key to the clustering of genius must be sought, therefore, not in the caprice of nature but in the peculiarly favorable conditions provided by society. After the Athens of Pericles, two great clusterings of genius appeared: the Florence of Michelangelo and the London of Shakespeare. The flowering of New England was still another such time, less prolonged and incandescent than its predecessors, but marked by the same phenomena of intense patriotism, expansion of travel and exploration, and accumulated wealth diverted to the subsidies of writers, artists, and learned men.

Readers will remember that George Eliot's *Romola* opens in a Florentine barber shop at the time of Leonardo. As the customer lies back to be shaved, he sees on the ceiling, looking down at him, a sculptured head. Thus ran the insanity of the day: each store, however humble, cherished a painting or a sculpture or a beautiful bronze or silver bowl. Because the people as a whole cherished art as they cherished good wine, the talented young men went into art as today they turn to electronics or nuclear physics. To this insanity of a populace, Florence owed its prolonged inducement to growth of talent, even as Shakespeare and his fellows, living in an age of nationalist enthusiasm and new world horizons, found their best customers in the penny-paying citizens who filled the pit of the Elizabethan theatre.

There have been many wealthy cities and countries (like America today) without the insanity of art, music, poetry, fiction, and sculpture. But the greatest clusterings of genius thus far have possessed the leisure and the wealth to support the unfolding of genius, which can only flourish when the nation as a whole has first met its primary needs of sustenance and shelter in war and peace.

The remarkable growth of some seventy art centers on the American scene in recent years, the development of civic theatres, and the expansion of courses in creative writing throughout America are evidence that America is more conscious of the need for the development of talent than at any time in its history. In dozens of colleges and universities, English departments are employing talented poets and novelists to teach undergraduates, while continuing to write their own books. This expansion of writing courses is based on the assumption that talent is not the gift of nature; it is the gift of growth, in part obscure and unpredictable, but nevertheless a growth in which no man begins by writing a whole page of magical sentences.

We are all born wordless and languageless. Whatever uniqueness we inherit, it is not the ability to write. The vast range of courses given in creative writing, from those at the humblest college to those taught recently at Harvard by MacLeish, at Iowa by Paul Engle, and at Stanford by Wallace Stegner, are all based on the assumption that talent is in part the mastery of a craft in which there is a predictable apprenticeship.

II

I am always astonished at the statement that writing cannot be taught. This is to my mind as absurd as saying it cannot be learned. Certainly every writer had a teacher, as Shakespeare had his Marlowe and the group at the Mermaid Tavern; more inspiring teachers one cannot imagine. As Bret Harte was Mark Twain's teacher, so Hawthorne taught Melville, and Conrad taught Crane. Say they taught each other; still they had teachers, as Maupassant had Flaubert. Every novelist goes to school to his predecessors and often to his contemporaries, as Faulkner and Hemingway learned from Anderson, and Thomas Wolfe learned much from a great teacher, Maxwell Perkins.

Ah, say the critics (among them John Aldridge), that is different. I mean teaching writing in classes. That is impossible. Such critics forget that there are as many different classes as there are writing teachers. Every young novelist learns in a different way, and almost every teacher I know approaches a novelist as a unique human being who should develop a style of his own and a vision of his own.

At the New School, where I have taught a novel-writing seminar for some years, no two of us approach the teaching of writing in the same way. The young novelists go from teacher to teacher (as they go from writer to writer among themselves), learning as much as they can from each. When they read the great books, they begin to see that Melville or Conrad has achieved in a superlative degree what they have achieved perhaps in only a sentence on a page.

One incandescent image of genuine literary power is a victory; it means that other victories are in the offing; if the writer keeps on, he can eventually write a sentence, then a paragraph, then a whole page of such images. Even a teacher who is not a writer himself can help the young writer thus far. There are a hundred things in the craft of style a young writer can learn from a gifted teacher.

Even when he has an acceptable style, however, the young writer is still far from being a short story writer or a novelist. But he has, let us say, indomitable energy and will for the next steps. Who can advise him? Who can teach him? Many people: his writing teachers, his struggling colleagues, books by writers about their art, but especially great writers, even as Keats buried himself in Shakespeare while he was writing *Endymion*.

The writing teacher can be the coach who knows all the resources, all the teachers, from whom the writer learns. He can show the young writer the structure of the short story, with emphasis on the quality of the dilemma; he can show the writer how to search for the dilemma in his own life that is new in literature and needs to be explored. He can help the writer to depend on himself, to select the criticism of his work that he feels most valid; only the writer can finally decide which road to take in developing his style or choosing a theme of significance for his generation.

III

To the unpublished writer, wavering between creative flight and the certain earth of professional advancement beneath his feet, no question is more pressing or so little delineated as the origin and growth of talent. When a man at twenty or twenty-five decides to give five years to the slow acquisition of talent, he acts on an assumption like that of Milton when he wrote to Diodati, "You ask what I am meditating? By the help of heaven, an immortality of fame. I am letting my wings grow and preparing to fly." To this young man talent is in part a craft learned by apprenticeship, like that of Giotto to Cimabue, or Dickens to Fielding and Smollett.

On the other hand, when an editor or a teacher says to an aspiring writer, "You have no talent and probably never will have," the assumption is that talent for writing has no traceable or dependable apprenticeship. The young writer who accepts the assumption that talent is essentially an inborn magic denied to some and granted to others will usually yield to the unfavorable verdicts of his first professional critics and go his way to professions giving certain rewards and family security.

These are the extremes of the argument for and against inborn talent debated each year in the minds of thousands of young men and women pondering their potential destiny in American literature: extremes which agitate the minds, too, of editors, teachers, and critics who feel a serious responsibility for private or public investment in the nation's reservoir of creative power.

Those critics who hold that genius has no decipherable apprenticeship point justifiably to the sudden blossoming of Stephen

Crane, who wrote *Maggie* at twenty; Truman Capote, a few years out of high school when he wrote *Other Voices, Other Rooms;* Charles Dickens, famous for *Pickwick Papers* before he was twenty-five. True, none of these works justifies the name of genius for its author, as do such books as *Moby Dick, The Scarlet Letter,* or *An American Tragedy,* written after the age of forty.

To some writers even the desire to write has no explicable origin in childhood surroundings. When Helen Upshaw was seven, living in a little Louisiana town, she stood one June morning on her back porch amid a blaze of sunshine and morning-glories. A hummingbird flew through the vines, sunlight glimmering on its wings. Suddenly the child Helen wanted to write a poem. After a few moments of concentration she showed her poem to her mother, who kissed her and praised her words. "I cannot remember a time," says Miss Upshaw, "when I did not want to write."

What is the origin of the hummingbird moment, of Helen Upshaw's self-sustained passion? Pearl Buck writes, "We are wound up before we are born and it is for life." To some critics the mystery of the creative impulse in speech or writing, full and vigirous in some early lives, weak or absent in others, can be explained only by the writer's genetic pattern.

On the side of accident and circumstance, each writer may trace in his own mind moments that ignited his hope and gave direction to his creative energy. Looking back on his early years in *Defensio Secunda,* Milton wrote, "My father destined me from a child to the pursuits of literature." What words from a father, a friend, a stranger, may unknowingly siphon energy toward a creative end?

Living near the Henry Street Settlement on the Lower East Side, Leonard Bishop one day picked up a piece of clay outside a modeling class and threw it into the room. Catching sight of him, the teacher called out, "Come in here a minute, kid, I wanta show ya somethin." When Leonard went inside, the teacher gave him a piece of clay, saying, "Make a statue with it, a dog, a hand, an ear, anything you like." As Leonard's fingers worked, he experienced a transformation: For the first time in his life, he felt he could change something in his harsh environment into a unique expression of his personality.

Such moments as Leonard's and Helen's and a thousand others we cannot yet trace to their roots. Yet those moments of sudden illumination may call forth in time a host of other blazes, some of them explicable. If a parent, a teacher, watched for such a moment from each child, could a nation thus enhance or multiply its creative potential?

What talent the writer may inherit is a question none can now answer from the yet scanty science of man. Certainly man inherits his uniqueness, but does he also inherit unique sentence rhythms, a unique talent for making images, or a unique idea for a work of art? These questions are useful if only to call our attention to the enormous range of apprenticeship patterns in the growth of talent, many of them still undocumented. What can an aspiring young writer do to nourish his ambition, intensify his style, enlarge the resources of his craft, create a design for a novel of permanent worth? Some answers to these questions, however incomplete, may be traced in the experience of master writers.

In this search for apprenticeship patterns, few books are more instructive than Vasari's *Lives,* though apparently remote from writing problems. To Vasari such humble virtues as fiery concentration and prolonged labor were more often than not the keys by which the artist opened the door to supreme artistic achievement. Luca della Robbia spent "all his days in chiseling, and his nights in designing," on cold nights warming his feet in a basket of shavings. "No one ever excels in any worthy exercise," writes Vasari, "who does not begin, while still a child, to support cold and heat, hunger and thirst" for the sake of his creative dream.

Whatever the womb of talent, its birth and growth are inseparable from energy. "The longer I live," writes Pearl Buck, "the less I understand the origins of creative energy." In her judgment the energies of most people are consumed in "growing up, earning a living, marrying and having children and growing old." Beyond these needs and compulsions, the artist has energy to shape his impressions into forms and patterns that he hopes will be imperishable. Miss Buck goes so far as to assert, "A talent is merely a possession to be used by the force of energy."

How can a young writer's energy be diverted from his job, his marriage, his children, to the expression of his talent? We think it nothing remarkable that a youth's daily energies go into his studies for eight or twelve or sixteen years. Yet as a nation we provide few opportunities for the diversion of energy to artistic forms. Such means failing, each young writer must work as an individual to build, conserve, and direct his energy to the expression of his talent.

Mark Twain's boundless energy permitted him to write his first books while earning a living as a reporter and a lecturer. While they wrote their first books, Melville subsisted on his father's bounty, Bernard Shaw on his mother's industry. Until after Ellen Tucker's death, when Emerson was able to live in good part on the income of her estate, he could not give his full energies to literature.

When a gifted man has leisure, he has daily energy which he may now and then transmute into literature. If America by a national fellowship plan enlarged the leisure of every aspiring youth a thousandfold, would the result be a proportionate multiplication of works of art? As yet we have only guesses to answer this crucial question. No nation, not even enlightened Athens, has thus far attempted a collective measure of the genius its energy might unfold.

Often with a sign of talent comes along a vision of one's place in the world of poetry or fiction or painting. In trailing his vision, a youth wishfully or realistically gauges his own potential in the immense scale of human endeavor. Milton as a boy aspired to be a clergyman, then a poet; only after years of meditation did his vision of himself take on a meaning full of portent for centuries of readers and poets to come: to make of himself a great national poet speaking for England as David had done for Israel, Homer for Athens, and Virgil for Rome.

Such a vision finds only one imperfect parallel on the American scene: Walt Whitman. One cannot escape the conviction that the paucity of superlative talent on the American scene may be traced, not to lack of genius, but to lack of soaring aspiration such as Milton hugged daily to his heart. "You ask what I am meditating," he wrote to Diodati. "By the help of heaven an immortality of fame. I am letting my wings grow and preparing to fly."

There can be no greatness of achievement without a sustaining vision of greatness in one's youth. How does a country teach its youth the soaring aspirations of the men and boys who passed Ghiberti and Leonardo or Brunelleschi daily on the streets of Florence or Pericles and Phidias on the streets of ancient Athens? Our greatest deficiency is our failure to hold before our youth those images of greatness that have set boyish imaginations on fire in past ages.

IV

An early vision of oneself may gauge one's potential without tracing the nature of his future creative life. "All through my boyhood," writes Farrell, "I believed I was growing up to have a destiny, to become known to many, to thousands." Yet he pictured himself as a great baseball player, not as a writer.

When Theodore Dreiser was sixteen, as he tells us in *Dawn*, while he was working in a Chicago hardware store, an older fellow-worker named Christian Aaberg introduced him to the world of great books and ideas. Aaberg convinced him that "mind, and mind alone, makes the essential difference between the masses and the classes. . . . Either I had it or I did not have it. If I had it, I might do much; if not, nothing." Dreiser feverishly began to read. His estimate of himself mounted. However low his salary, he had a mind. "One could rise! One could rise!" Between this new vision of his powers, still undefined in application, and his conception of himself as the artist architect of *An American Tragedy*, Dreiser wrestled with aspirations of many shapes and colors; one aspiration gives birth to another, in the artist's mind still more glorious than the last, if often frustrated in the end.

Wihout early visions of limited or unworthy perspective, then, there can be no superb aspirations of later years. "Living in solitude till the fullness of time was come," wrote Hawthorne of his own vision, "I still kept the dew of my youth and the freshness of my heart." An early vision may change in a few brief years, like that of Mark Twain from the outlook of a frontier humorist to that of a great novelist and social critic. The gap between the Melville of *Typee* and the Melville of *Moby Dick:* the result of Melville's new vision of his powers.

In Steinbeck's career, the gap between *Tortilla Flat* and *The Grapes of Wrath*, or between *Of Mice and Men* and *East of Eden*, should be perennial refreshment to every young writer distrustful of his powers. For genius is growth, not genetic magic: but growth first of an aspiration. "He grew slowly," writes Ruth Firor of Thomas Hardy, "but he grew till the day of his death." Steinbeck at sixty is still growing; whereas Hemingway's powers as a novelist were never more maturely realized than in *A Farewell to Arms*, written in his twenties.

In 1958 I heard Faulkner speak at the Nassau Club at Princeton. I can never forget him as he stood before us that evening, dressed impeccably in brown, a short gray-haired man with a gray moustache, his speech rhythmical as ballet steps and pointed as a rapier, answering the most barbed question with a courtesy and illumination that reduced the imagined faults of the man to sudden ashes. He said, as I recall, that he had never finished a book without a deep despair at viewing the gap between his vision and the ultimate reality. Yet he never began a new book without a great hope built up that he would this time write the great novel he knew lay within his powers. Looking back, I cannot think that Faulkner would write any greater novel than *Light in August*; but this work I cannot imagine Faulkner would have placed beside *The Brothers Karamazov* or *The Mayor of Casterbridge*. Yet in "Barn Burning," it seems to me, Faulkner has written as piercing and classic a short story as one finds in American literature. In this story, more than in any other achievement of Faulkner, his vision of himself filled the mold of reality to the brim.

V

The writing of autobiography is a recurring and indispensable ingredient of the author's apprenticeship. Only through autobiography, from the earliest fumblings in adolescence to the incandescent diction one finds in the last pages of *The Woodlanders* or Camus' *The Fall*, does the writer discover his unique materials or that authentic voice that represents the essence of his personality.

xviii

Even in the earliest autobiographies a skillful critic may discern the quality of dilemma or setting which no other writer in embryo possesses. In Peter Kotsogean's story, "Anemones," an American buries his Greek wife and child, slaughtered by the enemy. Without such a narrative, written long after the event, when life has nibbled away at the heartbreak of death, a novel on the same theme cannot take shape in the writer's imagination.

As no work of imagination such as *Othello* is without autobiography in its very diction, so no autobiography is without additions from the imagination. Art makes a harmony truthful to the writer's vision of life, a vision supported by selected actual and imaginary scenes, not sequential ones. But how can any great work of art, however far removed from particular scenes of the author's life, be devoid of the deepest autobiography of thought and feeling?

The best writing wisdom is to go back to one's roots, whatever one's obscurity or fame, as both Faulkner and Steinbeck have done in their best books, both men returning time after time to the land and people who moved them unfailingly to depths of thought and feeling no strange town or face could call forth. I do not deny that some of the greatest books have sprung from the imagination, such as the *Antigone* of Sophocles and the *Faust* of Goethe. But how much of *War and Peace* is autobiography? How much of *Buddenbrooks?* How much of *The Brothers Karamazov?*

When Dostoievsky wrote, "Precious memories may remain even of a bad home, if the heart knows how to find what is precious," he was tracing a deep tunnel of his own memories. But the story of the Grand Inquisitor is a master stroke of the imagination.

VI

What are the early signs and omens of a creative talent? To this question critics and writers give curiously varied answers. Milton took an early sign to be the ease with which he could imitate the master poets. Later, after more experimentation and praise from Italian literati, he became convinced that his poetic style, "by certain vital signes it had, was likely to live."

Elements of a unique stylistic magic have usually appeared early, as in the sketches of Dostoievsky and Dickens, the reportorial accounts of Tolstoi at Sebastopol and Mark Twain in the Sandwich Islands. An important sign is the sense that a writer or his critics may have from a single page of the confident flow of a style as unique in flavor as that of Faulkner or Melville. In this volume, for example, I have this feeling about a single page of William Alfred's "Stand by Me, Kate," Maurice Posner's "We Steal the Coal," Dora Johnson's "Paid with Moan," Claude Koch's "Fiddler's Bow," and Chayym Zeldis' "Burial." I know of no other writer who has a stylistic flow such as Charles Bryan achieves in "Through the August Night," Helen Hudson in "Sunday Mourning," Mildred Jeffrey in "Persephone Lost."

At eighteen or twenty the writer may be able to achieve only a line of stylistic uniqueness on a page; ten years later his style may glow and burn in every sentence.

Another early sign may be the writer's power to communicate more fully than his fellows his mastery of one department of experience, such as James Farrell relates about his debate on baseball in a Chicago classroom. A creative boy's choice of a theme may in itself foreshadow a unique creative bent, such as Farrell's early composition about two boys who talked and acted in a tough manner but really did not want to fight each other. A cast of mind flowing free into prose or verse, such as Hawthorne's tone of somber mystery, Twain's saber-like humor, Sigrid de Lima's compassionate appraisal of life's dead ends, John Burress' sense of wonder in the lives of simple people, the free flowing of such an outlook in early writing years is a sign of high hope for the flourishing growth of a creative mind.

VII

The young writer cannot reach his full stature while shutting the curtains to the world's ills. If his duty is to interpret man, as John Maloney asserts, not solve his problems, he must consider that the greatest art is also the most permanent propaganda for the values in which he believes. *The Scarlet Letter* is timeless propaganda for honesty in the definition of marriage: but how is the definition of marriage to be separated in any era from the exigencies of social reform?

When a writer bores deep down into the frustrations of a unique man or woman, he cannot help clarifying consciously or unconsciously the social concomitants of personal despair. In Willa Cather's "A Wagner Matinee," for example, we have a portrait of Aunt Georgiana, a woman apparently remote from problems of social salvation. From thirty years of existence on an ugly Nebraska farm, where she has borne six children and labored for over a decade without seeing a musical instrument, Aunt Georgiana returns to Boston, where she attends a Wagner program with her nephew.

In her early life in New England, before eloping with Howard Carpenter, Aunt Georgiana had been a pianist and a teacher of music. Slowly the symphony arouses the memory of cherished beauty: "It never really dies, then—the soul which can suffer so excruciatingly and so interminably; it withers to the outward eye only; like that strange moss which can lie on a dusty shelf half a century, and yet, if placed in water, grows green again."

At the end of the story Aunt Georgiana breaks into tears and sobs, "I don't want to go, Clark, I don't want to go!" In contrast to this reassertion of the soul's greenness is the ugliness of pioneer life to which Georgiana must now return: "the tall unpainted house with the weather-curled boards, naked as a tower; the crook-backed ash ceilings where the dishclothes hung to dry; the gaunt moulting turkeys picking up refuse about the kitchen door."

At first glance, as Willa Cather intended, "A Wagner Matinee" is a portrait of Aunt Georgiana, seduced on one side by the beauty clasped in youth and driven on the other by family ties knotted amid insufferable ugliness. But it is true that millions of Aunt Georgianas have been "carried out where the myriad graves are, into the gray, nameless burying grounds of the sea, or into some world of death vaster yet, where, from the beginning of the world, hope has lain down with hope and dream with dream and, renouncing, slept."

Not Aunt Georgiana alone, but the pervading tragedy, must be the artist's concern. The answer to Aunt Georgiana's riddle is to be sought neither in acquiescing in her suffering nor in the renunciation of her dreams. The prevailing ugliness of frontier homes, the spiritual barrenness of long labor, whether in farm slum or city slum, the nagging torment of survival, that destroyer of dreams and dreamers—these realities will vanish only under the impact of social resolution and cooperative spearheads. In "A Wagner Matinee" Willa Cather has rendered the artist's timeless service of planting a question so deep in human life that you and I, and the generations to come, seek desperately an answer.

No great art, then, is without social meaning, and the greatest art possesses the deepest social meaning; but it is part of the true artist's detachment that he acts, as in *The Scarlet Letter,* as an interpreter of the question for a unique character, rather than as the voice of the answer for us all.

Not only will the artist plant deep questions that require new answers from each generation, but he will probe the deep recesses of the nature of man and leave in his books the crystal insight of his probing. Of Zola's great scheme of fiction Henry James wrote, "His general subject in the last analysis was the nature of man; in dealing with which he took up, obviously, the harp of most numerous strings. His business was to make these strings sound true, and there was none that he did not, so far as his general economy permitted, persistently try." But Zola, like Dreiser and Farrell, could record more deftly the nether reaches of man's nature than the upper. As *L'Assommoir* portrays the degradation of man buffeted by poverty and ignorance, and Henry James the middle stations of man's flight, Thomas Hardy in Tess and Michael Henchard delineates the triumph of man's soaring spirit.

Of such infinite range is man that great books have emerged from all levels of his behavior. But as Browning wrote in *Pauline,* "a perfect bard was one who shadowed forth the stages of all life." Except from the insight of a Shakespeare, a Fielding, a Cervantes, a Hardy, this is a perspective to be hoped for rather than expected. These artists, like Tolstoi and Dostoievski, have approached the nature of man humbly, without predilections, their eyes on the world beyond the window, sensing the magic of ideas, the impersonal cruelty of encircling whips, objectifying evil not in man, but in the forces beyond him.

Such a great artist, like Thomas Hardy, it is futile to describe as a pessimist or a fatalist: he is rather a superb analyst of cause and effect, superstitious neither about the inheritance of sadism and cruelty nor the genetic transmission of divinity. "If the way to the Better there be," asserted Hardy, "it exacts a full look at the Worst."

To look at the worst in man is not necessarily to pigeonhole his nature at the chimpanzee level. In the supreme artist it is rather to trace beyond man the seeds of his behavior in forces and patterns beyond his choice. The artist senses that the priceless ingredient of human nature is not free will, but plasticity. If man yields to the poisons of sadism and hatred, he yields by the same magic process to the persuasions of a St. Francis, a Thomas More, an Abraham Lincoln.

VIII

To select material from the stock of memories is a genuinely creative effort only when the author compels belief in his unique world with sharpened images no one else can muster. "To evoke in oneself a feeling one has once experienced," wrote Tolstoi in *What is Art?*, "then by means of movement, lines, colours, sounds, or forms expressed in words, so to transmit that feeling that others experience the same feeling—this is the activity of art."

The essence of particularity is this visualization, profuse and massed, as in Wolfe, Lewis, and Dreiser, or selective and sparing, as in Hawthorne, Cather, and Stephen Crane. A torrent of images, throwing structure awry, may uncover unexpectedly an outpost of mind or motive, leaving a more thorough record than any yet set down.

For this illumination, rarely in the short story, often in the novel, we gladly digress; and the young author, as in Sinclair Lewis's description of the store windows of Gopher Prairie, may risk profuse imagery with less danger than sparse, especially if through it he releases the flow of his rhythm resources. But even from the mass of images emerges a decisive and unforgettable one that pierces the mind with a lifelong memory: like the single stone in Wordsworth's "Michael," the moulting turkeys and cattle tracks in "A Wagner Matinee," the dead goldfinch in *The Mayor of Casterbridge,* the red bandanna handkerchief in "Tennessee's Partner," the leather thongs in Hector's ankles and the dust around his bobbing head. Such a culminating image Kenneth Henry has used with startling power in "The Wake" of the rosary beads scattered over the carpet at the moment of the hero's capitulation to hatred and despair. Such images in this volume are the mother's love felt on the fire escape in Gwynneth Grobin's "The Seed of a Giant"; the face of Joe in the coffin in "Stranger at a Wake"; the sheets over the mirrors in "Where Is My Father?"; the butter biscuit in "Paid with Moan"; the mother with her arm around her younger son in "Proud Words."

In selection of the sharpened image, the safe guide for the young writer, as for the old, is not invention, but experience. But nothing takes the place of the imagined calamity image, such as that of the wings struggling with the drop of ink at the end of Mansfield's "The Fly."

One of the first tasks of the young writer is to release from his memory streams of authentic images carrying with them, as in Ismith Kahn's "In Search of Stella" and Lily Poritz' "The Circle on the Grass," the confident language rhythms of an independent spirit. Only in this flow of personality can he achieve the integration of his creative forces, sensory, emotional, and philosophical, as does Dostoievsky in *The House of the Dead,* Melville in *White Jacket,* Wolfe in *Look Homeward, Angel.*

Like these men, the young writer must have confidence that relentless delineation of his own unique life will bear a unique vitality, resisting what Edith Wharton calls "that common symptom of immaturity, the dread of doing what has been done before."

Any childhood fully recorded will call up universal patterns: rejection by a brother one loves as in Jack Fields' "Alex," the first day of womanhood, the first emission, the first detached impression of a father as a person, the first impact of death, strike no two lives with identical shadows or effects. By recording any experience in the full flow of impassioned memory, enclosing both the relevant and the apparently irrelevant images, the young writer makes his experience unique in proportion as he extracts from it the uttermost differentiation. "You must squeeze out of yourself every sensation," wrote Joseph Conrad, "every thought, every image,—mercilessly, without reserve and without remorse: you must search the darkest corners of your heart, the most remote recesses of your brain,—and you must search them for the image, for the glamour, for the right expression."

To achieve the free flow of one's creative powers enforces a temporary disregard of classic form and structure. Thomas Wolfe's record of the ride through Virginia in *Of Time and the River* was as long as a novel in its original form; but this waiving of proportion was a necessary consequence of Wolfe's fierce hunger for exhaustive delineation of life. In this sense the novel provides a more suitable medium for the young writer than the short story, accommodating itself easily to digressions incidental, even irrelevant, to requirements of form, but crucial to the illumination of the author's unique vitality.

VIII

From the dominant themes of childhood and love the young writer often turns by one path or another into the crucial social dilemmas of his day. As Arthur Koestler points out in "The Novelist's Temptations," the artist is like a man sitting at a window as he writes, aware or not of the world outside. If the writer chooses, he can, like Henry James, immerse himself in the inner life of his characters, closing the curtains to the outside world, insulating his spirit against the madding crowd, the blackened slum, the bones of the gas chamber, the black man dangling from the rope, the eyes of children crying for bread, the words of Vanzetti before his execution.

Still another choice of the novelist is that of Thackeray and Hawthorne: he may observe with a telescope one segment of the world outside, mastering the intricacies and subtleties of one great theme or one segment of the social scene. Then, too, the novelist may become so absorbed in the outside world that he can no longer remain aloof. He injects himself vehemently into that world, as did Sinclair in *The Jungle* and Norris in *The Octopus,* losing somewhat of the detachment of the artist in the documentation of the boiling present.

Finally the novelist may, like Tolstoi and Dreiser, preserve artistic equilibrium with the window wide open, his spirit heavy with the labor of slaves, the shadow of the atom bomb, the ragged Greek at the mountain top, the Palestinian astride his tractor; yet with his creative faculties in such profound equilibrium that his people, like Levin, Clyde Griffiths, and Anna Karenina, live and breathe long after the old ills of society have passed away. What novelist has penned a more damning indictment of Czarist Russia than has Tolstoi in *Resurrection*? Yet Tolstoi has bestowed on Katusha and Nekludoff unique and unforgettable characters.

A writer may well spend a year on one short story to gain mastery of structure alone, writing and rewriting, studying meanwhile the dilemma presented in such stories as Conrad's "Heart of Darkness," Fitzgerald's "Babylon Revisited," Cather's "The Sculptor's Funeral," Galsworthy's "The Apple Tree." Gradually the time comes when the writer conceives for his story a series of dramatic scenes pointed to one interior dilemma, avoiding the entrapment of flashbacks, mingling dialogue, action, and description in each scene.

Once a writer understands the necessity for a march of scenes, varied in mood, place, and stylistic resources, he is ready to concentrate on the poignancy of the dilemmas and road blocks in the life about him, visualizing the scenes in his mind. "So often when I hear a story in my class," said Martha Foley once, "my mind itches to take hold and see how I would fashion it." This is the expectant feeling of the experienced craftsman who sees instantly the potential of a new dilemma, extending its meaning in scenes from the imagination.

IX

One of the surest ways to learn the structure of a novel is to complete the first draft while fired with the theme, then seek advice from a trusted editor or critic, and think through the structure again. On this point Ellen Glasgow writes, in *The*

Woman Within, "Of all my later books I had written three drafts, the first for vitality and vividness of theme and of characterization, the second, for arrangement and balance of scene and of structure, and the third, for style and manner and the effort toward an unattainable perfection."

The greatest temptation of the novelist is the use of materials irrelevant to his theme, though fascinating in themselves. In such a book as *Look Homeward, Angel,* the theme is so broad and the structure is so loose that Wolfe could insert a great many episodes of childhood and youth without a central meaning; but in a closely knit novel such as *Lord Jim* or *Cry, the Beloved Country* or Sigrid de Lima's *The Swift Cloud,* the writer must conceive of each chapter as heightening the dilemma of the hero in relation to the complex of forces and people who surround him.

Among the great range of apprenticeship patterns, some, then, we may trace with assurance; others are still hidden in the mysterious alchemy of the creative mind unaware of its workings, knowing only that in a certain mood and after long travail a story, a novel emerged that satisfied the unique demands of the writer upon himself. Perhaps no other master has sought isolation, like Hawthorne, to preserve freshness and youth; but every writer must live long months, sometimes years, in enforced isolation, steeping himself in the seminal creations, mastering humbly the techniques of his craft, trusting to the ultimate emergence of his unique self.

I do not deny that the richest gifts of the creative man are such a mysterious outgrowth as to be unteachable to another. No writer indeed without destroying himself can follow mechanically the dictates of his teachers or the models of his masters. The imitations of Hemingway's style now in vogue (and worse, still, the imitation of Hemingway themes and attitudes) have spread wide desolation among budding American writers. Though Hemingway has a "special charm" for critics like John Aldridge, in *After the Lost Generation,* what great books his imitators have produced Mr. Aldridge omits to say.

The young writer would do well to study Faulkner, Conrad, Cather, and Dreiser, whose stature as creative artists has been reinforced by a mature intellectual outlook lacking in Hemingway and his disciples. In his vision of life no writer, however young, needs to be an imitator. The young writer should search himself for the exact emotional and intellectual coloring of his vision of American life. Here he should allow himself no teacher but the roots of his childhood and the gradual shaping of the moods and values he cherishes most, as distinct and memorable as those in Ellen Glasgow's *Vein of Iron* or D. H. Lawrence's *Sons and Lovers*.

X

The young writer can take a hundred short steps toward professional stature before trusting exclusively his own conceptions of style, theme, and structure. The more creative the writer, the more teachable he is, the more receptive to the response of the reader and the suggestions of his critics. The less talented the novice, the quicker his anger when his writing is under fire. Nothing is more vital to a writer than an unerring sense of the reader's response to a page of his writing; the more creative the beginner, the more quickly he makes imaginative use of criticism, searching for the modicum of truth on which he can build a more mature creative outlook.

It is easier for the young writer to trust in his own undeveloped genius than to ways of slow growth traced for him by his critics and teachers. Yet writing, like music and painting, whatever the touch of genius, the sign of talent, requires a slow accumulation of skills, the growth of a mature critical sense, the habit of close and accurate observation. "He wants for purpose of his craft," wrote Sherwood Anderson, "to develop to the highest pitch his own senses . . . He is continually watching others, noting the way in which people walk, the way they hold their heads, the shape and meaning of their hands."

The steps by which a writer learns the art of observation, the elements of an electric style, the requirements of design, are limited only by the energy he channels to these ends. Whatever trickle of genius nature bestows upon him at birth, the writer finds that talent is the result of toil resolution, and the willingness to pay in years of trial for the possession of the tools of the craft and the insight of the artist. He should remeber, too, that even after he writes a work of art the world may still shun him as it did Hawthorne. "Here I sat," he wrote, "waiting patiently for the world to know me, and sometimes wondering why it did not know me sooner, or whether it would ever know me at all—at least till I were in my grave."

What talent is inborn none of us can gauge. What talent the young writer can build for himself, though the unique stamp of one author's personality must remain unteachable to another, bulks large and traceable and infinitely valuable among America's human resources. As in the golden age of Florence, when one master learned from another, and a thousand young artists burned with energy to emulate the skills and genius of their great contemporaries, so in America talent grows apace when writers assemble in groups and take fire with old dreams each time a comrade, like Edward Wallant with his *The Human Season*, publishes a new novel. Who is Wallant? A few years ago he was unknown, living and writing in obscurity, as many of his predecessors at the New School had done: Leonard Bishop, Mario Puzo, William Styron, Sigrid de Lima.

When a young writer watches in an unknown comrade a long struggle of years end in triumph, at least the march of chapters, the theme strong and clear in the opening pages, the resources varied, the unique rhythms of a confident spirit strong on every page, then he knows that talent can grow in himself, too, and in thousands of creative minds yet untouched by the spur of fame, but groping as in a narrow tunnel toward a chink of light.

Nature is not so capricious as to produce in Athens a thousand geniuses and deny them, twenty centuries later, to Chicago and Los Angeles and Atlanta. Every generation gives birth to creative minds. But alas for the tares, the stony ground! The creative minds await only the fire of the dream in their teachers, their friends, and the proof of its reality in themselves; then they build apace the resources of talent and give birth perhaps at last to a work of genius as well.

—Don M. Wolfe

Paul M. Wolfe

1. Love of a Kind

In Search of Stella

EXCERPT FROM A NOVEL BY ISMITH KHAN

THE STREET itself runs for a single block. There are still some streets like that in New York City; one short diagonal mistake on the drafting-board for snow to fall upon, inch upon inch, foot upon foot in winter; for wind to blow through in the autumn, stop like a child chasing a ball that has run down the gutter, then turn and run back up the street at a slower pace, forlorn and puzzled. I have seen the wind look puzzled on this street.

It is a street of parked cars incongruously tilted half up on the sidewalk. It is a narrow street. There is a painter's studio in a basement with an arrow pointing the way; on the sharp angle of the arrow is written in a fine feminine hand: gallery. And in the summer there rises from the basement that sweet smell of turpentine, and paints and oils, and canvases recently finished. And from a few doors away there is the smell of dough of Italian bread in that strange little bakery with its ever empty glass cases. And in the very next door, I have wondered if the young matron with a tight bun who sews and minds the antique shop really came from the time and place of all the rag dolls, the magic lanterns and spinning wheels which surround her.

The street has its own quiet as you turn onto it, for you have left behind all those harsh noises, those horns and hurrying eyes; yet, it is not a quiet of death and decay, but one of lives being lived out, perhaps not as frantic as on the avenue you have left behind, but slowly and deliberately, with the quiet sound of teeth that grind upon themselves in sleep.

And since the street is so unfrequented, it is not unusual in the summer, after the pavements crack, to see a pale green stalk, a blade of unknown grass, pushing through the sidewalk. And

3

in the late summer, its top has been knocked off, its body bruised and blackened with crankcase oil as cars have driven over and stood above it, both as executioner and deliverer. And then in the autumn, the grass turns a mirrored gold, snaps and crumbles into flecks of golden dust beside the oil marks, then blows away.

I have seen this street in many lights. I have seen the people of the street in many lights, or so I think. Of one thing I am certain, I have seen Stella in many lights; or so I think, I do not know. But since it is possible that you yourself may be the one who is changing, attributing your changing tempers to others, reading your moods into their lives, it is better to reserve judgment.

I remember how I loved New York that May morning, loved the thought that I was going to call this city "home." As I rode downtown in the subway to Stella's apartment, I kept thinking, "This city is mine. I shall make it know that I am here, that I have come from nowhere to spend the mornings, evenings, afternoons . . ." I felt that hunger for all of its streets and alleyways. And even then I knew that it had heard my voice and answered that above were the streets and the houses, the stores and apartment buildings and the eight million lives that would keep me company, and that was a feeling of such intense joy, paralleled only by those dreams you dream of finding your lover at first sight; she moves toward you and takes you by the hand without a word.

I do not mean that I had come to this city like some conqueror; I have no conquering blood in my being. I do not mean to say by all this that I had come to climb to dizzy heights. I did not come to be a millionaire tycoon nor at the same time to sit in all-night cafeterias with old men's smoke from stale cigars and dried out watermelon slices that will make tomorrow's fruit salads in the cafeterias.

I came because of a quiet horror that steals across my soul in summer back in Lansing, Michigan, and the faces of the quiet gaunt old men who sit in dress suits in front of the Hotel Clinton and the Calhoun Palace at home. I came to erase those places and those faces from my brain. I came because I was tired of the sprawling flat distances of the Midwest. I came because all

4

the Great Lakes are not the Atlantic Ocean, and I have always wanted to be near to the sea. I came because we had talked about New York over many coffee cups across the street from the campus, all of my friends had gone on ahead of me, and now I was finished with school, and then, too, I think I came because of Stella.

Some moments are like music felt. Some visions of a street like love possessed. Some days are etched out on your consciousness with a glimpse of eternity . . . you know that no one nor anything can take away that ecstasy, that it will stay with you forever, and then when you meet other people, when you see the same ecstasy in their faces, when you feel the infectiousness of the day spreading and growing from their eye sockets to their ankle bones, when you listen to the golden voices of your friends mounting, climbing, as they speak of things they have been doing in this magic city, and you feel their excitement, you know that they will do great things one day.

It was morning on that one-block street, one of those languorous mornings when you feel the perspiration prick your skin in pinpoints, then grow into balls which roll down your skin, and as the wind fans against your body, you feel its life pulsing in all its cells, begging to walk, to run, to take to the sea before its season. I knew that Stella slept late into the mornings. She would work far into the night at her painting, then go out for coffee, or for what she used to call "unwinding." We had met quite by chance a few times back in school at the little restaurant called the Kewpee Doll across from the campus. In a way I have always admired, rather envied, the kind of energy she always had. She seemed ready to go on until morning at those times, while I am more or less finishing off the day at that hour, but then I am up by the first light of day and have used up my time, if you can put it that way.

I had my last cup of coffee at Kewpee's as a sort of farewell gesture to the campus. The Greyhound Station is right next door, I told myself, so that I would not have to call it nostalgia. It was then that I started wondering about Sid and Stella, who were usually together on those evenings, but the feeling was that they were good friends, and I really thought for the first time that I

5

had not known Sid at all. I did not even know where he lived, and probably the only reason he stays in my mind is because he has the kind of face and looks that I place among the very few men I think of as good looking, and when Stella left a year ago, I passed him on the campus once or twice with only a nod. It never occurred to me to ask him if he had heard from Stella, although I had from time to time, and yet, he never asked me if I had heard from her either.

From the time I got on the Greyhound bus the evening before, I kept thinking of all these things and all the things she must have been doing up to this moment. We had parted very simply, again at Kewpee's and, as usual, I had left her and Sid and gone home earlier. "When you come to New York, you must look me up," she had said. Was she going in a day? A week? I don't think I really knew, but she was going to New York to study, to paint, to haunt the art galleries and museums, and with a few letters exchanged during that year, here I was at last, I thought.

I was envious of all the people on the streets for having been here, lived here . . . their faces were a pleasure to watch, the bodies of girls in slacks and their casual hair styles on the way to their Saturday shopping. They moved almost with a kind of display of their bodies that had been covered up all winter, and now each muscle, each curve and undulation, came as a reminder of something beautiful but long lost or forgotten which had had life breathed into it again. Do we really forget how a woman's body looks during the long winter, I wondered, or do we have during those months the kind of remembered vision such as one who has lost his sight does of all these things?

And in the streets I wanted to stop and look long at everything, down to the screwdrivers, the locks and lamp bulbs, the drills and saws and magic cements crowded in the hardware store. Feeling that pull of pleasure as I thought of Stella waiting, I felt like a child stretching out the sweetness of the second best in a box of biscuits, saving the best one for last. As I walked along the avenue, I passed one of those long deep bars where it is eternal night, down to the smells that come pouring out of them. Night smells, I thought, like a sour note in a symphony. There were people inside the bar already, mostly men, looking out from their

6

darkness into the street. I hurried past, I do not know why; I did not want their eyes to meet mine.

At the corner of this improbable street is a small restaurant nestled into the point of a wedge that the street makes with an adjoining street. There are stools and a few small tables where men in shirt sleeves were having breakfast. It must have been about ten-thirty or eleven. Some of them were reading newspapers beside their plates, and one girl had a book propped up against a sugar shaker. This was not a scene of people shoveling food down their gullets, but one of leisureliness and long hours in the day for small indulgences, like more coffee, because the first cup had gone cold instead of being emptied down two at a time on the run.

The table and the counter in the restaurant were made of a heavy unfinished wood with all the softer pulp worn away from age and use, leaving a high brown grain, smoothed and shined by use and time, like the body of someone who has used it for all the natural purposes for which it was intended. "I'm going to have breakfast just like that one of these days, long and leisurely, many, many breakfasts like that," I thought.

I supposed that Stella must have come in here many times, sat like that girl, her book propped up the same way, and spent a leisurely hour or more having breakfast. It was very different from the hundreds, thousands, of students on campus (there were twenty thousand at State) cramming down cereal, toast, two cartons of milk, pounding the bottom of the catsup over scrambled eggs . . . all to be downed in time to catch an eight o'clock class. "I'm not one for huge breakfasts," I remember Stella saying, "and if it is unreasonable to dislike people who are, or those who consume vast quantities of food, then I have to own up, it is my way."

The building could not be more than a few doors away now; whichever end of the street you started on, number twelve would have to be close by. As I thought this, my heart leaped, and I suddenly wondered: What if Stella wasn't home? What if she had gone away for the weekend? She would have received my letter, but how was she to know that I would simply check in my suitcase at the bus stop on Thirty-Fourth Street and come right down here. Perhaps she would expect me to settle into a hotel or an apartment and then call her up one day after I had straightened myself out. I wondered how I had come to bring myself all this way with so many expectations, which had by now become fact and taken for granted, while in truth there had been no reason for them whatsoever?

As I entered the small alcove off the street, there was a little stooped man polishing the brass mail boxes and name plates. He was dressed in one of those gray uniforms that janitors wear, with his name "Charlie" stitched out in red on the shirt pocket.

"Morning," I said, scanning the names on the bells. He went on with his polishing, paying no attention to me. I noticed that he had one of those hearing-aid plugs stuck in his ear, so I tried again.

"Do you know if Miss Barrow is in?" I said a little louder.

He must have heard me this time, even if he did not hear just what I said, because he moved slightly enough to let me look at the name plates. He waved a sallow vein-tormented hand at the brass plaque where I saw her name under apartment five. I pushed the button, and the little man stood with his head cocked to one side, looking me up and down like some common thief. His baby-blue eyes had a tremor in them that drew those seconds out into minutes as I waited. He had a great bunch of keys at his side, one of which I was sure could open the door and let me in. But no, he kept looking me up and down as if to say, "All right, mister . . . let's see if you really know someone here who'll let you in, 'cause I sure as hell ain't." For the most part I walk with my eyes to the ground. I rarely look people in the face, but now I put my hands to my hips and started looking at him in much the same way he looked me over. It is amazing how people freeze up and change and get all flustered when you take this tack. It's as if you let them know that you speak their own language and can kick in a few of the choice words they won't use too often. He fumbled a little, his eyes fell back to his polishing cloth, and he went back to his work. Just then the bell rang, and I walked in. I saw his dirty little eyes go over my hand as I took hold of the newly polished door knob, and all the way through the corridor, I could feel his eyes piercing into my back.

8

The tunneled corridor ran beside the front apartment. At the end, it opened on to a small garden with jet black earth divided up in an irregular pattern like cracked marble. The black earth was wet, as if someone had just watered it, and loose rose petals of pink and deep red had fallen from the many rose bushes in the garden. At the far side, against a wall, was a half-circle pond with a drip-drip-drip of water from the mouth of a lion or some other animal's head. There were bright orange-colored fish in the pond that broke and at the same time added to the wonderful silence as they jumped past the surface and fell into the water again.

The most pleasant of surprises is not to be surprised at all, but to find your expectations, your anticipations answered down to every detail. This was Stella, this street, this garden. It is hard to say just what I expected, or just what I had in mind when I had thought of her and where she lived, yet I was reminded only of thousands of possible things I had formulated in my mind and associated with Stella, so that for me, although I had little by way of fact, I nonetheless had a complete picture of her at all times, and this delightful little garden with its bent rose bushes touching the ground only added to my feeling that you could know someone intimately with the fewest of meetings and exchanges of conversation.

Stella lived in one of the rear apartments. There were four of them, two above, two below, each with two windows looking out on the garden with passageway in the center above which were brass numerals, 5, 6, 7, 8. As I entered the passageway, I heard a door open to my right. She's on the ground floor, I thought, and then I thought of the rain, that you could hear the rain falling on the garden if you lived on the ground floor. It was something I missed in those huge dormitories at State, and I knew, without ever having asked Stella, that she too would have agreed that there is an unusual feeling, one of incompleteness only to see the rain falling in thin long threads of opalescence, and never hear the small mouths of the earth open in their thirst for its drops.

9

The Cardboard Screen

BY HOLLIS SUMMERS

I T HAD BEEN a mistake to invite them, but at the moment it had seemed as natural as the breeze which pulled at the soft ribbons of the heaped flowers. Della had not closed her eyes during the benediction; she looked steadily at the yellow glads she and Charlie had sent. One streamer of the white ribbon flipped itself over at the Amen. She turned; she lifted her feet high so that she would not step on any graves, even the old ones, and moved to each of the girls. "We'll sew tomorrow," Della said. "As usual." Her face felt drawn from not crying, as if she were a child who had left soap to dry on her skin. Her mother had always said, "Be sure and dry your face, Della." And all of their mothers had told them not to step on the graves. Other Junes they had walked through the cemetery with their mothers, taking a short cut to the park.

Betty Kay bobbed her head; her eyes were squeezed tight; she pressed her gloved hand hard against her mouth. Winifred's eyes swam almost invisible in her tears, but she smiled down at Della. "We'll sew tomorrow as usual." Three times Della said the words. Lillian did not cry, but her face looked as old as her mother's face beside her. Of course the woman who wore Lillian's suit was Lillian. Della was conscious of the woof and warp of the linen. She thought, as briefly as the ribbon's flip, that she should pat Lillian's arm. Instead, she went to find Charlie, her own invitation still in her ears. "We'll sew tomorrow, Della," she said to herself. None of the girls had answered her.

In the car Charlie said, "It was a nice service."

"What are we going to do, Charlie?" she asked before she thought of what to say.

She could not look at his face. His shoe pressed against the gas pedal, then relaxed. He was wearing the black shoes she had bought for him a long time ago. They needed polishing. "But I got black shoes," Charlie said. "They're so old, the other ones. You need black shoes when you dress up," Della said. Dust lay on the shoes. It was dust from Charlie's closet. The cemetery was green.

"Della, look at me," the man in the old black shoes said. "I love you, Della."

The car trembled. If she closed her eyes perhaps she could know which person in Charlie's body was saying, "I love you, Della, you know that." There was Charlie who sold Fords, and Charlie Somebody on the School Board, and somebody else who lived on Parkview with his wife and two sons, but the boys were away at camp. There was Charlie who had had an affair.

"Look at me, Della, honey."

"I just don't want to cry." Charlie's wife could not close her eyes. As suddenly as the turn of a ribbon or Amen she could not close her eyes.

"Please."

His hand moved across the seat toward her. The hand was big and freckled; fine red hair covered it. She nodded at three blurred faces in a black car which pulled past them over the gravel drive. The hand disappeared.

He said, "Josephine didn't have anything to do with us. Listen to me. I'm trying to talk to you."

"I said we wouldn't mention her again, not ever again," she said aloud, or to herself. "We weren't going to mention her. You promised."

"She was a sick woman, in her mind, too. I told you I was sorry. I try to tell you. You don't give me a chance."

Charlie spoke the words easily. He could have been addressing his employees. She thought of saying, "Maybe you just know the easy words."

"It's why she drank so much. And slept around. A lot of men could tell you. I'm not saying it was right. I'm just trying to tell you." His voice was a straight line. "It didn't mean anything. I've been trying to tell you."

She was calm. It was the car that trembled, waiting to pull into the string of traffic which only an hour ago had been a funeral procession. "The way's clear," she said. "You can get in line now." She said, "I don't mean that. I don't mean anything. Just don't talk to me."

She could have said, "We have each other." That would have been something to say. Perhaps, if she had not invited the girls, she would have said, the way people in real life were always saying, "We have each other." She could have cried, and Charlie could have comforted her in the empty house. They could have held each other in the empty house. She could remember Charlie's face above her, saying, "I love you, I love you."

"We had a letter from Tim," she said. "They like camp. Bobby finally passed his swimming test. You can read it."

"Later," Charlie said.

They were in the driveway beside a house on Parkview Road. She held her gloved hand on the knob of the car door. She did not say, "You don't have to go back to the office?" She said, "You're not coming in." She was not sure if he spoke a question or a statement.

"Later, later," Charlie said. The tires of his car turned slowly, and then the driveway held only the blotched shade of the maple tree they had planted a long time ago.

She had not cried. Even after the moon came up white and round she had not cried. She undressed and lay at the foot of the bed, looking at the moon. Several times the telephone rang. It is Winifred. It's Lillian. It's Betty Kay. It's Charlie, even, calling, she told herself, but she did not move from the bed.

Once upon a time there was a time before Charlie. He hadn't even known about Madison, Kentucky, where kites sailed over the park. When the five girls were growing up he hadn't ever been out of Tennessee. It was strange to think about. They played hide-and-seek. They took turns giving slumber parties. They went to dances. Josephine was first. Josephine had the first permanent, and the first two-piece bathing suit, and the first car of her own. She was married first. But they had followed quickly. Josephine was divorced first. She was the only one to be divorced. Josephine knew about death first, too. Death was a word like hide-and-seek. It was something to remember, like time.

But Della did not look at her watch when Charlie finally came home. It was late. She hurried her body around to lie straight in the bed, the way bodies were supposed to lie in bed. She covered herself carefully with the sheet. She breathed carefully, like a sleeping body. Charlie tiptoed to his closet to get his pajamas. He stood by the bed. He breathed harshly. And after a while he went away to sleep in another bed in the cool dark house; and after a while she slept, the night heavy against her eyelids. All of them slept alone. When she awoke Charlie had left the house again; there was no proof he had stood beside her on the night of Josephine's funeral.

It was ten o'clock. She watched her own hand with the kitchen scissors whose broken prongs bit into the chicken. She had already taken the transparent pies from the oven. When Mamma was alive she always said transparent pies were the nicest compliment you could pay your guests. And now Mamma had passed away. All of their mothers had passed away. And their fathers, too. Except Lillian's mother. Lillian's mother had looked very young at Josephine's funeral.

"Josephine Nye Martin Foster is dead," Della said aloud.

She called all of Josephine's names. Josephine no longer pretended to sleep under the flowers. Josephine Nye Martin Foster was and isn't.

Della leaned heavily against the sink. She had wished herself dead. For five months she had almost wished herself dead. Death was a real word, like scissors or salad. She could not think of anything to wish.

On four white Spode plates she arranged lettuce; it expanded, and she heard the movement of the lettuce, like breath. She reached her hand toward the table. In a little while Winifred and Betty Kay and Lillian, grown women, almost forty-year-old women, would stand on the front porch, breathing against the screen. "Anybody home?" Winifred would call, as she had been calling all of their lives; with their needles and their fabrics they would enter the house; their faces loomed as large as billboards. Winifred's face said to itself: "Della is having a funeral party." No, honestly no, it's not a celebration. I didn't want Josephine to die of a heart attack. I don't want anybody to die of anything. "Honestly, honestly, no."

13

She would telephone them. She would say, "Don't come. Don't come at all. Honestly."

Or they weren't planning to come. "We'll sew tomorrow," Della Norris said. Not one of them had answered. They had not heard her invitation. And, anyhow, at the cemetery she wasn't even thinking about Josephine and Charlie. Before God, she was only remembering that today was their sewing day. For over a year they had sewed together on the third Tuesday of every month, ever since Josephine moved back from Louisville, before God.

It was snowing the day Winifred came to tell about Charlie and Josephine. Winifred sat in the wing chair, filling the room. Her pale eyes were kind. "Della, sweet, you musn't brood. Nobody else knows. I'll never tell a soul. It's our secret. But if I were in your position . . ." Della studied the fire in the fireplace as if it were a painting in a frame. In the presence of the painting it was difficult to hear Winifred's voice, or to think about Charlie, or Josephine, or the fire itself. Once old Doctor Ed told Della that her appendix had burst. "If I were in your place, I'd want to know," Winifred said. Her square face was kind. Her heavy body leaned forward in the chair; her hands with their unpainted nails moved toward Della.

"What would you do?" Della whispered. "What does anybody do?"

"It's simple," Winifred said. "It's very simple."

It was simple to pour one's mind into the square efficient box of Winifred's mind. Even afterwards, when she spoke to Charlie, it was simple. In Winifred's mind Della said, "I thought it was only fair for you to know I know." She said, "Charles, when faith is gone, there isn't anything else." She was not ashamed of Winifred's voice.

"Della, baby, I love you, you know that," he answered in one of his voices, but she did not bother to try to identify which Charles spoke to her. "I don't know how it happened. I don't know."

"We will not discuss it any more," she said, holding Winifred's mind carefully, bearing Charlie for the sake of the boys, moving through the rest of winter, through five sewing days, past spring,

14

into summer, softly so that she would not spill Winifred's mind. "Courage," Winifred said in their little talks. "That's my Della. You're keeping your chin up."

But Josephine was dead.

Della bit at the knuckles of her hand. "Did you hear? In the cemetery Della Norris lost Winifred's mind?" It was like a joke. If she had been alone in the house she could have laughed until she cried tears as salty as the blood on her hand. "She lost Winifred's mind, and she didn't miss it until the next day. She didn't actually miss it until she was getting ready for the funeral party." But she could not laugh because she was not alone in the house. Some place, back in time, she stood and watched herself against the sink. "You're not going to be sick," she said. "You can surely borrow another mind for the day."

"It's all right," somebody told her in the hospital—Mother, or old Doctor Ed, or somebody. "You're going to feel fine when you wake up." She was thirteen. It was almost her thirteenth birthday. But she had not felt wonderful. "I feel wonderful," she said, and somebody pressed a cold enamel basin against her. And now Della Norris had lost Winifred's mind.

If Lillian or Betty Kay had told her about Charlie and Josephine, she would probably have acted as they expected her to act. But it was Winifred who said, "I think you ought to know. Josephine confessed to me herself." There was nothing in time to compare with, neither sickness nor death. "She confessed quite freely," Winifred said. "I made her confess."

Della Norris lost Winifred's mind. Sweet, adaptable Della lost everybody's mind. Have you heard? Have you heard?

Winifred had to call three times. "Anybody home? Anybody home? Anybody home?"

"I'm just going to steal your cleaning lady, everything looks so nice." Betty Kay pirouetted in the center of the living room, as graceful and slim as she had been in high school. The yellow folds of her skirt moved softly. "Your house always just sparkles."

"God, it's hot outside." Lillian tossed her sewing basket onto the gray couch. "I don't know why we don't get air conditioning. I could kill Ransom over things like air conditioning."

"It's sweet of you to have us." Winifred touched her lips to Della's hair. "It's so sweet, Della."

They moved as if they followed grooves in the carpet: Betty Kay to the mantel to place her purse, to pat her soft dark hair; Lillian to the couch where she sprawled, kicking off her sandals; Winifred to the wing chair by the piano; Betty Kay gliding on her high heels to swoop onto the ottoman, turning her head to smile at Della; Lillian reaching for a pillow to place behind her head; Winifred's large hands already threading a needle.

"My feet hurt," Lillian said. "It makes them hurt worse to see you in those heels."

"Silly," Betty Kay giggled, turning, and turning again. "Della, we're late because they had to wait on me. Everything was in such a mess this morning. Al couldn't find his car keys and then Kay insisted on . . ."

"I had a fight with little Ransom before breakfast," Lillian said. "He won't flush the commode. Sometimes I could kill that boy."

"You don't mean that, Lillian." Winifred's needle had already begun to outline a pink flower on a white pique collar.

"It's easy for you to shake your head," Lillian said to the ceiling. "Your girls are exactly like you, sweetness and light, and a place for everything. But that Ransom . . ."

"You're not being fair." Betty Kay pushed out her lips. "Ransom is just darling. Why, yesterday Kay was saying . . ."

"If you'll excuse me," Della said. She had planned the words. "If you'll excuse me."

"Sit down and relax," Lillian said.

"Della, you're white as a sheet. Are you feeling bad, Della?" Winifred's embroidery frame hung in the air, as if it would fly to the table, freeing Winifred to push herself up to her feet, to stand in front of Della Norris, encouraging her to tell about Charlie and Josephine.

"No, don't. Don't. I'm fine."

"You're tired. You've gone to trouble."

"How did you hurt your hand?" Lillian asked.

"Oh my goodness," Betty Kay said. In her lap lay a red felt stocking, half covered with green felt trees and silver sequins.

"At the sink," Della said, but Lillian was not listening.

"Oh that Ransom," Lillian said.

"Please, I'm fine." Della lowered herself to the leather chair by the dining room door. She leaned her head against the back of the chair. In the cool room the leather was warm against her neck.

"Did you say that stocking was for next year, or the year after?" Lillian said. "You make me sick being so far ahead."

"It's a beautiful stocking," Winifred's voice said. "You'll all make such pretty things."

"You don't consider hemming a tea towel as fancy work, do you? Or darning socks?" Lillian swung her legs around to the floor. Her legs were fat and flabby. "Oh God. Goddamn it."

"Lillian, dear. Please." Winifred placed her needle in the center of a pink leaf. "There is no need to be profane. We mustn't let ourselves get upset. We're all together, all of us. We're not taking sides."

"Josephine helped me cut out this stocking." Betty Kay's eyes were closed. Tears seeped through her long dark lashes. She bit her lips until she looked like a toothless old woman. "Poor Josephine."

"Oh God, I was afraid it would be this way," Lillian said.

Winifred was across the room. She inched her large body on to the edge of the ottoman; she put her arms around Betty Kay. "There, there. There, there, now."

"But Josephine of all people. She was so alive. And generous. She was so generous, whatever her little faults."

"Ever so generous. But Betty Kay, honey, listen to me." Winifred might have been speaking to one of her daughters. "This is a hard time for all of us. We have to be realistic. We have a lot to be thankful for."

Betty Kay's little dark eyes darted back and forth in her head. "She gave me this pin. I admired it one day, and she said, 'Here, take it.' You remember. She said, 'Here, take it.' "

"She was generous." Winifred's voice was like salve. "It's hard, just the four of us now, meeting to sew, and remembering." Winifred was gray salve.

"I almost wish she hadn't started us on these sewing days." The ends of the silk tie moved under the pin at Betty Kay's neck.

"It was crazy. And just because our mothers sewed." Lillian's voice was harsh. "I told Josephine it was crazy. She just laughed."

"Yes," Della said, but she could not remember her mother's face.

"I think it's been wonderful," Betty Kay said.

"We all thought our mothers were terribly secure in this crazy town. My mother's always telling me how secure they were."

"Josephine was a leader," Winifred said.

"Except having children," Betty Kay said. "It was the only thing she wasn't first in. Do you think she minded a lot?"

"Josephine was a strange one. She ran deep," Winifred said.

"Yes, yes," Della said. "Yes." She felt sly. She was proud of herself. For five months they had sewed together, and Josephine had never guessed she knew. And Lillian didn't know. And Betty Kay didn't know.

Winifred's pale eyes were looking at Della.

"Yes," Della said. And even Winifred didn't know that Della's mind had no words to think. And Della Norris could get through the funeral party all right. She could run the tape recorder and the camera. If she were careful, and she was careful, oh, marvelously careful, if she were careful she could get all the pictures straight and in order. She could say, "Yes, yes."

She could follow Lillian's glance. A film of dust lay quietly on the cross bar of the piano bench.

Winifred, Betty Kay, Lillian, Betty Kay. The sounds of their voices came slowly. Betty Kay, Winifred. Sometimes the sound almost disappeared, but there were the quick dark turns of Betty Kay's head, the rocking motion of Winifred's body, yes, yes, Lillian's hands clutching each other as they remembered Josephine.

"Our mothers were ladies, weren't they."

"Oh, God, yes, they were Kentucky ladies."

"Now, Lillian."

Their mothers and their grandmothers, poised as cameos or Godey's ladies, sat in the parlor of the house which once stood on this very lot. In the kitchen a maid helped the cook cut up chicken for the salad. The transparent pies waited in the great oven. Outside the girls played together. In a little while they would eat from real china, using linen napkins, in the playhouse which once stood under the willows. The maid—whatever was her name?—brought the food in two wicker hampers. "Now you all be nice," she said. "Now, be nice, ladies."

But Josephine was not at the table.

Betty Kay's head lay against Winifred's lavender shoulder. Winifred said, "There must be a special heaven for poor tortured souls like Josephine." Betty Kay said, "She was so alive. I don't understand." Winifred said, "Some things we aren't supposed to understand. It's God's will, Betty Kay."

Lillian said, "Oh, hell, you both make me sick. She's dead. That's all anybody knows."

"Lillian."

"Josephine would be getting a big laugh out of this."

Betty Kay was standing. "You hear me, Lillian. You're not to talk that way." Betty Kay was steadying herself against Winifred. "You and Josephine—both of you—you were always making fun of religion. And I let you do it because you were my friends. But now . . . Now, you're not to talk that way. You hear me?"

Josephine lay in Charlie's arms, smiling at Charlie, smoothing her hands over his body.

Lillian's weeping, close to laughter, whirred in the room. "Don't shout at me. I believe. I believe something," Lillian cried.

"I believe," the recorder said.

"Oh, of course you do, Lillian."

"Of course you do." Betty Kay and Winifred were on the couch. The girls fluttered together, almost like flames.

Once upon a time Della had a playhouse. In the playhouse was a grate. On a cardboard screen in front of the grate Della drew a picture of a fire. She colored the fire with yellow and orange and red crayons. The flames embraced each other and parted and embraced again.

"I'm scared, I guess, and I'm too old to be scared." It was Lillian. "We're old enough to have everything worked out."

"We're not so old, honey." It was Betty Kay.

"I'm scared of dying, I guess. Oh God."

"God's in his heaven." It was Betty Kay again.

"We love each other very much. All this . . ." Winifred said to

19

the air. "All this has brought us closer together. We mustn't be upset."

The machines moved very quickly. "We understand, Lillian." Betty Kay's face was as wet as if she had come from the pond beyond the willows. But there wasn't any pond now. Houses stood on the pond. Children they didn't know played in the square yards of the new houses. "I loved Josephine." Mascara streaked Betty Kay's face. They had not even worn lipstick when the pond stood. "I'd have done anything in the world for Josephine, you all know that. She loved me, too. But Josephine liked to be shocking. She always acted—I don't know—different."

They had forgotten her, the three of them, the four of them.

"She wasn't really one of us," Winifred said. "Not even when we were in grade school. She was different."

"But we made fun of things together," Lillian said.

"But Josephine did it most. That's right, isn't it, Winifred?"

Winifred nodded. She took her hand from Lillian's to pull at her own shoulder strap.

In the playhouse Della allowed herself to hide behind the screen of the fire only once a game. "Bushel of wheat, bushel of rye," Winifred called, or Lillian, or Betty Kay. Della crouched behind the fire. She was breathing so hard she tried to hold her breath. "Bushel of wheat, bushel of clover, all aren't hid, can't hide over." But none of them had found her hiding place. "Wherever were you?" they asked. "Della's a funny," Josephine said. "Ally ally out's in free," they called while Della hid in one of their minds.

"I don't mean to be disloyal," Lillian said. "We're not nice people. We're awful people."

"Yes," Della said, afraid for a moment that Lillian had discovered her.

"We're not disloyal. Nobody's being disloyal." The volume on Winifred's voice was too high. "Life has to go on."

"It's important to try to be honest," Betty Kay said.

"What's honest, oh my God?" Lillian was crying again. Her shoulders shook. Her voice had not changed really, not in all the years.

20

"Oh, Lillian, honey, Josephine would want us to be brave," Betty Kay said. "Whatever else, she was gallant and brave."

Once Della giggled when Josephine stood in the doorway of the playhouse. "I hear you, I hear you," Josephine said. You're some place around and I know it. Don't jump and scare me though. Promise you won't scare me, Della."

She had not come out. She did not mean to come out. The game wasn't over.

Winifred was pushing her into the circle when it wasn't her turn. "O-U-T spells Out." King's X. King's X a minute.

"It's so true." Winifred's picture was moving too fast. "Della's the brave one. Della has the bravery for all of us. Come over here, Della." Winifred patted the arm of the sofa. "We're all together. And you're so good to have us here, just like always, as if nothing had happened."

"It's the way Josephine would want it," Betty Kay said.

They were all three looking at her. They waited for her. Before it had been Betty Kay and Winifred; and Lillian and Josephine; and Della could belong to either side. "Choose. Choose a side," they said. "Whose side you going to be on?"

"No, really. Don't look at me."

"Della, sweet."

"No really." She held to the chair arms. "I didn't think anything." She spoke slowly, hoping they could hear her from far across the room.

"I've always said Della kept us together. You've always been the sweetest, and the kindest. I've always said that, haven't I?" Winifred asked the others.

"Josephine loved you, too," Betty Kay said. "I think you've just been wonderful, what with Charlie . . ."

"Betty Kay," Winifred whispered, but the sound carried.

"Oh you Freudian fools," Lillian said, closing her eyes.

Betty Kay put her palms to her cheeks. Her hands moved over her face until they covered her mouth. Her hands dropped to her lap, like papers falling. "I didn't mean anything. I didn't mean anything, Della."

Winifred organized the games. Winifred decided whether they

21

would play dolls or hide-and-seek. Winifred said, "Josephine grabbed at life, anybody's life." The age lines were deep around Winifred's mouth and eyes. "These sewing days were good. We could keep an eye on Josephine." Winifred decided whether they should play cards or Truth.

"You told them, didn't you?" Della said quietly. "You told them about Josephine and . . ." She was not angry. "You told them about Josephine and Charlie."

"She was a menace." The lines grew even deeper. "She was a menace all our lives."

"We loved her, of course," Betty Kay said.

"But we're loyal to you, Della. And we love our husbands and our families. You understand that."

Lillian's eyes had found the dust under the piano bench again.

The tape had run out. There wasn't any more film in the camera. Della had to clear her throat three times before she spoke into the quiet room where the three other women sat.

Perhaps she spoke in Josephine's voice, but she did not mind. "I loved Charlie," she said, wondering if her mind were Josephine's. "I love Charlie."

They were quiet again before Betty Kay said, "You're so wonderful, Della."

Winifred said. And Lillian said. And Betty Kay said. And Winifred said.

They spoke their words as their mothers had spoken, finishing out the morning. But they were not their mothers. Summer lay around them. A mind, or a word like faith, hung over Della, like a kite, tugging at her hands.

And Winifred said, and Betty Kay said, and Lillian said.

Della said, "It's ever so late. You must be starved."

Lillian said, "I am. I didn't have any breakfast."

Winifred said, "Nobody cooks like Della."

Betty Kay said, "I know we're going to have transparent pie."

Jean Abbott

EXCERPT FROM A NOVEL BY H. L. NEWBOLD

CHICAGO, April 1. It is a night I will not forget.

The automatic elevator eases to a hushed stop at the fourth floor. The brown metal doors click open. I step out into an atmosphere always left stained with odors of ether, alcohol, and iodoform which drift off the wrinkled uniforms of nurses as they return from work among rows of white iron beds and slack faces at Charity Hospital. Because I have broken the heel off of my left shoe, my steps make an irregular echo as I hobble down the empty hall of the nurses' dormitory to my room.

My hand trembles. The key scratches across the brass lock before finding the slot and slipping solidly into place. I push open the door and step into the room where I stay.

I cross over to the chair outlined by the hazy night light coming through the window. My hands find the security of the smooth maple chair arms. I ease myself down and relax my head backward until the rough upholstery cradles my neck. No one will disturb me here in the darkness behind that oak door.

When I left with Michael only six hours ago, I may not have been beautiful, but I was as beautiful as I could make myself. During the afternoon I had washed and set my short blond hair so that it was light and curly, ready for his eyes to touch. My face, which is too thin over the cheeks and makes me look older than twenty-one, was carefully powdered to keep away the shadows. I gave a red depth to my shallow lips and touched my pale eyelashes with mascara to enlarge the blue of my eyes.

My eyebrows have been too thin since I was fifteen and plucked them one rainy Saturday night with my mother's tweezers before going on stage for a high school dance recital. So these, as always, I had carefully shaped with a brown pencil. But they are always too long or too short or too thin. My face seems slightly artificial, not as soft and feminine as I would like. But my nose is straight. The bony framework of my face is delicate and symmetrical.

There is something about my face which shows I can be destroyed, the same weakness I have seen in the faces of tired women with small children gathered about them, sitting on wooden benches, waiting to be examined by a doctor at some charity clinic.

Perhaps my high school dancing teacher was right when she said my figure, rather than my face, was my beauty. My breasts are full for a girl with a slender neck and shoulders, yet they stand out from my ribs so well there is no fold of skin beneath them. I think my breasts were meant for work. Sometimes they feel a prick of tenderness when I walk past the nursery and glance through the window at the moving lips of newborn babies. The tight muscles fall away sharply from my chest to form a small waist from which a curving line goes out over my hips and thighs to my knees. Another line stands out over the calves of my legs and quickly falls away into slender ankles and small feet.

When I turn in the chair and lift the window, warm April flows over me, carrying the scent of moist earth which has blown in from the prairie farms and, for once, has driven away the throat-drying soot of the city. Somewhere in the quiet blackness an automobile horn blows, but the sound is quickly absorbed by the Chicago night. I hear a loose metallic noise as the door of a second-hand car slams shut in front of the dormitory. A nurse laughs and then her feet make quick happy scrapes on the concrete as she runs up the steps and disappears into the building.

Last night I felt lonely as I sat here looking out at the soot-soiled yellow bricks of the hospital across the street, but now I have a sick loneliness a hundred times worse, even though less than an hour ago I felt the heaviness of Michael's body against mine.

During these past few weeks something strange, a mysterious force I sensed once before, seems to have taken control of my body, an urgency which is a part of me and yet is a stranger to

24

me. It is as if my feet are being guided through the intricate steps of a dance even though my mind knows nothing of the pattern.

II

When I left the dormitory tonight, holding Michael's arm and laughing up at his dark face, I was wearing my blue wool dress, the one with the black buttons running down the front all the way to the bottom of the full princess skirt.

Now the dress has a long ragged tear at the shoulder and the two top buttons have been snapped off by the bulge of his quick hands. The neat picture he saw when I ran up to where he was waiting for me at the end of the lobby has been smeared. My hair is a mass of jumbled blondness. Both stockings have wide runs in them. One hook has been torn from my girdle. The heel of my left shoe was broken off as I struggled on the floor at his apartment. When I screamed, he struck me across the face so hard the corner of my lip is swollen and will be black when I go on duty in the morning. From where I fought with my back scraping the floor, I saw the dark angular shadows of his face, his white teeth as his breath heaved in and out, the rigid fire in his black eyes, which were nearly closed, which did not care whether I was Jean or Julie or Joyce.

"All right! All right!" I shouted because I was afraid he would kill me.

Michael is a resident in surgery at Charity Hospital where he has come to complete his training before returning home to Mexico. He must be ten years older than I, a strange, intense, often silent man.

His head is not square, but the short clip of his black hair gives the effect of squareness. There are dark shadows, angles and triangles all over his hungry face. His skin is lighter than many Mexicans' (you might think he had just returned from two weeks in the Florida sun), probably because his grandfather was from Texas.

Michael has a strong neck, wide shoulders, and a full chest. When he wears a short-sleeved scrub suit, you can see the lights and shadows wander over the long muscles in his arms. In spite

of his beautiful body, he does not have that soap-scented masculine loveliness you see in the men who pose for the covers of
health magazines. Even with their bulging bodies, they are not
quite masculine. Michael is so masculine I missed a breath the
first time I saw him walk down a hospital corridor.

Even with all his muscles he moves with ease. Just to watch him
reach for a cup of coffee is a joy. They say he plays tennis well,
and I am certain he does. I can see his body stepping smoothly
from one side of the tennis court to the other as he accurately,
almost lazily, drives the ball back at his opponent with what
must seem like a mere movement of his wrist.

But I imagine he is much different in the operating room.
There he would be accurate and precise, but would tolerate
nothing but perfection in others. I can hear him calling out the
names of his various Mexican saints as he curses the scrub nurse
and throws a steel instrument against the floor when she makes
a mistake and slaps a Kelly instead of a Halstead clamp into his
gloved hand.

His hands are narrow, lean, and long, so that his fingers seem
to be made only of bones over which stretch narrow tendons
covered with brown skin. The tips of his fingers are nearly square,
his fingernails always freshly scrubbed.

If you watch his fingers, you see them reflect all his emotions.
When he is surprised, they straighten out. When he is restless,
as he often is, they move from coffee cup to cigarette and then
dance on the table top. When he is content, they curl up and
go to sleep.

He was sitting at a booth drinking coffee in the bar across from
the hospital when I first looked down at his hands as I walked by.
Suddenly I had the feeling he had plunged them up through the
center of my body and was holding onto that oval cradle within
me so tightly I would never be able to step away from him.

III

A month ago I was introduced to him at a Saturday night party
given in the musky intimacy of a nurse's candlelighted apartment
where couples were seated arm in arm around the edge of the

floor, drinking red wine, or dancing slowly to the deep drum rhythms of sensuous music from the phonograph. Michael asked me for a date while we were dancing. I was probably the first girl who ever said no to him. His fingers made tight circles around each of my arms and the moving candlelight shifted the shadows back and forth over his glistening face as he looked at my eyes to ask why not.

Sometimes Michael and I would have coffee or a beer together after work when we happened to meet at the Greek's, a nickname given to the bar-restaurant across the street from the hospital. Each time he asked me for a date, I shook my head and told him no, but sometimes at night I would dream of a tall magician with a shadowy face, dressed in a black cloak, standing in the corner of my room. He would touch a velvet hat with his magic wand and draw out a kicking white rabbit. Then he would point his magic wand at me. I would reach out to steal its power and just as my fingers closed about it, a flash of exploding yellow light would fill the room, dissolving me and the magician. The only thing left in the room would be the white rabbit hopping slowly from corner to corner, searching.

Suddenly I would jerk awake and find myself throwing the bed clothes aside, terror-eyed, choking, so frightened my throat would be dry and as tight as if I had been screaming.

IV

Two weeks ago Michael asked me out again. For some strange reason I went with him to a movie, but not to his apartment, because I had heard of his bad reputation and there was something about his unknown face and his quick magic hands which frightened me. All the time we were together I kept remembering the gaunt man in the dream who wore a black cloak.

Something inside me must have known what was about to happen. I did everything to avoid him after that first date. I even moved out of the dormitory and ran home to Springdale to live with my parents and younger sister.

But it was an hour ride to work each day on the train. It was annoying to share a room with my thirteen-year-old sister who constantly prattled about male TV stars and lay on her bed every afternoon, her brown eyes glossy with shallow dreams as she listened to the wax sobs of Johnny Mathis records, over and over again. She had even taken Dad away from me. When he stepped through the doorway at night, she would lock her arms around his neck as if he had slain a hundred dragons since breakfast. She would tease him to his easy chair, loosen his tie, and even bring him a bourbon and water while I stood by forcing my mouth to smile, holding my hands together because there was nothing left for them to do.

I felt like a stranger at home and moved back to this room after being away only one week.

Tonight, on our second date, I followed Michael up those dark complaining stairs, past the cooked-cabbage odors to where he lives in that bare room of his. Ten minutes later my back was scraping against the floor as I fought him off with both arms and both legs.

I still cannot understand why I went there with him, or even let him take me to a movie. It was as though the fall and winter of me stayed in my room, an April stranger entered my body, guided it to the lobby below and put my arm through his as we left the dormitory together.

I push myself up from where I have been sitting by the window and begin undressing, still without turning on the light. The shrill siren of an ambulance speeding toward Charity Hospital cries through the night, closer and closer, and then suddenly hoarsens and dies.

If my father knew what had happened he would call me names: whore, tramp. I say them over to myself, but they are only names. The only thing I feel is a quiet anger towards someone who tricked me, I am not sure who.

Perhaps I should be angry with Charles. He is the only other man who has known me, that thirty-eight year old doctor with the sagging brown eyes and sad face who six months ago . . . that cold, tight snow . . .

But I do not want to think about either of them any more.

As I pull back the covers and ease myself into the bed, feeling the cool smoothness of the fresh sheets, I realize I should do something to protect myself. But if I walked into the emergency room and asked to see a doctor, the whole hospital would be laughing at me by morning.

It is probably too late anyway. By now those restless seeds have had their chance.

John Edgar and the Floozie

BY SALLY THOMPSON

EVERYONE followed someone, that summer at the small, elegant northern California resort. My father followed my mother, and I, though only fifteen, followed the Floozie. No one knew anything about her. Only that she was there alone, had platinum hair, sunned late when others did not, and laughed somewhat loudly. Evenings, she appeared in the dining room in aqua or coral dresses that left shoulders bare, and the outlines of her hips clear. She came in with different men each night, two of whom looked as black-haired and large-featured as gangsters. By day she looked shadowy under the eyes; by night, she glittered.

They began calling her the Floozie.

The Floozie was doomed from the start. People watched her coldly. Mother hated her, Father made inquiries.

"There is certainly no apparent commercial aspect to it, Maria," he told my mother. "She pays a stiff bill to stay here, just as you do."

"As *we* do, Jonathan," Mother corrected him, as always. "It's *our* money."

Father ignored her correction. He was a tall, thin writer with a Van Dyke beard who had not been very successful, but then he did not have to be. Mother had enough for all of us.

"Now, whether this lady has friends who add to the coffers, I can't say," Father added.

"I've never seen anything like that at Du Lac."

"The reservation clerk does not require photographs. What can one woman do to change Du Lac?"

"It doesn't look right, with children around," she said. She was referring to me.

They had visited the resort, a place which excluded children under fifteen, yearly since I was ten. I had always been sent on all-male camping trips and museum expeditions, or shuttled between birdwatches and what few nature-loving relatives we possessed, particularly those who dwelt on the edge of lake, ocean or forest. It had long been my mother's notion that after nine months in the confines of boarding school, I should be let loose on guided tours or in familial dog-runs, for outlet.

Father had never agreed. And this year he had insisted I accompany them to the resort.

"He's big now, Maria," Father had said. We were in the living room and he was restless. School was just out, and I had wondered what summer tour I was signed up for.

"He's only fifteen," Mother had answered. Mother was very beautiful, but I seldom saw her beauty face-on. She never looked at me. She looked above my right eye. I secretly adored my mother, despite the fact that she still wanted me to be a child, and disliked children.

"Fifteen is not exactly a child," Father said. "It may be that he is ready for something more than hikes and bed-rolls."

"He's doing what other children his age do," Mother said.

"Let's take him," Father said. "He needs manners. Lessons in food, what wine to order. He needs to grow up."

"Surely his growth is adequate," Mother said, dryly. She had, I gathered, stolen a recent look at my general size and shape. I stood five eleven, and had always been good at sports.

Father bent before her, smiling.

"Maria, will your friends be surprised to find him so big?"

"*Our* friends, Jonathan," was her only answer.

"You can't keep hidden forever the fact that he has had fifteen birthdays, and is apt to have more."

I was accustomed to being invisible and mute during their con-
versations. But I was allowed to stare.

Father laughed. He rubbed her shoulders gently. Always, when
they touched before me, I could feel it.

"Don't worry, darling, your beauty is intact." His hands went
to her neck, her ears, cheeks. She was very still.

"Let's take him," Father said softly. "You won't be ashamed
of him. He'll learn quickly among snobs."

"Du Lac isn't snobbish. It's respectable."

"Yes, Maria," he said. "Respectable, rich Du Lac." He held
out both hands to her and drew her up to him. My throat tightened. I watched my mother rise. I still longed for her love, yet I
wondered how anyone else could love her.

Mother put her hands on my father's shoulders, and I knew
that I would go to Du Lac. It must have been that day when my
father began following my mother, in rehearsal for the summer
ahead.

The Floozie was there when we arrived. We walked into the
dining room at seven thirty, and her hair lit up one entire corner
of the room. She had a long, thinnish face for the rest of her body,
and the most wonderful bones in her cheeks and shoulders. Her
vivid coloring, the incessant motions with her large, tanned hands
made her seem the one real woman in a storeroom of mannequins.

She wore a blue, sparkling, low-cut dress, and a white furpiece
about her shoulders. It would slip, and she, caressing it as if it
were a cat, would replace it. She smiled in our general direction.
I felt my mother's stiffness ahead of me.

After we were seated, my mother found my father and me both
staring at the Floozie. The Floozie laughed, quite audibly. Heads
turned. Her mouth was wide, full and red.

"Who could that be?" Mother asked.

My father shrugged. I kept staring.

"You were right, Jonathan," Mother said. "This child needs
manners."

"He's not a child, Maria," my father said. He turned to me,
nodding a trifle in the direction of the Floozie.

"Do you know what that might be?" he asked me, ready to
smile.

31

My stomach and groin had already told me, but I dared not answer.

"Jonathan, is that nice, in front of me?" Mother said. She wore white, and her black hair stayed steady in every strand. Her enormous gray eyes, arched over with black brows, were set wide apart above perfect features. She was a beautiful statue; how beautiful, I kept a secret, even from myself.

"For a young man to learn discrimination, he must first know that there are choices," my father said.

Mother rose, affronted, her back to the Floozie. I was excited by this sudden quarrel.

"Maria, I'm sorry," Father began. He rose, too.

"Excuse us, son," he said. "Order your own dinner. Then we can see how much you have to learn."

My mother, without a glance at me, walked away from the table. My father winked at me and followed her out, wrapping his hand about her elbow as if it were a breast.

I was alone at a great white table in the middle of a sea of tables. I pretended I was shipwrecked and alone with the Floozie, and I provided her and myself with the most expensive dinner on the island menu. It was guinea hen dressed with ham and a quivery yellow sauce. I ate very fast and stared at the Floozie. The man with her stared at her. The maitre d' and the other men stared at her. Everyone stared at someone, that summer.

My first meeting with the Floozie made me her slave. There were no other young people about, and foolish as it seemed, I had begun a gigantic sand fort, for something to do. I worked under the broad, open, palmetto-thatched hut, and hoped the fort might never be finished.

The Floozie ducked her head under the palmetto strings of the hut, and put down her sunning things. I felt her there, but I had no courage to look up.

"What are you building, sonny?"

I dug both fists under the sand, to keep their trembling from showing.

"The biggest, best sand fort in the world," I answered.

"Well," she laughed, placing herself rather tiredly on the plastic ropes of the lounge, pulling her bathing suit leg-bands looser with a snapping, somehow intimate sound, while I leaned over to secure a moat and see how much of her was outlined by the ropes, "if you're going to bother and do it, then *make* it the biggest and best."

"My name's not sonny," I said. My voice was childish; it had changed years ago, but occasionally, as if to remind me that I was not yet grown, it gave way to cracking.

She lay back and closed her eyes, only her head in the shade. She brought up near-perfect knees for sunning.

"Sonny, Little Lord Fauntleroy, I couldn't care less *what* your name is. I do know your mother is that tall, black-headed icicle."

"She's really my stepmother," I lied.

The Floozie turned her head slowly on the lounge and, frowning comfortably as a friend, eyed me up and down. I liked that. I looked back at her. I quit working so that we could see each other.

"You look so much like her it's pitiful," she said.

"I don't want to look like that," I said.

"You could do worse. She's a looker."

"She's hideous."

"That tall skinny guy your daddy?"

"He's her lover," I said. My voice went again. What meager hopes I had had of some new companionship with my parents had gone. I had come to Du Lac, and that was that.

I rose to get some palmetto strings for reinforcing a tower.

"He's no kin to you?" the Floozie asked.

"None whatsoever."

"You're just a boy on the loose?"

"She has a terrible scar on her back," I lied again.

"Christ," she said. She laughed, and I moved nearer to watch her. It was a lovely, loud sound she made, but without any jarring to it, like church bells when you're dressed up and going there.

"I don't think your *step*mother approves of me," she said.

"She doesn't like anybody," I said.

"Go on. Bet she's proud of a good-looking kid like *you*," she said.

"She can't stand the sight of me," I said. I blushed. I hadn't meant to make it sound so true.

33

She was watching me. I went beyond the fort to gather shells for gun emplacements and officers.

"She likes that tall skinny guy, and don't tell me she doesn't," the Floozie called after me.

"She has a new lover every year," I called back.

"Oh, God," the Floozie laughed. "Let me go to sleep. I never knew a kid lie as much as you."

She covered her eyes with a silver-winged, black plastic eye-cover, and kept on smiling. I came back with the shells and stood above her. I had not seen such an eye cover at Du Lac.

"I'm not a kid," I said. "I'm eighteen."

"Go to hell," she said. "You're not a day over sixteen."

I stood quietly, relishing my progress. I had gained a year, and fallen in love with the Floozie.

Father wrote, mornings; Mother read. Father smiled, and asked me to take advantage of every moment at Du Lac; Mother asked me to stay out. Father looked closely at me from time to time as if he would speak, but said nothing. He gave me money and stayed with my mother.

My mother lay on a chaise, secretly the most beautiful woman in the entire universe. Except, perhaps, for the Floozie, who *looked* at a man, and knew how to laugh.

I had quick lunches and stiff dinners with my parents. Mother told me what I was eating, Father told me the year and origin of my wine. Father mentioned a fishing trip, Mother changed the subject. Mother told their friends that I was fourteen, and that all her family was tall. My parents spent their evenings with their friends, playing bridge or listening to music. I was not invited. I walked the empty, palm-lined, dimly-lit terraces outside the lobby, or read.

Without the Floozie, I would have been desperately lonely. She, too, left me after dinner, going off in long automobiles to secret places. But every day at one, when the others had gone inside, she was back under the hut. The Floozie was wonderful: she was kind; and, more, she wore about her as closely as her

bathing suits and gowns the worldliness, the appearance of be-
longing, for which I so strove.

The entire hotel wore that air: everyone had, or could have,
someone. People touched. I owned no one, yet the atmosphere
about me felt warm in promise, wise, and tumescent with possibility. Though I waked each morning alone in a child's world,
aware of the desire to run, swim and build, by noon I verged on
another world: that of the Floozie.

I would rush to eat lunch, race through the lobby, which got
me called down twice. I raced on, seeing few faces, aware only
of the morning's growth, and the approaching hour with the
Floozie. I watched, as I ran, the lobby floor for those transparent
shoes on women which showed painted toes. They were not
usual, in the midst of our elegance, but the ones there made me
want to whistle one time, cry the next, just as the Floozie's laugh
and thighs did.

People shook their heads at me, but I ran on, from the air-
conditioning of the lobby smack into the glare and blast of the
one o'clock sun. I was always there before she came.

"When's that thing going to be finished?" she would ask me.

"Not as long as you're here," I said.

She would lie far back on the lounge and close her eyes.

"Does your mother know you spend all this time with me?"

I would crawl forward in the sand to deploy troops and see her
legs better.

"It's you who stays near me," I teased her. "All you have to do
is move your lounge."

She would smile slightly. She always looked tired, her white
platinum hair dulled by the greater light on her body.

"And have you break down in tears? But what if Mamma gets
the wrong impression?"

"She doesn't worry about me," I said. "She's pretty busy."

"That right?" She would look at me, and we would both laugh.

"Just how old are you, kid?"

"Eighteen. I told you."

"Shut up," she would say. "And don't pine your heart out for
that black-headed icicle. She isn't worth it. No woman is."

"She's afraid she's getting old," I said.

"She's afraid *you're* getting old!"

"Will you marry me when I'm twenty-one?" I asked.

She threw sand at me, and even if some went into my mouth, I didn't mind. I loved the Floozie, next to my mother. Everyone loved someone, that summer.

"Why aren't you eating, son?" Father asked me at lunch one day.

"He's fidgeting to go out and see the cheap blond. They sunbathe," Mother said. She looked nowhere near me.

"He's fifteen, Maria," Father said. "Maybe he could answer for himself."

I had a poppy seed roll in my hand. I was surprised to see how I had crushed it.

"I'm not very hungry," I said.

"Why don't you speak to him about her, Jonathan?" Mother asked. "Of all the people here, he has singled her out for a friend."

"She talks to me," I said.

"I can't think of a better reason for him to like her," Father said. "No one else bothers."

"And what do you talk about? A woman like that, and you, such a child?" Mother asked.

"He's not a child, Maria," my father said. "And she must surely be the youngest woman here."

"Then," and my mother turned her face full to me; I was stunned at its sudden age in the midst of such beauty, "I suppose that you have some ridiculous romantic notion about her?"

I reddened all the way to my middle. I could scarcely endure seeing age and anger on that beloved face. I carefully buttered what remained of my roll.

"We talk about my sand fort."

"Out of all those hours? People say that they have come up on the two of you laughing like idiots."

"The respectable spies are out," Father said.

"She says very funny things," I said.

"Maria, you are intruding," Father said. "Let him be."

"I told you he was too young to come here. If it continues, he will leave, or *she* will."

My heart turned over.

"Where is the harm?" Father asked. "If he is such a child?"

One day I was working on a tunnel that happened to run parallel with the Floozie's lounge. I had, half-heartedly, worked myself out into the sun, even with her knees. She had one knee raised, as women do on lounges, and as I leveled the tunnel top, bracing sides with palmetto bits, I admired her calf. It hung loosely, a tanned, beautiful pouch of flesh, even more shapely than her thigh whose flesh thinned at the knee, swelled in the middle, and was nipped at her groin by the tight bathing-suit leg, much like a sausage in casing.

The Floozie had been quiet a long time. I turned and looked about me. There were no sun-bathers anywhere near us, and the idea of us being alone appealed to me.

Suddenly, however, I sat back on my haunches. The fort looked silly. The ridiculousness of my position in the sand, like that of a child being guarded by its dozing nurse, hit me all at once.

"Damn it," I said.

The Floozie stirred, turned her face languidly toward me. Her eyes were circled and cat-green, her face was lined in the glare; but her lips, especially the lower one, were so full and soft-looking that I raised on my knees to see them better.

"What's eating *you?*" she asked.

The lower lip moved wondrously, lazily.

"Just damn it," I said.

"Does the black-headed icicle know you swear?"

I walked on my knees the three steps it took me to reach her side. I leaned over her slightly. Her elbow, resting on the arm of the lounge, touched my diaphragm.

"My mother thinks I'm a child," I said.

She laughed and moved her elbow.

"Your mother thinks *I'm* a whore," she said.

"*Are* you a whore?" I asked.

"Are *you* a child?" she teased me.

37

We shook our heads "no" simultaneously. Then we smiled at each other.

"Now beat it back to your fort, General. I hear the bugle," she said.

I leaned over her and quickly touched my lips just to her lower one. I whirled from her and threw myself in the sand. My heart had kicked up a noise anyone could hear, and my face felt smeared with flames.

The Floozie was frowning and sitting erect, looking all around, when I sat up.

"What if somebody saw that?" she said.

"You're the only person I like to be with."

"Listen, kid, you may not know anything about it, but I'm on thin ice anyhow! All your rich mother has to do is tell the manager I am seducing her sixteen-year-old son—"

"Eighteen," I interrupted.

"*Seventeen*-year-old son, and I'm *out!*"

"I'm sorry," I said, my head throbbing with my progress. "I really am."

"I'm no goddamn cradle-snatcher," she said, loudly.

"I'm no goddamn baby," I said, faintly.

"Tell that to your black-headed mother," the Floozie said.

The next day when I went out to the hut at one, the Floozie was not in sight. Nor did she come. The sun was bright and hot, but the fort, staunch and firm as it stood, embarrassed me.

I looked everywhere. Then, far down the beach. I saw two men staring, to this side of them, at a familiar figure. I tore loose four palmetto strings to plait, and walked to where the Floozie lay.

"What are you doing away down here?" I asked.

She took off her eye cover. She began at my legs, and went up. Then she covered her eyes again.

"Mama's letting baby run awfully wild," she said.

"You always sun outside the hut," I said.

"Well, I've changed my suuing place. Anything wrong with that?"

"No. I guess not." I stood there wishing I were dead. I looked

38

at her wonderful legs, her hips and breasts. I thought of the clam shells and wished I might place one on each breast tip. I thought of my mother's frailer beauty.

She removed the eye cover.

"You still here?"

"I was wondering if I should move the fort here," I said.

"Jesus," the Floozie said, more in her old voice, "the sand buckets you'd need."

"I haven't had a sand bucket in twelve years."

She sat up. Her face had turned hard and unfamiliar.

"Look, kid, I'm busy. I don't want to talk."

"I could even begin a new fort here, maybe make *two* big ones," I said, hopefully.

"Get lost."

"But I'd have to be sure you'd stay here."

"I can sun any damned place I want to," she said. "Today and *tomorrow,* anyway."

In her voice I heard an end to something.

"Is anything wrong?" I asked.

"*Yes,* anything's wrong. I've been asked for my room. Two weeks ahead of time."

I stared at her. I mashed the half-done plait in my fingers behind me.

"What does that mean?"

"I'm very politely invited to leave. They forgot they promised my room to the King of Arabia."

"I wonder if my mother said something to the manager," I said, unbelieving.

"For all I know, somebody saw that little-boy kiss you hung on me," she said. "Now beat it, kid. Vacation's almost over."

I walked toward the thatched hut, feeling my knees doughy, and my arms as long as my legs. I tore down the entire fort.

I poured my own second glass of lunch wine. I had been moping for twenty-two hours. I couldn't find the Floozie anywhere, and as I walked the beach and lobby, and watched the elevators, people shook their heads at me. I sat now, angry with my mother, half listening to my father maintain gloomily that there was less peace here this year than ever before. Too many people knee-deep in money, and look at their shattering colors.

I was thinking I might very easily drink myself to death.

"Our most colorful guest leaves shortly," Mother said. "Then perhaps things will be as they used to be."

"Respectable," Father said. "Classless. Very, very rich."

I poured a third glass of wine, drank it, and waited for a reprimand. When it did not come, I lost interest in the wine. But I felt its warmth, like new blood in my veins.

I looked, with Father, out the great window of our suite, over the beach. I looked for the Floozie. People came and went: colorful big ants in the sand.

"She's leaving two weeks early," I said. "She said her room had been asked for."

"In a place like this, the demand—" Mother began.

"He knows the truth," Father said.

"She said she is being kicked out," I said. "They've been mean to her."

"Jonathan, he is very rude," Mother said.

Father wiped his mouth.

"Do you expect him to *like* this civilized stoning of his playmate?"

"Someone must have complained to the manager," I heard my bold voice saying.

"You are both rude. She is a—floozie, a nothing," Mother said. "Everyone knows what was seen."

My heart sank. The Floozie's wild guess had been right.

"Son," Father said, "there has been a debate at Du Lac over what constitutes immoral behavior. Item: a young woman is here alone with a hearty laugh, dyed hair, and many admirers. To cap all *that* corruption, she is seen being kissed by a fifteen-year-old roué in plain view of respectable, rich people."

Father sounded a little bit drunk. I swallowed, whole, a bite of meat and reached for my water glass, to avoid choking.

"I won't bother you with the details," Father continued to me, "but the respectable people have rebelled. Your floozie has been accused, judged, and sentenced to exile."

"Jonathan!" Mother said.

"It was all my fault," I said. "I kissed *her*."

"The idea is repulsive to me," Mother said, sharply. "You, just a boy, a mere child!"

"You'd be surprised, Maria, how soon—" Father began.

"I don't want to hear any more about it," Mother said. "This is for the child's own good. Heaven only knows what it might have led to, if he had been older."

"Or if she had stayed longer. As I was trying to tell you—" Fathed went on.

"Jonathan, please!"

"Would it help if I told the manager it was my fault?" I asked my father.

"You'd be laughed out of his office. Everyone's already laughing," Mother said.

"Your precocity as a fourteen-year-old playboy is being widely admired," my father laughed. "And, I might add, envied."

Mother rose, furious.

"That was a crude, vulgar remark, Jonathan."

The room was silent. Father's head went down, his face purple with anger. Mother stood taut and pale. I quit trying to swallow.

Father slowly wiped his spotless mouth and mustache, and laid the linen napkin on the cloth. He rose, then, and looked down at me.

"Let your friend go. How fortunate she is that she *can* leave."

He turned to Mother, who looked frozen.

"Relax, Maria. You are temporarily safe from the danger of being exposed as the mother of a grown son."

He walked stiffly to the door of their bedroom, and stopped.

"Send your child back to his sand pile, and come to bed."

I rose, and fled from the room.

I passed two newcomers, boys about my age or slightly older. They came whooping out of the lobby and began playing catch. People shook their heads at them. I was not even interested.

I walked toward the thatched hut. I liked the feeling of burn on the bottoms of my feet.

The Floozie was on her old, former lounge, by the ruins of my fort. She looked up just as I saw her. My heart skipped and ran.

She looked from the destroyed fort to me, and back to it.

"I got homesick," she said. "I came to say goodbye to it."

"It was only a toy." I fell into the sand beside it.

"No survivors?" she asked, gently.

"No survivors."

She lay back on the lounge. I picked up a handful of rubble. In it was the largest clam shell I had assigned.

"Here's the General," I said. "Bombed to hell and back."

"Worst bastard of the lot," she said.

"I'm tired of playing."

"I'll miss you, kid."

"You're too old for me," I said.

She threw sand at me. It was nothing wonderful, just cooled sand, and I spit it out. I wiped the back of my hand across my mouth, and stood up. I thought I was going to start crying. I stood, uncertain, a moment. Then, walking to the lounge, I leaned over the Floozie, and put my mouth directly on hers. In a moment my hand, wise on its own, went to her breast.

This time I did not whirl and fall in the sand. I drew back from her slowly, still tasting her mouth with its fresh-smoke smell, and the faint, perfume-like odor of gin. The only girls I had ever kissed had tasted of soft drinks, or sweet soap, or chewing gum.

She stayed still, looking at me.

"How old *are* you, kid?" she asked.

"Fifteen."

She narrowed her eyes, watching me.

"You look so much like your mother it's pitiful," she said.

I picked out the aide-de-camp and three lieutenants, and buried them.

"My mother's a beautiful woman," I said. "She doesn't have a scar to her name."

The Floozie was very quiet. She looked out to the ocean.

"You needn't have kissed me," she said. "Men usually don't kiss whores."

The truth between us at that instant was more than I could

42

endure. This time the tears came, but I bent over her again and kissed her in my new, man's way. Her lips parted for me, and her breast, soft as a bag of water, was quiet under my hand.

"Look, sonny," she said. "I mean, what's your name?"

"John Edgar."

She laughed. "Well, we'll pardon you that."

"What's your name?" I asked.

"Myrtle. I answer to Clarice here."

"We'll pardon you that," I said, miserably.

I sat back in the sand, looking at her.

"John Edgar. Wipe off that long face and listen to me."

"I'm listening."

"Don't worry about all this business."

"I made a mess of everything. Now even my father thinks I'm a child."

"It won't last forever. And does it matter, as long as *you're* sure?"

Suddenly she sat up. She looked at me. She eyed me up and down. I liked that.

"You're on your way, John Edgar," she said. "And in case there's any doubt left, I have an idea that might help."

She picked up her bathing cap and sun-tan lotion bottle. I handed her her beach towel.

She stood, and reached her hand to mine. I rose, dizzily, and followed her out of the thatched hut. Everyone followed someone, that summer.

2. Early Years:
Paid with Moan

We Steal the Coal

EXCERPT FROM A NOVEL BY MAURICE POSNER

AT LAST I WAS TO GO with my brother Lazar to steal the coal.

Tonight, after supper, Mama had yielded to my pleading. "Yes, tatanu, you may go," she had sighed wearily.

I was wild with the joy that only a seven-year-old can know who is to share an adventure with an oldest brother. Racing up and down Carbon Lane to spread the news among my buddies, I had rent the icy November evening with my happy shouts.

"Hush," Lazar had cautioned me, gently cuffing my ears. "All Wilkes-Barre will hear you."

In the kitchen, sitting next to the coal stove, I dressed in a fever of anticipation. I squeezed into my corduroy breeches, panting in the struggle against their thronged laces and brittle stiffness. Over gray, knee-length stockings I put on my felt snow-boots. Mama coiled about my neck the brown wool scarf she had knitted me. Then she took from a cupboard drawer the long black comb, fine-toothed on both sides, that she reserved for me.

Lazar snorted in disgust. "Is it *schul* you are dressing him for, Mama? Comb the hair later."

I writhed impatiently. Unmoved, Mama slowly combed and brushed my unshorn hair until it gleamed like her silver candlesticks in the parlor. She buttoned my sheepskin mackinaw around my neck and tucked my hair inside the upturned collar. Finally, stretching my knitted blue cap over my ears, she declared me dressed.

"Why is the hair still uncut? Is the young one to be anointed?" scoffed Lazar.

From behind the stove Lazar lifted two battered coal hods and a small wooden bucket. Then, reaching down behind the iron

47

washstand, he pulled out my old baby carriage. After having served me honorably, its cracked blue canvas and rusty, wire-spoked wheels had been converted to use as a carry-all. Into it Lazar dumped the hods and bucket. Tonight it would carry the coal.

We were ready. With a shout I pulled Lazar after me into the winter evening. I ran before him as he wheeled the carriage down Carbon Lane, my boots crunching on left-over patches of the first snow. Our breaths frosted in the crisp night air. The smell of coal-smoke and burning wood tugged at me with the faint waft of remembered winters. Low above the horizon shone the moon, thin and bleached, a bone picked clean by black carrion clouds.

We passed Molly Parr's bake-shop, from whose ovens floated the earth-smell of hot pumpernickel loaves and the spicy bite of cinnamon buns, and such siren smells as would another time have bewitched me from my purpose. We passed McLaughlin the watchmaker. The chimes of his old clocks regulated the neighborhood workday as much as the colliery whistles, and even now tolled and signaled us on our way. At the fork near Coal Street, through the door of Griffith's blacksmith shop, I saw the cindering embers of his forge, and the black bellows, round and accordioned, that hung above it. His shop held for me a secret terror. I fought to keep from scurrying by, lest I reveal my shame. We passed the sooted company shacks, their foundations so undercut by mine blasts that they tilted forward like pines bending in the wind. From behind them echoed the lonesome child-cry of back-yard cats.

Then we ran down Coal Street which coursed unpaved to the valley below. Near the colliery gates, where he had scouted it earlier, Lazar pulled up a loose board in the weathered paling, and we burrowed under.

II

For the first time I was within the colliery gates. It was for me a place of storied wonder, for here toiled the miners. With other neighborhood boys I had chased after them mornings as they filed to work down Carbon Lane. I had listened slack-mouthed as they shouted to each other with friendly curses, spitting black spume, and boastfully displayed to us their amputated thumbs. I saw them as helmeted cavaliers on parade, heroic men of the scarred, soot-webbed faces, their black coats draped across their shoulders, swinging dinner pails that glinted blue in the misted Pennsylvania morning.

Now, half afraid of their presence, I edged along the paling away from the main gates. We climbed an embankment to the railroad tracks. On its slopes, Lazar told me, lay stray pieces of coal fallen by day from the flat cars. Alongside the twin bands of steel that gleamed in the moonlight, we found unbroken chunks of the blue-black ore. At each new discovery, cupping the coal in my hands, proud and wide-eyed, I called out to Lazar, "Lookit me! Lookit me!"

"Pebbles," he said scornfully. "Just load the carriage. When the cops find us, you will talk less."

Swinging my bucket, I ran out in front of him, vowing for myself a manly share in the search. I raced along the railroad ties, hunting and probing, until sweat matted my hair. Coal dust hung in the air, stinging my nose and throat. At a siding that shunted off the main track, a locomotive loomed before me. I remembered nights when, with snow blowing in on the east wind, I had lain awake listening to its anguished animal shrieks that pierced the night, echoing down the banks of the Susquehanna and out across the endless pine barrens. Now, timidly, I touched the shining flanks and for a moment stood in awe before its towering, sinewed blackness. Then, scraping its sides for a toe-hold, and grasping the steel pull, I hoisted myself into the cab. From my sovereign perch I joyfully surveyed the colliery in the valley below.

Flames jetted from bellied, earthen furnaces, briefly searing the night like the whiplash crackle of lightning. I saw long trails of coal chutes and tipping cradles as they coursed in a network of black, rough-hewn symmetry. Up from the ground towered two breakers, their heavy warped timbers crusted with coal tar. From the roof, steel booms scaffolded over the yards, dropping from their trolleys slender, tentacled cables. At their base, resting on the pyramided and shining coal piles, black-jawed shovels yawned. Twin smokestacks stabbed sheer and soaring into the sky, belching black smoke in a rhythm ceaseless as breath. Under a belfry of latticed timbers, beneath a frame of wheels and counterweights, I saw hanging the three-tiered cage that lowered the miners into the pits. Finally, as if lured by horror, I stared into the open shaftway, gaping black and bottomless. Then the flames recoiled and flickered out, blackening the valley.

III

Suddenly, below me, voices hissed muted in the darkness. I climbed quickly from the cab, grabbing my bucket.

"Chickie!" I shouted to Lazar. "Chickie the cops!"

I ran across the railroad siding, short-cutting behind a row of empty flatcars. Lazar was not in the clearing where I had left him. I retraced my steps, angling in and out among the cars. I searched for him behind a water tank, and then behind a pile of loose railroad ties. Alone and lost in the darkness, I felt panic claw at my throat. "Lazar!" I called hoarsely, running and weaving wildly. In terror I retraced my steps, and between two cars I stumbled into the waiting hands of a company guard.

Soundlessly, swiftly, he locked my neck with his arm and shook me back and forth. I struggled, kicking and flailing, my screams choked off. I felt suffocated by the sweated stench of his clothes and the stale reek of his alcohol breath. For the first time I felt shame and fury scorch my body. Wrenching my head free, I spat in his face.

"Why, ye thievin' bastard!" he snarled. He pulled at my hair, and in long backstrokes slapped my face with hard-boned knuckles that bloodied my mouth.

Before me, out of the darkness, a coal hod rose, then cracked down with a metallic grind. The guard crumpled at my feet. Suddenly I was freed.

"Run!" hissed Lazar, grabbing my arm.

We raced along the shadows of the flat cars and among the slag heaps, heading for the gates. I heard voices behind us. As we passed a siding near the embankment, I saw the locomotive again.

"Up here," I said, pointing. Lazar hoisted me into the cab, then climbed in after me.

We crouched low on the floor of the cab. I heard the shouts and curses of the guards as they ran beneath us in the darkness. Their boots kicked up cinders and gravel that pelted the wheels. Lazar put his arm around me as we listened and waited. Huddled against him, I heard his deep breathing, and against the warmth of his body I felt fear leave me. In the valley below, I saw lights go on in the company offices. Soon the shouts grew fainter, echoing off the distant coal banks. After a while we climbed down stiffly, and stretched frozen arms and legs.

"Home, now," said Lazar. "Go on alone. And bed for you."

"The coal," I said. "I can carry some."

"What? You like the beatings?"

"We need the coal," I said stubbornly.

"A cholera upon you!" cried Lazar, angrily seizing me by the hair. "Next time I come alone. You are a yoke about my neck. Never before was there such a stupid brother, and may the Lord of the universe never create such another!"

My mouth and chin puckered as I felt the tears well up in me, and my throat go dry. With my small fists I pummeled his chest fiercely.

"We need the coal!" I sobbed.

Lazar knelt down beside me and rumpled my hair. With a grimy, red checkered handkerchief that he drew from his jacket pocket, he wiped my tears and blew my nose. Suddenly he crushed me to him and kissed my cheeks and mouth.

"Yes, young one," he whispered softly. "We need the coal."

And so again we began our quest. We searched futilely for the hods and bucket, but thrown aside on a slag heap, I found my carriage, more battered than ever but staunchly loyal. Slowly, carefully, we scratched for more coal, and tenderly protected it as if it were life's blood. We filled the carriage with such chunks as it could safely bear and headed home. Cold and wet, I welcomed the prospect of warm bed sheets.

As we wheeled the carriage, puffing and snorting up the hill,

I glanced admiringly at Lazar. I watched again the handsome face, the long-lashed brown eyes with the play of light in them, and the full red lips that curled in soft mockery. Of all of us, he was the most in Mama's image, even to her erect, soldierly bearing. Beneath his peaked cap his straight black hair glistened. I pressed close to him, reveling in his willowy young strength.

He looked down at me, then threw back his head in peals of loud laughter.

"Wait till Mama sees you!" he said. "One will truly think the walls of Jerusalem have been breached."

IV

As quietly as we could, we stole into the kitchen. Her back to us, Mama gently rocked to her knitting. Lazar leaned over and kissed her on the back of the neck. She turned around, sighting me.

"Lord of the universe!" she wailed, dropping her needles. She rolled her eyes and flailed her arms heavenward.

"Oi, what has happened?" She glowered at Lazar. "Look at him!"

"True, there is little to recommend him," said Lazar, winking at me.

Pulling me to her bosom, and covering my face with wet, passionate kisses, Mama began to cry.

"Tatanu, mine! Little Tata!" she said, rocking me gently and smothering me in the folds of her blouse. "The oldest brother is too ashamed to look after the young one. A cholera upon him and his oxen head!"

"He needs this oxen head to look after him as he needs the toothache. And I repeat, it is time to cut the hair." Lazar winked at me again.

Seating me on a chair next to the coal stove, Mama opened the door to the baking oven. She wadded down strips of torn white toweling. After pulling off my boots and wet stockings, she placed my bare feet inside.

"Mama," I boasted, "I stole the coal."

Unheeding, she reached above the kitchen sink and took down a large copper tub, oval in shape, with black handles on the ends. She used it to boil bedsheets and white gauze curtains. I had watched her often as she bent over the steaming tub, sweating heavily, and seen how, with a sawed-off baseball bat, she had stirred with loving care the wet sheets as they swelled and billowed in the soapy froth. Mama placed the tub on the kitchen table. Into it she emptied pots of boiling water that hissed against the dented sides and steamed the kitchen walls. She peeled off my layered sweaters. Then she pulled over my head my sacred under-vest, soft and gold-striped, with white silken fringes that clung sweat-clotted to my body. Reverently she folded it and laid it aside. With the back of her hand she tested the water. She lifted me, and despite my howls, immersed me in the tub.

Through the kitchen door walked my sister Esther, her freckled face aflame from the burn of the winter evening. I shouted over to her.

"I stole the coal!"

"Well, now, aren't you the hero!"

Kissing me, she brushed me with a swirl of her long auburn hair. She took from Mama a ball of coarse brown soap, and while Lazar related the events of the evening, she lathered me until I tingled and soap suds frothed above me. I smelled the sweet-sour exhalation of her body.

My brother Shimmon, dull-witted and forever underfoot to the vexation of the family, sat down next to me, his hands laced childlike on his lap. He squinted near-sightedly, heedless of the black hair fallen over his eyes. He hung his head, too abashed to speak, grinning at me to tell me he comprehended all, and was pleased with me.

Then, home from hawking newspapers on Market Street, my brother Herschel walked into the kitchen, blowing on his finger-nails, his wrists lashed with white frozen welts. Beneath his blue wool cap his carroty hair spiked out wildly.

"Up with yer dukes," he said, crouching and squaring off like a boxer. I splashed him with soap suds. Bobbing and weaving, he hit my cheek softly with straight left jabs.

"Ha! Gotcher!"

Then Tata opened the kitchen door from the side alley. He touched the brass-cased scrolls on the door-jamb, then lightly kissed his fingers. For warmth, he flapped his arms across his chest, like an alighting bird, pounding the shoulders of his sheepskin greatcoat.

I shouted to him. "Tata, I stole the coal!"

His brows arched in surprise. Lazar again assumed his storytelling chores. As Tata listened, his black eyes sparkled until finally, slapping his thighs, he threw back his head in booming laughter.

"Truly," he roared to Mama, "you have whelped a cub of Judah!"

He lifted me from the tub and tossed me into the air, then pressed me wet and streaming against himself. He chafed my cheek with his wiry, iron-gray beard that smelled of stale tobacco juice. Standing me on the table, he wrapped a large coarse towel about me and rubbed me dry. Making Lazar retell the story, he danced me about the kitchen. His boots pounded the linoleum floor and sent the overhead gas lamp singing and flickering. Suddenly he lost his footing and we crashed to the floor, while everyone howled and jeered.

"Enough!" cried Mama. "I am accursed with a family of lunatics! Everyone to bed!" She thrashed about her with a towel, and all fled before her in mock terror.

She took the black comb from the cupboard. While I sat on a chair, she combed and brushed my hair again. Then she prepared my bed. On the kitchen floor, near the stove, she rolled out a cotton mattress, which she pounded flat with her fists. She drew over it fresh sheets, and then a down quilt cased in a checked yellow coverlet. Under them she placed hot stones wrapped in towels. I slid beneath the sheets, naked.

From bed I watched her as she banked the coals for the night. She wrapped a soiled woolen shawl about her shoulders, outlining the short heavy figure with the oddly erect sentinel carriage. As she knelt beside me, her long black hair fell on my shoulders. For a moment, the sunken eyes smiled and danced blue, then darkened into deep pools of sadness. With shy tenderness she

54

drew my hand across her cheek. The pockmarked skin rasped my fingers.

"This is to keep off the mists of the night," she said. She hung from my neck a cloth sack of dried herbs.

"And this is to keep away the Evil One." She placed about my neck a brass amulet with a tiny scroll inscribed in Hebrew.

"And this is to keep away bad luck." With the palm of her hand she pressed hard against all the orifices of my face and head, my mouth, my nose, my eyes, my ears, and she kissed each in turn.

"And drink this that one day I will have grandchildren." She gave me a cup of steaming broth prepared from dried mushrooms and mandrake root.

She told me of gehenna where bad boys burned in everlasting ovens, and where the flames shot higher than the colliery furnaces and blazed hotter than Griffith's forge. But I was not to fear, for was I not her tatanu? She kissed me good night, then turned off the gas lamp. In the dark I heard her tread wearily upstairs.

I lay alone on the kitchen floor. I tried to recapture sitting in the cab of the locomotive, but in my sudden weariness the keen edge of elation blunted like a futile daydream. Coals glowed through cracks in the stove shield. For a while I watched their long bony shadows clutching across the walls. Then I slept.

Last Day in Church

BY KENNETH JENKINS

NO, GRANDPA! I felt like jumping up, standing on the pew yelling to him to stop. I felt like running up to the choir, yanking their robes off, smashing Elder Harris's guitar, ramming my fist into Sister Lena's tambourine so that everybody would run after me out of the church and Grandpa would have to stop. But I didn't because I knew the best way to shut my grandfather's mouth tight—to keep him from saying a single word against my sister Ellen in his sermon. I simply prayed to God. I remember that twelve-year-old prayer even now—years later—and I can see Elizabeth, New Jersey, River Street, and the River Street African Zion Church—small, white clapboard; see myself bent over in that hard front pew; see the red windows flushed with the May afternoon sun; smell the lilac perfume of my grandmother who sat on my left, small, shaking from age, wearing her Sunday starched black dress, always smiling up at my grandfather, telling him in that cracking voice to preach, preach, no matter what he said; smell from my right my big sister Ellen's lemon hair oil; smell, too, the stale cabbage smell of the Elizabeth River coming through the one or two windows that were open on the other side of the church. Bent over, putting my fingers over my ears to drown out my grandfather's sermon, I prayed silently. Dear God, don't let him hurt her. She won't do it again. Ellen doesn't know that Grandpa found out what she did. Just me. I know. Don't let him speak against her in church. She'll die. Dear God, she said that she knows Raymond is married and she's not going to go out with him again. She told me this morning right after she fixed breakfast for us that she's going to try to stop loving him, too. Dear God, help her to stop loving him. Ellen's good. She's better than Mom was. She can keep a secret—I tell Ellen everything just the way I do with you, Dear God, and she never let me down. Not once. And she saved up the money herself to buy me this blue suit I'm wearing. She's good. Don't let Grandpa ruin everything for her. And Mom just walked out, left us both to Grandpa, and Pop doesn't come to see us. Don't let Grandpa preach against Ellen. I love Ellen more than anybody else except for You. I, Simon Henry Gordon, will never ask for anything else again. Amen, Dear God, in Jesus name. Amen. I closed my eyes letting that warm feeling move over me that meant my prayer was answered.

When I sat up, my back aching, Grandpa was talking about Sodom and Gomorrah, but I felt safe. Looking ahead at my grandfather in the pulpit, I saw the yellow sunlight on the bumps on his bald head, on his great white eyebrows, on his heavy chin —the yellow even coloring his black robes; I saw the full choir sections on either side of the pulpit. From the corner of my eye, I glanced at Ellen. I couldn't look straight at her because after church Grandpa would say the Devil had hold of me if he thought I wasn't paying attention. I wanted to tell Ellen that everything would be all right. She was fanning herself with those brown cardboard fans with the funeral parlor ads that the Ladies' Auxiliary place in all the pews. The wind from the fan ruffled up the lace around the collar of her blue dress, blew bits of her hair away from her brown face. Ellen was twenty-three then; her eyelashes were long, her nose was straight, her chin smooth, round; but in full face Ellen was off balance—even to me. She told me it was because of an accident she had five years before I was born. She fell in the kitchen while she was cleaning off the top of the refrigerator, ripping her face on the handle. She almost lost an eye, but after they gave her stitches in the hospital her right eye drooped at the end and one nostril lifted higher than the other. The stitches don't show unless you look real close; but her face is off balance when you look straight at her. Everyone says I look like her, except for that. But I don't care. I loved Ellen more than anyone else in the world. I patted her knee carefully so Grandpa couldn't see, but Ellen must have been thinking about something else; she fanned herself slowly, looking up at Grandpa, listening to him as if I wasn't there. I sat back against the hard pew listening to Grandpa's sermon, watching his face, lighter than mine—the color of bone—hard as bone; seeing his black robes flap around his legs as he walked back and forth behind the pulpit, his voice screaming, yelling, shrieking, then whispering as he raised his arms over the pulpit toward us.

"Yes, yes. The Lord struck it down. Struck it down!" He slammed both fists on the pulpit. "Evil can't stay long in God's world. You know that?" he added softly. "Sooner or later God speaks. Do you know that? Sisters. Brothers. God speaks. Did he speak to the people in Sodom?"

"Preach, preach," my grandmother said, smiling up at my grandfather.

I heard many other voices in back of me saying, "Yes, yes." Without turning around I knew that squeaky voice yelling,

"Speak to us, Reverend Dawes, speak," belonged to old Mrs. Bailey who was asked to leave the choir because of that voice.

"Did he speak to the people in Gomorrah?" he whispered.

"Preach, preach," my grandmother said, glancing at me.

"He spoke to them. He destroyed their evil!" He looked from one side of the small church to the other as if he expected us any minute to flash up in a puff of smoke.

The congregation said, "Amen, amen." I felt Ellen move away from me a little, toward the aisle. My grandfather paused, looked behind him at the choir seated on his right, on his left. "But then that was before He gave us Jesus."

"Yes, Lord."

"And Jesus came here to take up all our sins. Do you know that?" He looked right at Ellen, but I knew God wouldn't let him do more than give her hard looks. God wouldn't let him say a word against her. "Yes, Jesus knows we're all sinners. All of us."

"Preach, preach."

Ellen fanned herself, stopped, rested the fan in her lap. I saw the corner of her mouth pull down, the way it did when she came home last December telling me to stop doing my homework for a minute, to circle the day on the kitchen calendar, because she decided to give up housework; she said she wasn't going to clean no madam's house again, only house she would clean would be her own. She was going to find herself a new job, no matter how hard they are to get in Elizabeth.

"Rich and poor," he yelled, "man and woman, old and young. We're all sinners. Sinners!" he stamped his foot hard on the floor.

"Yes, yes," said old Mrs. Bailey.

"You know," he bent over the pulpit, "white people ought to be in church all the time."

"Amen. Amen."

"But no need for us to feel righteous, because we all of us sinners! Jesus knows it and only reason He let them drive those nails into the soft flesh of his palm"—he stood in front of the pulpit, arms, legs, spread eagle fashion—"only reason He let them drive those nails into his feet—Yes Yes—was to save us. Only reason He let them whip Him till the blood run down—"

"Tell it. Preach!"

"—was to save us."

"Amen."

"All you have to do is say I'm sorry." He stepped to the edge of the platform, smiling. "That's all."

"I'm sorry. Sorry."

"All you have to do is stand up before God—before His bleeding hands—" he shook his head from side to side as if he himself were in agony "—and His bleeding body and say, 'I'm a sinner. I'm sorry. I won't sin no more.' Even if your sins are red. Even if your sins are scarlet, say 'I'm sorry—.' "

"Yes, Lord."

"Now stand up for Jesus."

As if at a signal the choir stood erect in their red velvet robes, Elder Harris playing his big steel guitar stepping away from the basses, Sister Edna sitting with the sopranos slowly shaking the tambourine as we all bowed our heads, humming to the words of the hymn. But all during the hymn I saw the tears running down Ellen's face. I whispered to her, as loud as I dared, over and over that it was all right, all right. God made everything all right.

> *We has a hard time,*
> *We has a hard time,*
> *Don't God's children have a hard time?*
> *Just stop right still and steady yourself,*
> *Don't God's children have a hard time?*
> *God's going to move this ark Himself,*
> *Don't God's children have a hard time?*

"Everything will be all right. Don't cry," I whispered to Ellen. My grandmother reached over, her starched black dress touching me, reminding me to attend to my grandfather who was standing right in front of me, arms folded, staring at Ellen.

> *Religion is like a blooming rose.*
> *Don't God's children have a hard time?*
> *None can tell it but them that knows.*
> *Don't God's children have a hard time?*

He motioned the choir to silence; they stopped singing in ragged edges, the altos and basses first, the sopranos holding on for two or three measures.

"Now all you have to do is stand up," he said straight to Ellen. "Jesus knows we sin. We all sinners. Preachers—even though we do the Lord's work—Devil can creep around to us, too."

His eyes were on Ellen who, head bowed, looked at the fan in her lap. I knew he couldn't say any more than he did—God wouldn't let him; I wanted to tell her a joke about Dirty Parker whose ears were so dirty Miss McCready said right out in class that the flies were going to lay their eggs and raise a family where his brains should be. But I didn't say anything; I didn't even reach over to tell her that everything would be all right.

"Now the Devil got to my own family," he said in his everyday speaking voice—the one he uses around the house to ask about the furnace, how Grandma is feeling, what Ellen is cooking for dinner. He hung his head. "To my own daughter's child."

"Yes, he did," said my grandmother.

She knew. My hands shaking, I looked over at her dark face, blurred with wrinkles, at her eyes yellow with the misery that she said God saw fit to give her. Grandpa is talking against Ellen.

"Stand up, Ellen. You're a sinner. Stand up! Jesus will forgive you, honey."

"Yes, He will, child," someone said behind me.

My prayer. God let him say it. God let him hurt Ellen.

"All you have to do is say before Jesus that you won't sin no more. Trust in God. He'll never let you down. Stand up, child." He stepped down from the raised platform, into the aisle, leaning over Ellen, arms outstretched as if Ellen were a baby taking her first step and he ready to catch her if she fell.

Ellen sat still looking down at the fan in her lap, the corner of her mouth drawn down, the curls around her forehead falling over her face, over the lace collar.

"Stand up, child!" He yelled so loudly Ellen jumped to her feet, the fan clattering to the floor, her hand rushing to the right side of her face where the eye drooped. "God knows we all sin. You been seen sinning with Raymond Small—coming out MacGovern's Tavern at night, then going with him to his parked car. You been seen, girl. What you do at night comes out in the day. Can't hide nothing from the Lord. But all you got to do is say 'I'm sorry, Jesus. I'll sin no more.'"

"Yes. Yes. Sin no more," said my grandmother.

God didn't answer my prayer. I prayed right here in church. I looked up at my grandfather and at Ellen, saw the tears in both their eyes.

"I ain't sorry," said Ellen.

My grandfather stepped back as if the Devil himself said how do you do to him. The church was quiet. The shuffling in the choir as they arranged their robes—silence. Only the sloshing of the Elizabeth River coming through the windows on the other side.

"I ain't sorry." Both of her hands were fist; her mouth a straight line. "I didn't do nothing wrong. He asked me out; I went out. We just sat there in that place and talked. I did go there but I didn't drink nothing; he didn't ask me to neither. I just sat there listening to him."

"Stop! Don't let the Devil lay hold to you," he shouted. "Listen to Jesus telling you that all you have to do is say you're sorry, come to Me."

"I can't. I didn't do nothing wrong."

"Then Sister Ellen, we going to have to pray for you." He walked to the pulpit, stretching his arms out for everyone to bow down.

She turned to me. "What's wrong with you?"

"Nothing."

"No need for them to pray for me. It happened just like I told you this morning."

I held out the fan to give to her, but she shook her head.

"We going to pray for my granddaughter's saving." He fell to his knees. Ellen stood upright, her head high. I knew everyone behind me was bent over listening to his prayer that Ellen should listen to Jesus. I wanted to stand straight up like Ellen; I couldn't bend low and pray like the others. Not any more. I just hung my head listening to Ellen mumble as my grandfather prayed in a voice that made the windows shake.

"I'm leaving," she whispered to me. "Come on, let's go. You

have to live life as you see it. Come on. We can make it somehow."

"Sin is everywhere. We sin, because the devil is strong. He's bigger than the highest skyscraper man can make, and he's beautiful, too. Don't let the Devil win, Lord. . . ."

"Come on, Simon. We'll leave the church, we'll leave grandpa's house. Momma couldn't stand living his way. Pappa don't even try. Come on, Simon, we'll make it by ourselves."

I sat, my head half bowed, eyes closed, holding on to the fan with both hands, praying that God make Grandpa say he was sorry he said all that about Ellen. But no warm feeling came. I opened my eyes, reading "Makin's Funeral Parlor, 85 West Street, El. 5-4000" across the face of the fan.

"Shake the Devil loose from her, Lord. The man belongs to another woman, Lord, in your holy union. Set my only granddaughter free of this man. He's doing the Devil's work."

"I don't want to be set free of him," Ellen muttered. "Come on." After a while she stopped tugging me. "Don't you want to come?"

I said nothing.

"I'm going." I watched her walk up the aisle, heels clacking on the wooden floor. I saw the doors swing as she left the church.

"The Devil won." The choir began to sing the song we sing at funerals.

> *Just as well to love Me, Brother,*
> *You got to die,*
> *You got to die,*
> *Just as well to love Me, Sister,*
> *You got to die,*
> *You got to die,*
> *Just as well to love me, Brother . .*

I wanted to stand up to look through the window at Ellen. She would be crossing the narrow bridge over the river by now, walking toward Broad Street to catch the bus. While the choir sang again, "You got to die, you got to die," I held on to Ellen's fan, folding the hard cardboard in half, then in fourths, putting it in the inside pocket of the blue suit Ellen bought for me with her own money. While the choir was singing, I stood up, walking out of the church to follow Ellen. My grandmother reached out trying to stop me, but her hand shook; it could not hold on hard like Grandpa's.

Paid with Moan

BY DORA JEAN JOHNSON

> *Nothing begins, and nothing ends,*
> *That is not paid with moan;*
> *For we are born in other's pain,*
> *And perish in our own.*
>
> *—Francis Thompson*

THE WOODEN TABLE once laden with slabs of sugar-cured ham and platters of steaming white biscuits, soft and slightly suntanned, now offered only one biscuit per person and one-half cup of coffee for each adult. Fatback disappeared, replaced by fresh tomatoes for breakfast. The cream gravy became increasingly thinner, milk-white and bland as starch water. Salt was a commodity few could afford.

Thus hard times came to Greenlake, S. C., textile center of the South, "Garden Spot of the World." Except for this drastic, grotesque change in meals, it made very little difference in the external lives of the people. To cotton mill hands the years were always lean. True, there was more time now to sit in the seething July sun sewing panties, shirts, and slips out of printed flour sacks or sprawl on the floor whittling half-soles from cardboard boxes for shoes with holes in the bottom big as a half dollar piece. Suits, dresses, and coats blossomed forth with patches of green, yellow, and red, a virtual flower-box of colors, and still the people did not feel the difference. As always they lived quietly in their yellow clapboard houses for twenty cents a room, and deprivation, a companion familiar as their children's faces, held little fear. The pain, when it finally came, struck hard like a hammer blow straight to the pit of their pride. The battle lay now in somehow not reducing themselves to beg, borrow, or steal.

For fifteen years May Hunt had worked eight hours a day in Hudson mill. Her foot had pressed a large pedal while her eyes remained transfixed on the bolt of cloth rolling over a lighted frame. Her small cracked hands had shot forward deftly, plucking defects from the streaming cloth. The strained eyes, the swollen foot, and the cracked hands rested now. Four out of five days the mill was silent and dark. Time lay like a heavy shroud around her. The lives of her three children lay heavier on her heart. Dawn rode in, broke the back of night, the same as it had done for all her thirty-five years, and the days waned away in somnambulistic rhythm.

II

As soon as she saw the thin streak of gray light peep thru a slit in the green window shade, May's eyes opened wide. She lay quite still for a moment, feeling the tranquility of sleep slip from her body like a silk undergarment. Slowly the muscles tightened in the back of her neck. Finally the question itself crept in, hanging like a daily motto on the wall of her mind.

"What in the world we gonna do?"

She turned to look at her husband sleeping beside her, his long thin body stretching the length of the bed. For a moment, she listened to the short puffs of his breath, then reaching over tapped him lightly on the naked shoulder.

"Len, you better git up if you gonna go to town this morning."

"Huh? Uh, yeh. Okay."

He rolled over, grunted, and covered his naked shoulder with the sheet. May swung her body upright, let her feet slide to the floor, felt the first shock of the cool linoleum beneath them.

Stooping down, she groped under the bed for her oxfords, still talking aloud to the sleeping figure.

"Shore gonna be a scorcher today. Be hot'n nough to fry a egg out there in a while."

She slipped her feet into oxfords, leaving the strings untied so that they tapped a light rhythm against the linoleum as she shuffled around the foot of the bed.

"What ye want fer breakfast?"

The question was formulated out of sheer habit, and she left it trailing behind her, hanging in the bedroom air, not expecting an answer. At the end of the hall, she paused, opened the back bedroom door, and spoke to her children.

"Ya'll git up now. Breakfast'll be ready in a little bit."

"Yes, Mam."

In the familiar kitchen her body, now fully awakened, moved with precision from cabinet to table to stove. Removing a large wooden bowl from the cabinet, she sifted a mound of flour into it, added a dash of milk, a glass of water, then plunged her hands into the soft white mass, kneading it with her fingers. Sounds of banging closet doors, running water, flushing toilets, drifted in from the other rooms, mingled with the clatter of pots and the creak of the oven door, rising slowly to the symphonic pitch of a household shaking itself from sleep. The family finally sat together around the table.

"Gloria, I know fangers wuz made fore forks, but use ye fork anyway."

She reached over the table and placed the fork in the child's hand.

"Len, we aint got a speck a milk left in the house. I used the last bit fer gravy this morning."

He took a gulp of hot coffee, wiped his mouth with the back of his hand, then patted his pants pocket.

"Well, you know well as myself that's about empty. I got maybe a dime to my name. I'll leave it here, though. You'n take Gloria up to J.D.'s an git a can a milk ater while."

"Reckon you'll git sump'n to do today?"

"I jest dont know, May. I'll do my best. Time I walk all a way to town though they's done more people down there looking fer jobs'n you'n shake a stick at."

His voice heavy. Long weeks of weariness danced a little flat-footed jig on the edge of despair.

"Well, anyway I still got one day a week at the mill. I reckon that's better'n nothing a tall."

She tried to sound a note of cheerfulness.

"Be dogged if we dont have a Chinaman's luck though. Ye sister Lily said that Doc jest went down town the other morning'n this man give'm a job right off. He's selling the Piedmont paper down on Pendelton street. I reckon that's a bit of a come down fer them though. They so used to living high off the hog."

He pushed back his chair from the table.

"Well, what Doc's doing ain't helping us none. I gotta go. Don't guess I'll be back fore supper."

"We'll wait fer ye."

He left by the back door, his tall figure striding down the steps, through the uncut pasture grass, toward the Anderson road that led into town. She broke off a piece of biscuit and handed it across the table to her smallest child.

"Here, sop up the rest a that good gravy. It'll make ye grow."

III

By the time May and Gloria left the house, the street that ran up the hill to J.D.'s store was already steaming hot. The melting black tar stuck to their shoe soles. May reached down and tucked a strand of Gloria's hair behind her ear.

"We gotta melt some soap and wash that hair whenever we git back."

"Can I play some first?"

"You'n play out on the porch. Sun'll dry ye hair nice."

The child kicked a loose piece of gravel along in front of her.

"Honey, don't kick like that. Ye jest git that ole tar all over ye shoes and its a pain to git off."

The child stopped kicking but resumed her questioning.

"What we going to J.D.'s fer?"

66

"To git a can a milk, and listen now I want you to behave yerself'n not be asking fer ever thang ye see. You know mama'd buy anythang she could fer ye, but she jest aint got the money right now. Now will ye remember that?"

"Okay, but can we stop at Uncle Docs a few minutes?"

"Honey, they aint got no time to mess with us a visiting."

"Please, mam. Jest fer a minute."

"Okay, but we can't stay more'n a minute or two."

At the corner they turned, walked up between two neat rows of petunias, and knocked on the front door. Aunt Lily, a tall, slender, dark woman answered it.

"Well, look who's here. Ya'll come in."

She walked down the hall toward the kitchen. May and Gloria followed her.

"Ya'll come in the kitchen. We's jest having a bite to eat."

In the kitchen, uncle Doc and cousin Jo were already seated at the table. Steam rose from a bowl of scrambled eggs, hot biscuits lay on a platter piled high atop one another.

"Jo, look who's come to see ye. Well, can't ye say hello to ye aunt May'n Gloria."

"Hello."

"Hello, Jo. How you?"

"Fine."

Lily sat down at the table and began dishing out the steaming eggs. Doc made a motion toward a stool in a nearby corner.

"Jest pull up that stool'n sit down, May."

"No. Now ya'll jest go ahead'n dont mind us. Gloria jest wanted to stop by fer a minute on the way to the store."

"Well, ya'll don't have to rush right off. Sit down a while anyway."

May pulled up the stool, sat down, and pulled Gloria up on her knee. The child's eyes focused in a steady gaze on the bowl of eggs and pile of biscuits.

"Well Gloria. How you been? What you been doing since school's out?"

The child did not answer. May shook her vigorously.

"What'sa matter? Cat got ye tongue? Ye aunt Lily's talking to ye."

"I'm fine. I aint done nothing much, jest play."

Gloria leaned forward now, whispering into her mother's ear. May shook her again, looking sternly down at her.

"You don't need it."

Lily turned her head at the sound of their voices.

"What is it she wants?"

Gloria blurted out the words before her mother's protest could intervene.

"Thank ye, mam, for a butter biscuit."

May's voice took on the tone of embarrassed anger.

"Why Gloria, aint you ashamed a yourself. We jest got up from the table. She don't need a thang."

Lily buttered a biscuit and handed it to the child.

"Ah, here, May, let 'er have it. I jest never thought one time bout asking ya'll if you'd eat."

"That's all right. We jest got up from the table, but you know a young'n. They thank they got have some a everythang they see."

She stood up and gripped Gloria tightly by the hand.

"I guess we better git on up to the store. Ya'll come down to see us sometime. Gloria say bye to Jo and thank ye aunt Lily fer the biscuit."

"Thank ye fer the biscuit. Bye, Jo. Bye, Uncle Doc."

"Bye. Ya'll come back to see us."

The door closed behind them. May looked down at the child's cheeks puffed out with wads of bread.

"Gloria, I swear if I ever see you do that agin I'll tan your hide till you cant sit down. I taught you better'n that."

"But I wuz hongry."

They walked rapidly up the hill without speaking.

IV

The full moon floated up over the oak tree like a big balloon that just lost its string. May began setting the plates and calling the children to supper.

"Ya'll come on in now. Ye Daddy'll be here in a few minutes."

The front door screen slammed as Len walked in, wiping the back of his neck with a stained white handkerchief.

"Supper ready?"

"Yeh. All it likes is jest setting down to eat."

He stuffed the handkerchief into his back pocket and pulled a chair up to the table. The children came in and sat down on the other side. May set a bowl of pinto beans on the table, then put one corn fritter in each plate.

"Any luck today?"

"Yeh, but it wuz all bad. You know I walked slam from one end a town to the other. Beats anythang I ever seen. Even the littlest jobs scarceer'n hens teeth."

She looked down at her plate, crumbled up the corn fritter, and poured some bean soup over it.

"Well, I always said we could live on bread'n water if we had to. Be dogged if it don't look like we might have to fore long."

Len's face flushed. Beads of sweat stood out on his forehead. He raised his fork in the air and pointed across the table.

"It worries me, May, jest as much as you, but I've done everythang in my power. How ye thank I feel walking my legs off ever day'n gittin nothing fer it?"

Tears welled up in her eyes. She sniffed, swallowed hard, and held them back. He spoke apologetically.

"I'm sorry fer yelling at ye. It's jest that I'm tired, wore out'n cranky, I reckon. They ain't no need to cry bout it."

She looked up, the tears flowing freely now, racing in tiny rivulets along each side of her nose.

"It ain't that I'm crying bout no how."

"What'sa matter then?"

"I'm jest thanking bout the way Doc'n Lily treated me'n Gloria when we stop by there on the way to the store. You know, Len, they's settin down to eat'n Gloria jest kept looking at the table, and you know they never once ask that young'n to have sumpin to eat."

She rubbed her nose vigorously with the back of her hand.

"Gloria finally blated out fore I could stop'er ask fer a biscuit. An you know Lillian had the gall to jest pretend she fergot to ask us if we'd eat yet."

He ran his fingers slowly through his hair.

"Well, Lily's like that, ye know. I guess she jest didn't thank."

Her face paled with anger, and her words poured out now in a staccato rhythm like small firecrackers popping inside her.

"Well, they've fergot them days when Doc didn't have a job to his name'n Jo wuz jest a little bitty thang. You know yeself I split ever can a milk Gloria had with Lily jest so her young'n could stay alive, but no sir, they don't thank bout that no more."

He nodded his head. When he spoke, his words came forth heavy and labored like long gray ribbons of agony and confusion.

"I know, May. I remember all about it."

Her face slackened, and her eyes suddenly widened as if some unimagined horror had just presented itself before her. She shook her head in disbelief, strands of gray hair falling on her forehead, clinging to her wet cheeks where the tears flowed unrestrained.

"I tell you, Len, that hurt me. It hurt me right down to the quick. I never thought I'd live to see the day my young'nd be that hongrey."

"I wish to God I never had."

Where No Sea Runs

EXCERPT FROM A NOVEL BY AMANDA ROWE

> Light breaks where no sun shines;
> Where no sea runs, the waters of the heart
> Push in their tides;
> And, broken ghosts with glowworms in their heads;
> The things of light
> File through the flesh where no flesh decks the bones.
> —Dylan Thomas

AND WHO do you want to see come over the hill?" asked Anne.

"God and Jesus," said Jocelyn.

"No, I mean, who do you really want to see?"

"God and Jesus," was the insistent reply. Jocelyn knew that

Anne wanted her to say "the Harrison boys," but whenever she and Anne came to the Country Club grounds of the Massachusetts sea town to worship their special trees, rocks and hills, Jocelyn wished always that God and Jesus really would come.

The two girls walked quickly toward a large oak which had been their first "wood" idol. After repeating a long prayer which Jocelyn had written, they went to another tree, rock, or hill each week and gave it a special name, like Eden Tree or Jesus' Tree. Two weeks ago they named a tiny spruce tree Heaven Tree. Last week its rock of mottled granite was named Heaven Rock, and now, late in this early spring afternoon, they were going to name the hill.

The tallest hill on the club grounds! Their saddle shoes slushed through the soft earth as they crossed the dirt bridge of the brook and ran up slippery grass. No leaves yet; only tiny unopened buds on black tree branches. When they reached the top of the hill, the crisp blue sky was without a cloud. They began praying to the lovely spruce tree:

> *Oh, Heaven Tree; we worship thee . . .*
> *Oh, God of Heaven Tree.*

They kissed the tree and stood for two minutes in silence. The rock was next; Anne sprinkled holy brook water on the rock as they recited a hymn of praise:

> *Oh, blessed Heaven Rock; we worship thee . . .*
> *Oh, rock by Heaven Tree; we kneel to thee.*
> *Oh, God of Heaven Rock.*

Now they made final preparations for naming this tallest of all hills. From the top they could see the golden spire of the church on the village green; tiny houses marched into the serene orchid ocean; silver gulls swooped majestically across the faraway white beach; white pebbled cemeteries lay not too far away, awesome in their stillness; and to the west, the majestic pine forest where an old gray stone powder mill stood, remnant from a long-ago war, now a haven for sparrows and later on spring robins; no wind blew in the hushed air; only chapel bells singing their five o'clock Angelus and the yelping of happy dogs running freely at the bottom of the hill slope mingled with silence.

"I name thee Heaven Hill," cried Jocelyn. This was repeated three times. "Let us pray: *Oh, blessed Heaven Hill . . . Oh, blessed tallest hill of all. It is you we love most, oh, God of Heaven Hill."* They kissed the soft grass and earth; then, without speaking, they ran down the slippery slope as far as the brook.

"Let's wade," suggested Jocelyn. And they did, although a sudden bitter chill ran through the air as the sun dropped suddenly in the west. Icy water tingled their toes and ankles; after a futile attempt to dry their feet with handkerchiefs, they started home in soggy socks and shoes which burned their feet as they squished through the grass.

At the edge of the club they parted. Jocelyn walked through the new cemetery near the birches where they had first started tree worshipping by her friend Myra Gaskill's grave (so young to die, they said), across the old cemetery where, hidden beneath clusters of decayed gray ivy, was the rumored grave of John Wilkes Booth's brother. On the other side of the cemetery she passed the grave of her great-grandfather, "Solomon Rowe, died in 1776." Soon she came to her grandmother's house, which was white, large, and where only her grandmother, a New England mystic, lived.

She passed through her grandmother's garden, thinking of how lovely it would be when lilac bushes, golden daffodils, lavender columbines, red geraniums, and wild pink roses bloomed. She could see her grandmother's century plant in the window and remembered what an important event its blooming had been; why, the minister and all had come, and it was even written up in the *Manchester Cricket.*

As she reached the broken brown storm door of the four-room house where she and her parents lived behind her grandmother's, she suddenly stopped and huddled in the corner of the door: "They're fighting again. . . ."

"I don't care what the hell you say! You're not goin' to any damn bingo game again. You been out four nights this week; what's the matter with you? Can't stay in one night?"

"It's not that, Art." The spoon with which she stirred some-thing on the stove scraped the pan. "Its just that I can't hang around this house all day and night, too. You know that by now. God, my life's been miserable ever since I married you."

"Then why in the hell did you marry me? You knew I didn't have no money."

"Yes, I knew that, but I suppose I was afraid to be alone the rest of my life. If only Bill hadn't left me for that social-climbing bitch twelve years ago, I still might be going to the Astor Ball or the opera, living in New York . . . so what happens? I'll tell you what happens. I marry you, and you end up selling fruits and vegetables for six years!"

"Ya? Maybe so. But I got an electrician's job now, ain't I?"

"So what. Any money you do make goes to that mother of yours. That's what happens. And me? What happens to me? I get stuck in this four-room shack with no heat or hot water, while she lives in the lap of luxury, the lap of luxury, I tell you. That's what happens. I end up in this four-room fire trap—and she?" The scraping of the spoon in the pan became louder and faster.

"Shut your damn mouth or I'll rap you. Go ahead out tonight. Go on to your goddamn bingo; get the hell out. Who wants you anyway!"

"I swear if I hadn't been so lonely that summer, I'd never have married you, and don't forget it for one minute. I'd leave you today if it wasn't for the kid. Poor kid—if we keep fighting like this, we'll make a nervous wreck out of her. The doctor told me that, so you see what you're doin' to the kid?"

"Oh ya, well it wasn't me that emptied the kid's piggy bank and spent it on an old bingo game. Who did that to the poor kid? 'Poor kid' is right. Don't even have a decent mother to look after her nights."

"Shut up or I'll leave you, I'll leave you tonight!"

Jocelyn could hear a great movement now; a chair fell on the floor and she opened the door. Her father stood there, purple veins in his forehead vibrating as he grit his teeth, with one small hand grasping her mother's shoulder and shaking it; with the other he clenched a tarnished fork, the prongs about two inches away from her mother's heart.

73

"Don't daddy, please don't. Don't kill her. Please don't kill her!"

He put the fork down slowly; silence now, except for her father's heavy asthmatic breathing. Her mother swallowed bitter tears of fright and hatred.

"Come on, dear," she said. "We've been waiting supper for you. There now, don't cry. It's all over now; come on. Sit down and please eat your supper."

They sat in the dreary kitchen, none of them eating much. Canned beans and tomatoes again with peanut butter sandwiches for dessert. Burnt-orange and brown linoleum showed its scars unashamedly; a huge black coal stove overheated the tiny kitchen; a bathtub which they never used (it was easier to heat water on the stove and wash in the black porcelain sink) was covered with a dirty orange and green cretonne makeshift cover. On a shelf over the tub was a conglomeration of contest entry blanks her mother had saved; an old black clock with chipped dial and craggy bent hand; a smoky yellow hurricane lamp, in case lights went out during a storm; a large ashtray containing lost buttons, pins and old lottery tickets; and a peculiar old brown radio on which she and her father listened to their favorite stories, like Bulldog Drummond. Cabinets to the left of the stove, their green paint chipped and peeling, were filled with cracked dishes that didn't match. A strange aura, caused by the only new appurtenance, a long neon light with two sleek tubes which hung over the gloomy table, filled the room.

From the window, Jocelyn could see the light vaguely reflected on a dirt road, Stanley Avenue, which ran awkwardly beside another cemetery surrounded by gray broken clapboards; the grass always needed cutting, except for one spot where she and Myra had gathered chestnuts and made necklaces of them a few years before . . . but then, Myra had died.

More pleasant to look at was the picture above the table. Its glass frame was greasy and soot-covered, but behind the soot was a family of grouses, all in purple, gold, red, and blue, contentedly sitting in the middle of a rich green forest, plump and warm, caught in eternal sunlight.

"Eat dear," pleaded her mother.

74

"How in the hell you expect that kid to eat, after what goes on here?"

And she ate, because it would be better for all of them. She picked up the ugly-smelling squashy beans one by one on her tarnished fork. The peanut butter sandwiches weren't so bad; she washed them down with chocolate milk.

Her mother put on water to do the dishes; then she rushed into her imitation white fox coat, kissed Jocelyn goodby, and ran to get the six o'clock bus to Gloucester. On her way out, she cried to Jocelyn, "Maybe I'll hit a big one tonight, and if I hit enough big ones, dear, you and I'll get out of here. We'll go far away, and I'll give you piano lessons again, and maybe singing, too."

After Jocelyn finished the dishes, she went to the little Greek store and bought some ginger ale and ice cream. She and her father always enjoyed this as a treat later in the night.

Although she could read herself, he read the comics to her. Poor dumb Henry, Jiggs and Maggie, and best of all, Mandrake the Magician, who she dreamed might someday come and carry her away, or change everything; after all, something like that happened to Shirley Temple in "The Little Princess."

After the comics came Lowell Thomas, Gabriel Heatter, and Mr. Keene, Tracer of Lost Persons. They sat in the living room where they moved the peculiar brown radio. Another smaller black coal stove choked out heat here; a dilapidated studio couch (where her father slept) covered with old army blankets, two soiled cinnamon armchairs, and an out-of-tune upright piano (given her by Mr. Beach, leader of the town band concerts) rested on the cold green linoleum floor.

She loved to brush her father's silver hair because it was so soft; she stroked it, combed it with water, and then brushed it for hours. She could smell the Vicks Vapor rub under his flannel shirt and hear his rhythmic wheezing from the asthma.

"You better go to bed, sweetheart; school tomorrow. You keep doin' good in school and Daddy'll try to give you music lessons again. Do you like the piano?"

"I like it very much," she said. After kissing her father good night, she ran up the narrow stairs which lay between the kitchen and living room.

Her bedroom was the same size as the downstairs rooms. She had no closet and could see her new orchid Easter dress hanging first on the metal bar which ran across part of one wall. Myra was buried in orchid and white, she had been told (she wasn't allowed at the funeral, being so young).

New black patent leather sandals lay on the clapboard floor. The dressing table was covered with a faded green silk skirt, and yellowed white muslin curtains which hung at the window were beginning to tear; on the table were her Bible presented for excellence in saying the Ten Commandments and the Beatitudes the year before, several multicolored hair ribbons, a bottle of Evening in Paris perfume; an old gray tortoise-shell mirror; a cigar box holding tiny rings and a moonstone necklace given her by her grandmother a long time ago; but that was before her father's twin brother died of asthma. "Was that woman who did it! That no-good divorcee from New York. Marrying Art. Why, him and his brother'd been together for thirty-eight years. What'd she think? Landsakes, breakin' up a set of twins like that!"

Jocelyn's childhood stood on the bookcase: *Pollyana, The Bobbsey Twins, Now We Are Six, Black Beauty,* and *The Little Minister* beside *Heidi.* Thirteen dolls slept soundly in an orange and green cretonne-covered chest in the corner. She hadn't thought of them for a long time.

Jocelyn heard her father snoring downstairs. She shut off the naked light bulb with its long string, and sat in an old wicker rocking chair by her bedroom window. The silver moon slept over her grandmother's budding lilac bushes. She stared at the black silent night, and remembered the fight again (not really forgetting it, but being so used to this sort of thing by now, she often just quivered for long hours inside, didn't try to stop anything anymore). She decided to think of happier days now.

They were always poor, but for some years her father had a vegetable and fruit truck in which he often took her to Salem market at five o'clock in the morning. They ate breakfast at Hayes Bickford's, and all the giantlike men, especially Mr. Murphy, who had a bulbous red nose, gave her shiny copper pennies. She often went on her father's route around the village; always sure to receive freshly baked oatmeal cookies at Mrs.

Connor's, and always sure to devour half a crate of red cherries from the fruit truck.

On the Fourth of July her father took her and Myra to the Country Club where they could listen to Mr. Beach's Band Concert in the section roped-off for the townspeople; they then would go home and set off sparklers and caterpillars in the back yard.

She thought of her father's friend, Jim Burnside. He drank quite a bit, they said, and had a dog like Rin-Tin-Tin (a distant cousin, he told Jocelyn) who could count, and who once saved a little girl as she ran across the street in front of a car at the Catholic church. Jim made a footstool for Jocelyn's piano, where her feet wouldn't reach the floor.

And the time she was a bride in the Legion Minstrel show. How her mother had glowed over that, taking such care to make her lace satin costume, teaching her to walk like a bride and bow like a Metropolitan Opera star; afterwards she bought Jocelyn a real Mickey Mouse watch with some money she won at bingo.

Sometimes her mother took her to the movies to see Ginger Rogers, Jane Withers, or Abbott and Costello; once they saw a real stage show at the Paramount Theatre in Salem; Shep Fields was there and millions of crystal bubbles floated up to the ceiling. After the movies they had an ice cream sundae in Moustaki's overly candied ice cream parlor, with its multitudinous mirrors making millions of green and pink kisses and silver wrapped chocolates.

And then Jocelyn remembered her secret and Anne's; trees, rocks and hills at the club. She climbed into bed and soon dreamt of the biggest hill of all. She and Anne were there at the top. Five o'clock in the afternoon; only it didn't stop ever being five o'clock in the afternoon. Still no wind, and the sun didn't move in the west. She drank in the smells of the spruce and faintly salt air.

The spire of the church was golden forever, and the chapel bells sang forever. "It is you we love most, oh, God of Heaven Hill." And God and Jesus walked slowly across Heaven Hill and met them.

The First Stars Were Shining

BY SHEILA M. McMAHON

S T. PETER's was almost deserted on this Saturday afternoon, and as the heavy oak door shut behind Lucy it closed out the small Maine village of Ocean's Edge with its salty air and narrow winding streets that she had known for her fifteen years. There were only three other people scattered through the wooden rows that flanked her on either side as she stood on the worn maroon carpet in the center aisle. Although nearly four o'clock on a winter's afternoon, the lights had not yet been turned on, and the last rays of sunlight sifted in through the multicolored glass windows and spilled over Lucy's shoulders as she genuflected and sank down on the leather-covered wooden kneeler in a pew on the left, in the rear of the church.

Lucy blessed herself and lowered her head onto her clasped hands that were braced on the back of the pew in front of her. The small white frame church was cold and drafty, the candles lit on the black iron stands in the front of the church flickered, and the features of the large white marble statues seemed to be constantly shifting in the shadows. Lucy looked away from the cold unseeing stare of the Lady with her bare foot on a snake and back to the dark wooden floor under her. "How pure everything looks!" Lucy thought. "How peaceful it seems in here."

She watched as Father Murphy entered through the side door of the church and crossed to the center aisle. Tall and thin, he knelt for a moment on one knee, his head bowed before the altar with its white linen cloth and gold filigreed crucifix, and Lucy could see the grey fringe of hair over the white collar of his vestments.

Father Murphy had been with St. Peter's parish for more than fifteen years. Lucy couldn't remember ever thinking of church without the picture of Father Murphy coming to mind. As a first grader in St. Peter's grade school, Lucy remembered Father coming into the classroom almost every day after morning prayers, and all the children sitting up tall with folded hands and expectant smiles, hoping Father would take the time to tell one of his stories—stories of his boyhood in Chicago, stories of the children (just like them!) who had become Saints, a few words to explain some of the mysterious words of the catechism lesson. Lucy never tired of hearing stories of the lives of the Saints; when Father Murphy was telling the story, the person sounded real and human, not like the wooden statues that stood on the sunny window sills in the classrooms. When Father walked around the schoolyard at noontime, the children clustered around him, sometimes just listening, and sometimes asking the questions they could ask no one else.

"Father, is it true if you tell a lie, you'll go to Hell?"

"Why do you ask that, Jim?"

"Sister Joseph told us that this morning." Visions of an unknown place with never-ending fire swam before Lucy's eyes.

Father Murphy had bent down, folding his tall frame almost in half to get down to eye level with them, answering, "No, children. Not exactly. Not all lies could be that big or that important. Sister told you that so you would all remember to try never to tell a lie. Do you understand?"

A chorus of "Yes, Father" was their answer, as Hell's fires retreated a step for Lucy and the other six-year-olds.

II

"Father always has the right answer," Lucy thought, as she watched him walking down the side aisle toward the confessional, peeking through her fingers as he opened the grill-work door and settled himself, twisting the long black robe from under himself in the narrow box.

Lucy could taste her heart pounding in the back of her throat as she stood up and sidled over in the pew toward the confessional. She prayed silently, "Please help me, please help me," and pulling the thick green curtain aside, entered the small dark cubicle. The priest stirred and bent toward the wire screen that separated them, murmuring, "In nomine Patris, et Filii, et Spiritus Sancti."

The wooden kneeler had no covering; the worn wood was very hard under Lucy's knees. She began, as always, with the words she had been taught eight years ago in First Communion class, "Bless me, Father, for I have sinned."

There was a long moment of silence. Lucy could hear the soft even breathing of the priest, and concentrated on making her own respirations even and quiet. "I have sinned," she thought. "That's what I said so it must be what I really think. It must be so."

Only it hadn't seemed to be sinful last night, when she and Dave were parked on the bluff that overlooked the ocean. The movie had gotten out later than usual, and they had only forty minutes until Lucy was expected home. Lucy had unbuttoned her coat, it was warm in the car with the heater on, and they were laughing; Dave was telling her about an incident in his senior history class, Lucy was a freshman and new to the school.

Dave had leaned toward her, his dark head blotting out her view of the moon over the water, one eyebrow lifted in a manner that Lucy had grown to love, and whispered in her ear, "You're beautiful! And what a shape—you're really something!" His cheek was smooth against her own, and she had laughed, as he amended, "I mean for someone so young."

"What do you mean, young?" she asked indignantly. "I'm fifteen, that's not so young, and besides you're only two years older than me." Secretly she thought, "I like my body, too. Some of my friends still have little girl's bodies, but not me. I can see in the locker room when we change clothes after gym class; why Judy would be straight up and down if she didn't wear falsies."

Lucy watched, eyes wide open, as Dave leaned over her, hesitantly fondling her sweater-covered breasts with his large smooth hands, and lowering his head to kiss her through the sweater. Her first impulse was to push him away, and she feebly murmured "No, no," against his ear, a wave of excitement swelling within her. She forced herself closer to him, kissing his forehead and closed eyelids until he lifted his head to kiss her on the mouth.

He kissed her so long and hard her lips felt puffy and numb when they finally paused for breath. Lucy felt Dave's hand on her thigh, under her coat, and she could feel its warmth through the wool of her skirt. Her whole body felt swollen and turgid, warm and fluid, and she thought, "Don't stop, don't stop," leaning toward him; but Dave had fallen back against the door, taking his hands from her to search his pockets for a match. Lighting a cigarette, he smiled, "I'd better get you home before we have real trouble."

Lucy's face flushed in the darkness at the remembrance, and the musty smell of the heavy green curtain filled the narrow box, smothering her.

III

"Do you need help with your confession, my child?" Father Murphy's voice sounded weary as he intoned from behind the screen, soothing and professional.

"Yes, Father." Lucy shifted her weight from one knee to the other on the uncomfortable wooden bench; the edge of the wooden slab was cutting into her leg. "I'm confused about something."

"Yes, my child." The priest waited patiently as Lucy thought, "Confused is not the word. I was awake most of the night thinking about it. I love Dave, and I loved it when he touched me. But later I felt cheap and frightened and soiled." Later when she was alone in the pristine whiteness of her narrow bed, and remembering the many lectures that Sisters had given over the years on the evils of boys and their dishonorable intentions.

The words came in a rush, spilling over each other as Lucy forced herself to ask the unpleasant question, "Father, is petting really a sin, I mean a mortal sin?" She waited for his reply, thinking, "The word *petting* is such an ugly word."

"Why do you ask, my child? Start at the beginning." In the darkness Lucy could see him leaning toward her, his elbow on the ledge under the screened window, his large bony hand cradling his forehead as he bent his head to hear her words.

Lucy told Father Murphy what had happened, ending, "But

81

it didn't seem to be wrong at the time. That's why I'm so mixed up."

"How old are you?" the priest questioned, and when Lucy whispered, "Fifteen, going on sixteen," he continued, "Fifteen! Why you're just a child. You have committed a sin, a sin against the sixth commandment."

"I'm not a child," Lucy thought rebelliously, "I'm a woman. Dave thinks so, and I feel it. I'm not a child."

The priest continued in an earnest whisper. "You are entering a dangerous time of your life now. God has created man and woman with certain desires that are good and honorable in the right place at the right time. One of the reasons for this is that children might be conceived at the right time. Do you know what I mean when I say the right time?"

"Yes," answered Lucy, pausing only a split second. "After the sacrament of marriage. When I'm older."

"That's right. After marriage. Experimentation before then will only lead to trouble—it's like playing with matches. You wouldn't give a child a book of matches now, would you?"

"No, Father."

"Well, it's like this. You have the matches, only you must decide for yourself not to use them. This will not be easy, but if you pray to the Blessed Virgin, she will help you." The priest cleared his throat. "Now, are there any more questions?"

"Yes, Father, only one thing." She stared intently at the knuckles of her clasped hands. "Suppose, well suppose I love him now?" She remembered his smooth face and strong arms and the sturdy way he looked in his green practice uniform, running down the football field at the high school.

The priest shifted a little on his wooden chair so that it creaked loudly in the silence between them, and continued. "You're young, my child. You may feel old, but believe me, you have a lot ahead of you." He chuckled to himself. "Why, you'll fall for a dozen more boys before you find the right one."

"He is the one for me," Lucy thought. "I'll love him forever, I guess." She savored the flavor of this decision. "I'll love him forever."

82

Father Murphy continued. "This must not happen again. You must make up your mind to that."

Lucy answered, "I understand, Father. I see," not seeing, her confusion even more clouded than before.

Lucy hardly listened to the rest of the lecture, the box was so hot and stuffy, her knees hurt no matter how she leaned on them, and she could hear the shuffling of other feet in the church outside the confessional as the line formed to the right. "I wish he'd hurry up," she thought. "If I don't get out of here soon, the people out there will think I killed somebody or something."

She knelt down in the front of the church at the altar rail, her knees welcoming the soft cushion of maroon carpet on the steps, and stared at the placid white marble face of the Virgin. "Hail, Mary, Full of Grace," she began several times in an effort to say the prayers that had been prescribed as her penance, but her attention wandered and she kept seeing Dave's face as he bent to kiss her.

"I'll say them later," she thought, "later," and walked to the door at the rear of the church and blessed herself with the chilly water that stood in the font by the door. Stepping out into the clear windy dusk, she took several deep breaths of the clean, cold air and walked down the sidewalk, turning right at the hedge. As she walked under the leaf-stripped trees toward home, the first stars were shining dimly in the sky.

The village clock chimed loudly five times, and Lucy started to run, thinking, "I'll see Dave in just a few hours, and then everything will be all right." She felt clean again.

3. Dreams and Tinsel

Swinging Bridge to the Moon

BY MARION EARNSHAW

MICHAEL AWOKE with a start, his throat tight and dry. Had his mother called? He slept fitfully these April nights, waiting for her cry of pain. His body still taut, he turned on his side and waited. The window blind behind his head flapped idly in the hazy moonlight; he could feel the damp breeze on his face, with now and then the scent of lilacs from the yard below.

Beside him Harry stirred toward him, his knees drawn up against Michael's back. This sleeping trick of Harry's often enraged him, but now he only pushed the knees down gently. After all, was not he, Michael, who was just finishing the seventh grade, the head of the family now? Harry was only eleven. But they both had to be men now, he and Harry, and look after the young ones. He glanced at little Glenn's huddled form across the room, the moonlight brightening the yellow hair against the pillow. While Michael waited, his ears still straining, a surge of pride swept over him that he, the oldest, was awake while others slept. He would look after her, no harm would ever come . . .

"Michael!" His mother's low cry, and then a moan. He jumped quickly and ran barefoot through the narrow hall to his mother's room, reached frantically for the bare bulb above the foot of the iron bed. As the light flashed on, his mother winced and moaned again. She was sitting up at the head of the bed, her rugged brown face twisted with pain, her eyes touched with wildness, her black hair falling in tangled masses over the white nightgown. Her twitching mouth was pulled to one side, a sight Michael always dreaded at these moments.

She pointed toward the dresser, but Michael was already turning around to grasp the little bottle of chloroform, his mother's only relief in these spells. She took it eagerly, holding it close to her nose, inhaled long and deeply, her slight moans gradually fading away. Slowly the face softened, the twitching vanished, the left hand loosened its hold from the iron upright. She sank down weakly, Michael helping her with the blanket and sheet as he took the bottle again.

"Is Mommy better now?" A soft child's voice came from the bed in the corner: his little sister June. Michael could see her black eyes staring through tangled hair, her face thin and pale.

"Yes, honey, go to sleep now," said his mother sleepily. "Mommy's all right." She closed her eyes and spoke again, 'Go back to bed now, son. But see if Milly is wet first." Her voice trailed off.

Milly was sleeping in her crib quiet enough, but wet as a polecat, as his mother always said. He brought a dry diaper from the line in the kitchen, changed dry for wet with fumbling fingers, rearranged Milly's blanket to keep the wetness from her legs. Milly cried and whimpered a little, but soon found her two middle fingers, and was quiet as he turned out the light and tip-toed from the room and down the hall again.

For a long time he could not go to sleep. He watched the play of the moonlight on the bare unvarnished floor, the faded roses in the wallpaper, the mop of yellow hair across the room. Now and then the lilac smell, and the sound of creaking branches of the big oak tree by the front gate, and the creak of the swinging bridge as the wind stirred its boards and cables. He liked to run across the swinging bridge and feel the sway of boards under his feet; he liked to stand in the middle of the bridge and watch the catfish play in the clear green water far below. He was glad they lived by the river and near the swinging bridge in this house, their first home since his dad had left them. If only his mother did not have these terrible spells, *tic douloureux*, the doctor had called them. Lately they had been worse . . . the trip back to West Virginia, the strain of moving and getting settled . . . he had never noticed such things before.

Finally he felt himself drifting off to sleep with Harry's warmth at his back and the moonlight fading around the walls.

II

When Michael awoke, with the sun already warming the pillow and the sparrows chirping in the yard, he could smell his mother's coffee and hear the hum of voices in the kitchen. It was Saturday morning; they had let him sleep a little longer. For years he had awakened with red and golden bars of light across his closed eyes, or an ominous cloudy brown, with now and then a curious blending of bright colors and dark. Maybe he had told a lie and might get caught that day; maybe he hadn't done his arithmetic. This morning the colors were brown and black, and Michael knew why: he had to go and clean Uncle Ap's office. No basketball at the Y today, no tag in the sunny end of the pool. He could feel the basketball in his fingers and hear the swish of the net, the rush of feet, the thud of the ball on board; he could feel his feet flying under him and his arms reaching high. But none of this today. He and Harry had to clean Uncle Ap's office. He got out of bed slowly and drew on his overalls and shirt.

Down in the kitchen Harry, Glenn, and June sat around the table eating pancakes, with Milly on one side in her high chair, dabbling in her oatmeal, babbling and gurgling and cooing all the while. His mother stood at the stove baking pancakes on a black griddle, her brown cheeks red from the heat, her white apron listening in the streaming sunlight.

"Sit down, son. Here are some hot ones for you."

Michael sat down by Milly's high chair at the end of the table. He watched his mother's face. She sounded cheerful enough this morning, but he could see the tired marks around her eyes; her uncombed hair was curled in a rough knot atop her head. If only those spells could leave.

"How about you, Mom?" asked Harry, getting up from the table. "Let me bake for you and Mike. I thought you were going to sleep all day, Buddy." Harry grinned, his round face glowing. "And don't be a pig with this." He grinned again, passing the little red pitcher of syrup to Michael.

"I'll sit down in a minute. My coffee isn't quite ready. June, if you're through, feed Milly a little more oatmeal."

June rose instantly and stood by Milly's chair. Michael watched June's solemn little face, framed in black bobbed hair, her brown eyes heavy with worry and fear, a face like one of those madonnas he had seen in the penny prints at school. Already she was a little mother, her eyes wide and sad, her voice soft and anxious when angry words flew or her mother wept.

But now, as June fed Milly, she was smiling. She even giggled a little when Milly pounded with her spoon. The sunlight, flowing through the white curtain, swam round and round in her eyes and splashed on her bright white teeth. And Michael suddenly felt warmed as he often did at Saturday morning breakfasts, with the sunlight playing on the white oilcloth of the table, the red squares of the linoleum, the puffing coffee pot, and the mop of Glenn's yellow hair by the window. His mother relaxed by Milly's chair, sipping her coffee, the butter melting on her pancakes, the sunlight glancing off her plate and playing over her hands. It warmed hearts and eyes, too, this sunlight, and made his mother laugh again and Milly play with her fingers.

His mother glanced at the battered white clock on the window sill. "You'll have to leave soon, boys," she said. "Ap wants you there by ten o'clock this morning. And if he gives you fifty cents, get some butter with it on your way home. Don't pay no attention if he gets mad at something. You know how he is."

III

Over the swinging bridge, across the railroad tracks, along Clifton's red-bricked streets. The smell of spring was in the air as Michael and Harry swung along, with here and there the startling yellow of forsythia, the cool blue of lilacs in yards along the way. Far beyond, circling the town, they could see the mountains, blue and gray in the bright sunlight, with here and there patches of clouds around their crests. When they had bicycles, said Harry, they would ride out to the foothills and up into the mountains. Maybe they could even go as far as Job and see Uncle Abe, who sent them a barrel of apples and a slab of bacon now and then. "Maybe buyin' bicycles won't be as hard as we think," said Harry. "Maybe we can sell a lot of papers this summer."

Up two flights of dusty stairs to Uncle Ap's office and the black-lettered door: A. M. Cunningham, Attorney-at-Law. Michael knocked. They paused fearfully. A few heavy steps and Uncle Ap himself opened the door, a huge craglike man with a jutting chin, a great beak of a nose, and piercing black eyes. "Come in, boys," he said, with a surprisingly cheerful tone to his rumbling voice. "I'm just dictating some letters. You can begin in this room. How is your mother today?"

"Not as bad as sometimes," said Michael. "She's havin' two or three spells a day."

Uncle Ap frowned. "I hope we don't have to send her to the hospital," he said. As he turned toward the inner office, the great curve of his back framed in the doorway, he was muttering, "Annie and her children," and what more Michael and Harry could not hear.

They began to clean, Michael sweeping the heavy green rug, Harry dusting the chairs and tables, the typewriter stand, and finally the filing cabinets and bookcases full of heavy yellow law books stamped with black letters. Then came the cleaning of the spittoons, one in each office. It was Michael's turn, and he dreaded it. When his mother had first cleaned Uncle Ap's office, he had been with her; she had taught him how to sweep, and he had watched her clean this very spittoon, a fearful and loathsome thing of white enamel, with dried tobacco juice on itse sloping rim, and underneath a well of stinking blackness in which floated wads of tobacco and cigar stubs. First removing the rim, his mother had emptied this hideous mess into the toilet, then filled the well with soapy water and washed it with a cloth, and finally the rim, patiently dissolving the heavy stains. Now, as Michael carried the first spittoon into the toilet, holding his breath in disgust, he forced himself to do as his mother had done, mixing soap in a bucket of hot water, and pouring it into the well, bringing it back at last a spotless white, with clean soapy water in its belly.

Uncle Ap appeared suddenly at the doorway, glanced around searchingly. "Have you washed the window sills yet?" he asked. Then, without waiting, "Don't forget the baseboards. I'm going to court, won't be back."

As Uncle Ap opened the door, Michael and Harry looked at each other. Michael's mouth was dry; but Harry spoke up. "Uncle Ap!" he said. The heavy frame turned, the black eyes impatient. "Well?" he asked. "What is it?"

"You forgot to give us some money," said Harry. "We need fifty cents for butter."

Without a word Uncle Ap pulled out a half dollar and handed it to Harry. Then the door slammed, and he was gone.

IV

"Let's go round by the mill," said Michael to Harry, as they reached the street. Michael didn't want to tell Harry, but he was afraid of the short cut by the tracks, especially on Saturday afternoon. In the lot by the railroad tracks, behind an old watchman's shanty, John Ganard and his gang might be playing mumbly-peg and shooting dice, ready to fight and bully the younger boys.

But Harry was thinking of the same thing. "Mustn't let 'em know we're afraid of 'em," he said, and Michael was ashamed.

On Simpson Street, near the railroad tracks, they stopped at Wonn's grocery store, with its case of tempting candy, especially the orange corn and the peanut brittle. No candy today; not even a penny's worth. "How much is butter a pound?" asked Michael.

"Eighty-one cents, son," answered Mr. Wonn, round and solemn as ever, opening the glass door to a bucket of shining yellow. "How much do you want?"

"Fifty cents worth," answered Michael, and Mr. Wonn appeared with his wooden blade and flipped the butter on a piece of glazed paper. He weighed it, with hands aloft, wrapped it deftly, slid it into a paper bag.

Crossing the railroad tracks, Michael kept glancing fearfully ahead. Around the watchman's shanty rose mounds of cinders, sand, and rock, with here and there patches of coal, ammunition for neighborhood fights. A few of these fights Michael and Harry had watched from afar, new boys as yet without a gang of their own.

Suddenly, halfway across the lot, Michael heard a rush of feet from the shanty they had just passed. Four boys, John Ganard in the lead, stood in the front of them.

"Where ya think ya goin'?" asked John Ganard. He was a burly, pimply-faced boy of the eighth grade, his skin grimy, his black hair tousled.

"You let us alone," spoke up Harry. "Our mother's sick. We gotta get home." He edged around the leader, with Michael following him, holding the sack of butter.

"What's this, medicine?" sneered Ganard, grabbing the bag from Michael's hand and running behind a cinder pile, his gang at his heels. Michael stood rooted and helpless.

"This way, Mike! Behind this pile!" yelled Harry, as a shower of rocks and cinders came from the enemy. Huddled in a little valley of cinders, they cautiously looked over the top, rocks in hand, hurling fiercely when one of the gang across the path showed his head. Stones and chunks of coal flew over their heads to the bank of cinders behind them.

"Careful, Mike! Don't put your head out so far!" hissed Harry.

But it was too late. A blur of black and a crashing blow bore Michael backward into the cinders. He remembered the shooting lights across his eyes, and Harry holding his head up and screaming, "Stop it, you bastards, stop it! You've killed him! You've killed my brother!"

When Michael awoke, still in the cinders, Harry was holding a handkerchief over his right eye. The blood was dripping down his face and staining his blue overalls. He felt weak and far away from the faces round him, the hateful faces of the gang, John Ganard in the middle, his face pale and pleading.

"I'm sorry, I didn't mean to do it. You won't tell on me, will you, kid?" he was saying.

Michael was too weak to answer. At last he sat up, and Harry helped him to his feet, Ganard holding him, too.

"Is it a very bad cut?" he asked Harry.

"Pretty bad, Mike," said Harry. "About an inch long, just over your eye."

"We can't go home this way," said Michael. "Did you bring the butter?"

Ganard held it out, his face pale, his eyes pleading.

Michael and Harry walked slowly down the path, Michael holding the handkerchief to his head. He felt a numbness above his eye, but no pain. "Let's go to Mrs. Murphy's," said Michael. "We can call the doctor from there. If Mom sees me this way, she'll have a bad spell."

An hour later, when Dr. Moore had put some stitches in his head and bandaged the wound neatly, Michael and Harry walked across the swinging bridge, through the yard, and back to the kitchen door. His mother was sitting at the table, feeding Milly. "What kept you boys?" she asked, and then, seeing Michael's bandage, "My God, what's the matter?"

Michael grinned and kissed her on the cheek. I'm all right, Mom. Nothin' serious, is it, Buddy?"

Harry spoke up cheerfully. "Just a scratch, Mom. And here's your butter. Uncle Ap came across today." He proudly laid the paper bag on the kitchen table. As he opened it a little, some cinders fell out. Michael grabbed up the butter and looked closely. One of the gang had imbedded a handful of cinders in one end. He scraped them off with a knife, put the butter on a plate and slipped it in the icebox while Harry told the story of the rock fight, properly watered down for his mother's ears.

When Ben Awakened

EXCERPT FROM A NOVEL BY EDWARD WALLANT

AT FOUR in the morning, Ben woke up with a sensation of breathlessness. He opened his eyes and, if it hadn't been for the faint illumination of the window, would have thought someone had thrown a suffocating blanket over him. Everything was strangely still. It must have stopped raining just a short time before and the sudden silence, combined with the heat, had broken the rhythm of his sleep. His bed was drenched with sweat, and he knew he would have to get up for a while to let it become bearable again.

He groped his way over to the sink without turning on the light. The water was a godsend on his hair and face and shoulders. Drinking it from cupped hands in the dark, its rust invisible, it had a cool, sweet taste like springwater. For less than an instant, he was visited by a belief in miracle, and he felt he was being born, blind and strong and limitless. Then it was gone. He found his pants, pulled them on, fumbled for a cigarette and then, still barefooted, went downstairs and out onto the stoop. A figure was sitting there, all hunched up. When he lit his cigarette, he saw it was Lebedov.

"Hot," Ben said.

Lebedov turned around to him and, as Ben's eyes adjusted to the dimness, he could see the man's glittering eyes, the whole bestial face like that of an impaled lion, fierce and dangerous and sick with rage.

"People is animal," Lebedov said.

Ben shrugged and studied the glow of his cigarette. Sometimes I think the whole world is queer except thee and me and I have doubts about thee. He wondered if Lebedov noticed his smile.

"Coom froom Roosia, long time ago now," Lebedov said, waving his finger pedantically at Ben. "I see my fadder drroonk all time like crazy. All mens get drroonk like crazy from poor, from scare, from *everything!* Like animal only worse. My fadder—he punch, kick mudder. Get so crazy once he try to fuck my sister. Mudder stick him in wid knife. People kill like anything, no give a shit. Look on all dem . . ." He waved his disproportionately long arms at the four corners of the earth.

Ben kept his eyes on the vague openness at the end of the street. If there had been a moon he would have been able to see the great, Spartan cleanliness of the naked structures, casting complex geometric shadows on the ground. But here the shadows would be fathomless and undecipherable, dense and aged and hopeless.

". . . I go in Church when boy. Priddy picture, clothes on priest, smell nice. Pray to Jeez Chris. Bang him in my head." His voice was scratchy and raw as though he had never before used it in a normal, conversational volume. His forehead was deeply wrinkled, his whole face strained with the effort to say something that made sense to him. Ben sat without moving; it was just part of the night, something that, like a nightmare, was exempted from life.

"Church don' make difference to people. Just only eat, grab, drrink, take woomans. So I read book man gives me, then other books. Tell how Church no good, should make rewolts on Church, change things. Okay, *bam, bam*, smash 'em, right? Get foods for poor peoples. Make they should not have to bow down in front of rich peoples. Okay? Aghh, then same damn thing. Still everybody smash everybody. Same pains. Get tired of that also too. No sense. So jus grab things—what you find, *bam!* Like see a priddy butterfly. Okay, sneak up, grab him to enjoy. Got to crush him in hands. Little priddy thing, crush him. Jus like get old—nothing taste good even no more. Womans all dry up, fuck like old bone. Whole thing. Grab budderfly, you know . . ." He chuckled harshly, a sound as grating as an unlubricated machine. "Aggh."

Ben found himself nodding. Inside he felt a rawness as though something had scraped all the tissue.

"Yeah," Ben said. "Well, is hots, go sleep, else gets tireds too much. Think I go Ah-Ah-Baby."

Lebedov had an odd smile on his rough, broken face, but it was aimed *through* Ben. He didn't move a muscle when Ben flicked his cigarette over his head. But a moment later he turned to look at it lying in the gutter.

When he got back upstairs, Ben thought he heard Howard Miller moving around near his door, a scratchy, lightfooted sound as though he walked on tiny paws instead of feet. He waited in silence for a minute to see if Howard would come out. The pattering sounds continued and Ben gave it up. He went into his airless room and got into bed. It was cool and dry and before it could dampen and heat up from his body again, he fell fast asleep.

Monday morning was hotter than before the rain. Ben got up at his usual time even though he knew he was on vacation and that there was no place for him to get to. It wasn't a habit either. Perhaps he hoped to surprise something in the day. Like a man foolish enough to try and sneak up on his reflection in a mirror.

Well, he reasoned, might as well be conscious as much of the day on my own time as I am on that damned store's. He threw some cold water on his face and dressed in slacks and a white tee-shirt. His body looked handsomely muscular in the snug-fitting shirt; long, strong neck, powerful shoulders, thickly muscled arms, and the dark brown skin set off so dramatically by the white shirt. And with legs like a dwarf, he thought humorously. Too bad I can't do anything with all this manhood. He studied the envelope under the mirror, left there like a test of his personally determined discipline. In it was a letter from an old colleague who wrote him biannually, offering him a teaching job in the Negro university at which the man was a department head. And with the same biannual regularity, Ben wrote him the same answer. Neither he nor his friend seemed to learn by repetition; the monotonous correspondence, over five years old, might continue until one or the other of them died or lost his sanity. He shook his head almost fondly at the envelope; it was like a familiar totem.

He put some water in the little saucepan and waited for it to heat on the hotplate. While he waited, he looked through the papers he had committed himself to typing that week. Better get as much done today as possible, he thought. There was no knowing what shape he would be in by the end of the week.

He went over to the window. The sky was a merciless white, and the street looked soft as licorice. In one's, two's, and three's, people began trickling out of the houses on their way to work. They walked with Monday reluctance, stopping to light cigarettes, to look at the sky for excuses against moving.

Maria came out in her pink dress, her play as dedicated to the hour as the adults' work was. No dungarees or sunsuits for her; the Alvarez's were proud.

Lebedov came out, foreshortened from above, squat and ponderous with his black and gray hair, his cold blue denim shirt. He went down past Maria, and Ben observed how the child and the man were two different species really, all children and all men. Could Lebedov have had moments of beauty? Maybe with his children, grown and moved somewhere distant? Maybe even with that misshapen and battered creature who had once been a young woman? Who, *Lebedov?* Ben thought with bitter amusement.

97

That ape? My, my, Kellogg, see how your vacation affects you. You're getting positively lyrical!

He sipped the hot instant coffee and peered down over the rim of the cup. Howard Miller came out. Again Ben hadn't heard him. He thought for a moment of the possibility that the little bookkeeper might have a secret exit, perhaps over the roof somehow. Howard twitched past the child on the sidewalk. What is he? Ben wondered. Most likely a fag, maybe something else? Something phony and disgusting about him. The child didn't look up at him, and he went down the street on invisible eggs. Guy all alone like that, you can't know . . .

Ah, Sammy! He came flying down the steps, loose-jointed and silly, like a comic dancer. His threadbare white shirt was rolled up just past the elbows, and his thin arms looked as if they were made of china. Almost all his clothes were hand-me-downs, wouldn't spend a penny on any new ones. Ben wondered what he would look like in clothes that fit. Probably no different, all clothes would look like that on him; it was the *man* who was a misfit. "Man makes the clothes," he said aloud, trying to find pleasure in the inverted maxim. Sammy stopped suddenly at the foot of the steps, his hand resting on the blunt point of the railing. He began to talk to Maria. Ben couldn't hear what he said, only the sound of his high, tender voice. He touched the child's hair caressingly, smoothing the shiny darkness. Maria smiled up trustfully. Sammy was motionless; just his hand moved over the silky black hair.

"Go on, Maria," Eva called irritatedly. "Go play with Manuel."

Sammy stood still watching her go off, his face and body aimed after her. There was something taut and dolorous in his attitude; he was like a model for a sculpture of a weird tower.

"Get going, Sam," Ben called down, wondering what his motive was in calling. "Off to the salt mines," he said, trying to make it a normally humorous taunt.

Sammy looked startled. His eyes, when they lifted to the window, looked distracted, almost frightened. But then the savior grin lit his face with sunny idiocy. He waved with the tips of his fingers and hunched into his narrow shoulders, his expression an imitation of a quaint old man.

"Smart guy up there, making fun because you're the leisure

class. It should drop off, the tongue, mocking an honest worker. Go, drink up whiskey all day while I slave to the bone . . ."

Ben made an obscene gesture with his arm.

"Okay, okay," Sammy said. "See you later, Benny." He began walking down the street in the same direction Maria had gone.

"Where the hell you going?" Ben called after him.

Sammy stopped, looked both ways bewilderedly for a moment, and then smiled. "Boy," he shouted, "am I loused up." He shrugged goodnaturedly and walked off toward the redevelopment, the way he was supposed to go.

Soon the street was emptied except for the scattered children and the occasional housewife sweeping her dirt out into the street. Ben drained the cold coffee and went over to the typewriter. He glanced at the thesis, put a clean sheet of white paper in with two carbons and yellow second sheets, and began to type.

THE FERTILITY SYMBOLS IN ULYSSES.

He typed for some time, got up to open a can of warm beer, went back to the typewriter, and worked with occasional sips of the beer. Stay on beer as long as possible, he told himself. Otherwise, get slopped up too early. Once the keys jammed, and he stopped to flex his fingers before continuing. The metallic clicking numbed his mind comfortably. He typed for about an hour, then got up to change his position. He went to the window. Lebedov was going by with his rag cart.

"Raa-ags," he cried in his reamed voice.

He typed some more, got up for another break, typed, rested, making a pattern of it, losing track of the hour, of the planet even. Every time he went to the window he scanned the street. Half the times, Maria was there, sometimes with another child, sometimes with Manuel, her brother, sometimes alone, just bouncing her ball. Twisting his head to look up, Ben could see the hands of the old woman, Mrs. Colwell, watching from her eternal fourth floor guardtower. Just the old woman and him: the watchmen. All's well . . . He chuckled without amusement. The sound of Lebedov's one-word call came from a couple of blocks away. Maria dashed down almost to the condemned building and then back. There was the steady chattering of the drills and pneumatic hammers on the building site and dust clouded the stiltlike structure's bases as though they were gigantic automatons pawing at the ground, impatient to consume the doomed old street.

He typed some more in an unbelievable heat. The gazing through the window and then work, over and over again. Some vacation, but why not? No sense trying to seek out artificial pleasures; they couldn't convince him at this point. Maria was drawing a new hopscotch pattern over the blurred outlines of the old one. A couple of pigeons waddled over the black sidewalk, a squad car drove past, and the birds took off; guilty, hah! Howard Miller came home early and then went out again. Maria didn't look at him.

Clickety click, click, click.

"The Egyptian motif is quite prevalent in the . . ."

The ribbon jammed. He took another breather. He opened another can of warm beer, the sixth, and looked out at the street for the twentieth time. Maria was gone.

Rebecca by Any Other Name

A STORY BY FRANCES SILVERBERG

REBECCA HURRIED home for lunch, climbed the twelve steps of the brownstone house on East Sixty-Ninth Street, between First and Second Avenues, rang the bell three times, and shading her eyes from the brilliant May sun, craned her neck to watch for her mother's face from the parlor window on the top floor.

"A loaf of rye bread, a quarter-pound Swiss cheese, a box of candles, and a bar of Octagon soap," Mrs. Abramowitz called down, and threw the paper-wrapped money to her daughter. The packet fell into the areaway. She ran down and retrieved it near the grilled-iron doorway to the Felkin kitchen. Mrs. Felkin spied her and said, "Rebecca, would you please get me a dozen Sunkist oranges?" The child took the dollar. The fruit store was on First Avenue, the grocery on Second Avenue; two trips on this special day, and she was in such a hurry.

Today, Friday, was the day to hand in the map of the United States. She had decided against doing it in color; all the maps in the 7-B geography book were delicately tinted in light pinks, soft greens, pale blues, but Rebecca had wanted her map to be different, like an etching. With the money Mrs. Felkin gave her for running errands she had bought special pencils for this assignment, No. 1, No. 2, No. 3. She was proudest of the mountains, tiny semi-circles alternately spaced with the hard No. 3 lead. *I love you, Rocky Mountains,* she whispered to herself. *I love you, curving rivers. I love you, Great Lakes. I love you, divided states. I love you, capital cities, especially Baltimore. Maryland, my Maryland, how green thy boughs, my Maryland,* she hummed. Such a beautiful state to be born in!

"You forgot the soap," her mother said when she returned from the store.

"I'm sorry, Mama. Can't I get it at three o'clock?"

"You'd forget your head if it wasn't tied to your body. I'll make you a nice cheese sandwich for lunch."

"No, Mama, I have no time. I'm in a hurry to get back to school."

Her mother felt her forehead, "You haven't any temperature," she said, surprised her daughter wasn't hungry.

It would be nice if she could tell Mama what was going to happen today, why it was so special, but it seemed whenever she tried to tell her about things, either Mama didn't understand the importance of it, or she wasn't interested. It was better not to speak, nor let your face or eyes show what you were feeling, because if people didn't know how you felt about them, or things, or maybe thought you had no feelings at all, they couldn't hurt you as much, only a little. Nothing definite had ever happened that she could remember, but it was necessary never to let anybody see how important certain things are.

II

This afternoon Miss Prior, the seventh-grade geography teacher, was going to mark the maps. She had said she was going to grade them differently than last time when Rebecca had only gotten sixty-five per cent because the crayon was smeary. The girls were to write their names on the backs of the maps, and Miss Prior would put them on a cardboard and judge each one without knowing who had drawn it, then show it to the class and grade it. The best map was to win a copy of Daniel Defoe's *Robinson Crusoe*. Last time Alice Robinson had gotten ninety per cent for the map of North America, and won *Tom Sawyer*. Some of the girls had whispered "teacher's pet," and Miss Prior had then announced the new system for marking. Alice was smart, and beautiful, so blonde. Rebecca was sorry her hair had turned brown. It had once been blonde, too.

She went into the bedroom she used to share with her sister Sylvia, which was now hers alone. Sylvia was married and lived in Brooklyn. In the bottom drawer of Rebecca's mahogany dresser, under her pajamas and vest and panties, was hidden her diary. She felt the embossing on the brown leather cover, touched the fake lock that really didn't lock, and buried it deeper under the clothing. The diary was safe. Mama didn't read English, only Yiddish and German. Papa could, but wouldn't. Only Sylvia might. Sometimes she visited on Friday night for supper.

She removed the *Saturday Evening Post* and from its pages took the map of the United States, and allowed herself to admire it.

Mama hadn't understood that this was homework. She thought that Rebecca was spending every evening wasting her time playing, while she had done her work on the magazine spread on the kitchen table. She hadn't made a single erasure, not one. The hardest part had been the free-hand drawing of the outline of the United States. It was almost perfect, as correct as the printed map in her book. Tracing wasn't allowed, of course, and she had used up nearly the whole pad of specially-matted paper she had bought for twenty-five cents. After the outline it was easy, not a chore like homework usually was, but Mama was right, it was a game, like a wonderful game, knowing you were best and were going to win. Papa worked late every night. She was asleep when he got home. She wished she had remembered to show it to him. He was home on Sundays.

Passing the bureau mirror, she took a deep breath, sucked in her round cheeks, and flattened her stomach with the palms of her hands. She examined her reflection, admiring the slimming effect, then exhaled. Maybe next year. Her friend, Sarah Cohen, had overheard some 8-B girls talking about how the body changed when you got to be thirteen. So maybe next year.

As she hurried back to school, magazine with precious map tucked under her arm, she passed Julia Richman High School on Second Avenue, which the Prince of Wales had visited last year. It was the newest school in the city, all girls, and even had a swimming pool. She would go there and learn how to swim. She thought perhaps she had once known how to swim when she was younger, but had forgotten, as if she were afraid of the blue water, not so much of drowning in it, more like having to live in it, like a cold-blooded fish. It was a strange feeling.

Rebecca took different routes each day on the four trips to and from school, sometimes up one street and down another, passing the brownstone houses and picturing who lived inside them, even imagining their face and what kind of people they were. She wished she had more friends. None of the girls on her block went to her school. They attended St. Catherine of Siena, the Catholic school east of First Avenue; Sarah, her only other friend, lived on Sixty-Second and went to a different school.

Public School 176 was at Lexington Avenue and Sixty-Eighth Street; across the street, catty-cornered, was Hunter College. She looked up at the castlelike structure. This fairy tale would come true. She'd go to the all-girl Hunter, she didn't much care for boys, and become a teacher. Not a teacher like Miss Prior, who was always saying how it was destined she was teaching in this particular school, 176, talking about being a Daughter of the American Revolution, in capital letters she said it, as if that made her better than anyone else. The Prince of Wales had nothing to do with being born to the king and queen of England, instead of to the Abramowitzes or McGillicuddys. It had nothing to do with you as a person, it was more something you did youself, like picking the school you wanted to work in, or like falling off a horse, or like drawing an extra special map. No, not a teacher like Miss Prior, but a teacher like Mrs. Hempel, who wasn't even pretty, yet beautiful, like her eyes understood you.

III

Mrs. Hempel had been her fifth-grade teacher. Once, in the English class, Rebecca had written a composition about a Friday night supper. The assignment was really your birthday party, but she had never had a birthday party. The family didn't believe in it. So she had imagined that a Friday night was her birthday and described it. It was her turn to write on the blackboard, and proud of her Palmer script, careful to keep the lines straight, because they always slanted upward, she had chalked it on the board one afternoon before the rest of the class returned from lunch. Mrs. Hempel read it aloud. Most of the girls only tittered, but some of them laughed out loud, hard.

It told about a Friday night when her mother put a shawl on her head and lighted the candles, whispering a prayer into her hands as she cupped them over her face, swaying her body to and fro. It told about the gelid gefulte fish and the strong red horseradish that tickled the nose and made the eyes water. It described the clear chicken soup with the soft, curling noodles that Mama cut on the wooden board that Papa had made himself, sanding it down to smoothness; and the succulent boiled chicken, tender and tasty, served with a delicious crispy potato pudding that Rebecca had helped to make, grating the potatoes quickly so they wouldn't turn brown. Instead of the usual dessert of applesauce, she wrote of a chocolate cake her mother had baked with a colored candle on it, and her father had blown it out, making a wish for her, then she sang *"Happy Birthday."*

It was meant to be beautiful, it could have been like that, everything but the cake was true, just like a Friday night, only special. But they had all laughed, except Mrs. Hempel.

"That was well done, Rebecca," said Mrs. Hempel, and from

her desk drawer she took a book. "This is a prize for a very good composition," and patted her head.

The book was Rudyard Kipling's *Jungle Book*. If she could write like Mr. Kipling she would write about people, not animals.

Yes, it would be good to be a teacher like Mrs. Hempel, even when you knew she was being nice, maybe because she was sorry for you.

IV

The maps were on Miss Prior's desk, Rebecca slipped hers somewhere in the middle. Then, putting on her pince-nez, Miss Prior took a large cardboard, placed it under all the thirty-two maps, and said, "Now, we shall see what we shall see," and proceeded to mark the maps. Seventy-five, Mary, seventy, Josephine, eighty, Amelia, sixty-five, Matilda, calling the mark, turning the paper over and naming the first name of each girl. Amelia's was good, Rebecca thought, but not as good as mine. Then she saw hers. Miss Prior gasped, "Perfect!" she said, and adjusting her glasses which were slipping from her small nose, "Magnificent!" She held it high for all to see, carefully keeping the cardboard on the back so she could not see the name. Oh, Rebecca thought, it is beautiful, and tears came to her eyes. I made it, she said to herself, all by myself, I made it.

"This map deserves more than one hundred per cent, but what can be better than the perfect number?" Miss Prior waved her right hand, tightly holding the rest of the maps with her left, "I mark you one-hundred-five per cent," like a fairy queen transforming a toad into a princess. "One-hundred-five per cent." Her voice rose, "You can see it's drawn freehand, not traced. How wise the girl was not to cover it with crayon! We can clearly see each river, each mountain, each state, each capital city. Now, we shall see who drew this fine map." She seemed to be looking at Alice. The map looked like Alice, so clean, so neat, so perfect. Rebecca sat straighter in her seat, glad today had been an assembly day, happy that she looked nice in the white middy-blouse and pleated navy-blue serge skirt. With sweating hands she smoothed the pleats over her stomach.

Miss Prior turned the map over. "Rebecca Abramowitz?" Her voice dropped, and she looked at her. "You?" She examined the back of the paper, "Are you sure you didn't trace this?" she asked.

"No, Miss Prior," Rebecca said.

"Perhaps someone helped you with this? Like an older brother doing your homework for you?" Miss Prior smiled. It was an ugly thing.

Rebecca didn't answer. It didn't make much sense to defend yourself, or do your homework, or write things about yourself, or your family, or try to get people to understand you, and the things you daydreamed about. Not the night dreams—they were never any good, confused and frightening, only the dreams in the daytime were happy and hopeful; now that was being spoiled too. So she didn't answer, even if she wanted to, she couldn't, her mouth was all twisted and wouldn't work.

"As the Scots say, I ha' ma doots," Miss Prior continued, "I ha' ma doots." She fixed her with a stony stare, back to a toad, princess for such a short moment, "Know what that means, Rebecca Abramowitz?" She took off her glasses. "It means I have my doubts. But I marked it, and the mark stands. Some people never learn." She shook her head, then firmly replaced her spectacles, and finished marking the rest of the papers. But Rebecca didn't hear her voice after that. She didn't get *Robinson Crusoe*.

V

At three o'clock Rebecca walked home alone, as usual. She glanced across at the towered Hunter College. No, she wouldn't be a teacher. Maybe a reporter. Yes, she would go to Columbia University after she got out of high school, even if it was coeducational, and become a reporter, write for a newspaper, then she'd be able to tell the truth about things. Newspapers always printed the truth, didn't they? Like her diary, where she could write about what she felt, and dreamed, and wanted; nothing important ever happened to her, but it was nice to be able to tell someone what you were thinking about, and you could trust them, they wouldn't laugh or twist it around. Like her diary. That was good. If anything ever happened to her right hand and she couldn't write, she would die, surely die.

The map in her hand reminded her of Miss Prior's face. She crumpled it into a ball and threw it into a trash can in front of a house. Her hand hurt from the force of destroying the stiff paper.

At home she went immediately to her dresser and removed her diary.

"Rebecca," her mother called, "you forgot the soap again."

"Can I get it later, Mama?"

"No, now. Sylvia and Herman are coming for supper, and I need some things right away."

She thrust the diary under her pillow. It was only fair, she knew, that she do the shopping. The stairs were bad for Mama's heart which had been injured because Rebecca was so big when she was born, fourteen pounds. That's why she was the youngest. I guess I didn't come out right, she thought, few things do.

"Rebecca!" her mother called again, "take a pencil! Write it down. A pound of coffee, a dozen best white eggs, a pound of lima beans, not the small ones you bought last time, I don't know why I let you do the shopping, you never buy the right thing. Where's the pencil? Write it down."

The girl squeezed her eyes shut, tight, very tight, but the tears wouldn't come. She opened them, picked up the pencil, and wrote.

One pound of limas, *not small, but very large*

One dozen eggs, *I wish I'd never been born*

One pound of coffee, *ground into dust*

One bar of Octagon soap, *many-sided, to wash everything clean*

When she got back from the store, Sylvia, who had come too early, was sitting in the kitchen reading the diary aloud to her mother and brother-in-law Herman. The three of them were laughing, hard. She put the bag of groceries on the kitchen table, and face turned sideways, she slitted her eyes and squinted at them, a bad habit recently acquired. She put on a Miss Prior smile and went downstairs. Who cares about a silly dumb stupid stinking lousy freehand hundred-and-five per cent map? Or a diary? Or a composition? Or anybody? Or anything?

On the corner she went into Mrs. Wolf's candy store. With the quarter Mrs. Felkin had given her for the errand this noon, she bought a chocolate malted and a new *Frank Merriwell.* The malted was thick and delicious, felt good inside. Mrs. Wolf was a nice woman. She wished she hadn't bought the book, then she could have another malted. She felt in her pocket, she'd forgotten to give Mama the change. She bought another malted, two pretzels, and it was good, almost as good as the first one. She started to walk to Sarah Cohen's house.

On the way she changed her mind. She went to the public library on Sixty-Seventh Street, got a copy of *Robinson Crusoe* from the shelf, and began to read. When she got hungry, she went home.

The Magic White Slip

CHAPTER FROM A NOVEL BY RAE MAGAZINE

TORMENTED by hunger and aching feet and her head spinning like Yan's windmill at the edge of town, Sonya Bronsky stood shifting from foot to foot while waiting in line for her white slip of paper—the paper that would tell her whether or not she had been *accepted* in the Gymnasium of Bunionov.

It was Friday, like any other Friday in June, but to Sonya it had seemed like the Day of Atonement. *Who shall or who shall not attend the Gymnasium in the fall?*

The huge gray-walled room smelled of kerosene and cheap tobacco. The blond cross-eyed girl behind Sonya moaned like a wounded child: "Oooh, my feet . . . my feet. I'll die if I don't sit down." There was not a chair nor a stool in sight. There was nothing to do but wait, wait, wait.

Since six that morning they had been on their feet; now it was way past noon. Sonya could tell by glancing to her right, where the sun shimmered on the fly-speckled window-pane. She had learned from her grandfather to tell time by looking in the direction of the sun.

At the far-end room, beside a wall from which the plaster was peeling, sat a yellow-faced, hunchbacked man; black-rimmed glasses screened his eyes. He coughed shrilly, beating his fist on his desk, struggling for a breath. All eyes from the long line of students stared toward the hollow-cheeked man.

"That's the new principal," the blond girl pointed.

"What's his name?" asked the girl beside her.

"Who knows? Who cares? We'll call him *hunchman*."

"Good enough, good enough. Too good." They snickered, eyeing him with contempt.

One at a time he finally began calling up the girls to his desk; without so much as glancing at them, he shoved the printed slip in their hands. Sonya gazed at every student passing her on his way out, and knew at a glance that they were rejected. She could tell by the expression in the eyes that read the slips and the trembling hands that crushed them afterwards.

"Anzia Yakowich!" A sudden shout from the hunchman startled the line. He wheezed and cursed and pounded with his fist on the desk.

A tall attractive brunette stepped forward. "Present," she trilled and leisurely walked across the room, shaking her heavy buttocks and fluttering her long lashes, as though rehearsing for a play. As she neared the desk she smiled down at the hunchman, moving her shoulders coquettishly, her breasts rippling beneath her tight sweater caused the girls a hushed laugh. Two boys in back of the line snickered, mumbling words of vulgarity.

As the hunchman handed her the paper he caught a glimpse of her heaving bosom, then lowered his eyes.

On her way out Anzia Yakowich flashed her printed slip before the line and cried out giddily: "Oh, girls, look . . . I've made it! I'm in! My father'll be simply thrilled! thri-l-l-e-d . . ." Her echo was swallowed by the emptiness of the room as she closed the door behind her.

Sonya felt a pang of envy. It's an honor to be accepted in the Gymnasium, truly wonderful—but it's even more wonderful to have a father who would be thrilled. Thrilled, she sighed. What a beautiful word. Only the other day her stepfather had warned her to stay away from the *unyiddishe schule*. The *Szkola Pow-*

szechna from which she was graduating in June was bad enough. "Studying from any book except the Bible," he had told her, "distracts one from the belief of God. Remember! I'll beat you! I'll make you bleed if you don't obey me!" Sonya remembered every word, every threat. Yet there she was . . . in line with the other students, famished and drowsy and aching all over, waiting, wishing, hoping to see the miracle-word in her slip: *accepted.*

II

Anzia Yakowich had caused a stir among the students in the line. Like a flock of angry ducks they jabbered all at one time: "Sure, why shouldn't she?" stormed the blond girl. "Isn't her father the rich show-off?"

"Richest in town."

"Sure. He must've spent a fortune for coaching lessons for her."

"Must've bribed the principal. He's got the money."

"And he's clever, Yakowich."

"She's a snob, Anzia," the cross-eyed girl grumbled. "I hate her. Everybody does."

Sonya listened, indifferent to the grumbling, indifferent to the hands nudging at her back, and the elbows at her ribs before her. Her thoughts wandered toward her stepfather. She could see him standing up on the wagon, in the market square, unloading the sacks of rice and sugar and flour, and talking to himself: "Nu, so where is she, the Princessen? Why isn't she here to make record of the deliveries? Won't remember a thing when I'll come round to collect the money. Every storekeeper in town knows that I can't read and write. Oi . . . oi weh . . ."

"Imagine," Leah nudged Sonya "One out of a hundred girls, and the daughter of the richest man in town no less."

"He might accept one more," said the cross-eyed girl. "The day isn't over."

"Did you know," Leah said in a whisper, "that Yakowich is *her* best customer? Three times a week he comes to the *house.*" Sonya caught her meaning and bowed her head. After a silence she said:

"Where does it get you talking this way about your own mother?"

"So, who cares?" Leah snapped, then stabbing a friendly elbow in Sonya's bosom: "Take a look at our principal . . . our educator. What a laugh. He looks like the angel of death, the way he sits there, pounding with his sick claws, cursing, screaming for Jewish blood."

"Keep quiet." Sonya squeezed Leah's arm and reminded her that already the hunchman had shouted twice and threatened to tear up their slips, unless they kept their Jewish mouths shut.

III

Suddenly the side door was flung open and a crowd of Polish students rushed up to the hunchman's desk. Their giggling chatter filled the room, and their eyes glistened with joy as they read their printed slips. "A-ch, thank you, thank you, Pan Principal." They bowed and disappeared as quickly as they came in.

"D'you see what I see?" Leah whispered down to her friend, who stood a head shorter than herself, motioning with her head towards the side door. "There must be about two hundred of these Polish bastards, sliding in and out without wasting a minute. Bet nine out of ten were accepted." Leah held out her hand. "Look at their beaming faces and tell me I'm wrong."

"And they're not told to wait here for hours, either." Sonya supplied. "In this smelly old room."

"Stinky dungeon is more like it," Leah added.

"Shhhh," Sonya hushed her and told her to stop talking. She studied the room silently. It looked like a prison, bare and bleak, its walls glittering with dampness. The sky was bright, yet it seemed like twilight in here. A patch of sunlight cut through from the window, reflecting the black wooden floor; still the room was dim and cold. A kerosene lamp, hanging from the ceiling, waved a yellow flame, casting a yellow shadow on the gray wall, but the room was dim and cold in its enormity. Flies hummed and danced about the lamp, leaving their black specks on the glass cover.

After the last of the Polish students was gone, and the side door locked, the principal turned to the Jewish line again, calling up one at a time. A thin pale-faced girl staggered across the room as if in a trance. She glanced at her paper, then crushed it in her hand and dropped it near the door on her way out. Leah snatched it up.

"Look," she said to Sonya. "All it says here is *Not accepted*. Down here below the name."

"Can't understand." Sonya shook her head slowly. "You'd think they'd give us a reason, tell us why—"

"They don't have to," the cross-eyed girl broke in with a sardonic laugh. "You're so stupidly naive, Sonya, brilliant, but naive. I swear, you are." She shrugged and laughed again. "For three years now I've been taking entrance exams to the Gymnasium. The answers are always the same. It's simple." She leaned forward and snapped her fingers. "We're not wanted in their schools, that's all there's to it. Get it?"

"Bet it's different in America." Leah saw the smile spreading over her friend's face. "Bet you'll find it a whole lot easier there."

Sonya pressed Leah's hand and glanced up at her, beaming. "My mother says that in America everybody's got an equal chance. The people all speak one language, and the children start school at the age of six, mind you. Yes, it's compulsory. Isn't that something?"

"Telling me." The blond girl sighed, her head on Sonya's back. "They say that the streets there are strewn with gold and diamonds. I should live so, they are. Yes, yes."

Sonya and Leah giggled into their hands.

"Ohhh, my feet . . . my feet," the blond girl whimpered. "They're so numb and I'm dizzy with hunger. Ohhh . . . ohhh . . ." she whined, rubbing her head against Sonya's shoulder blade. "If only somebody would have the courage to tell the hunchman a thing or two."

"I think I will," Sonya told her. Yes, she thought. I will speak up when I get to his desk. He should be told, he should know the way we feel. Why not? So let him tear up my paper which no doubt reads: *Not accepted*. Besides, Mamma told me to fear God only.

Suddenly she recalled that unforgettable July evening. She had walked with her mother to a nearby village to visit some

112

Polish friend of Mamma's. She remembered it well because it was her sixth birthday, and she had worn that blue and white striped cretonne dress Mamma had made for her. On the way to the village Mamma had explained things. And Sonya had agreed to stay with the peasant woman until the rumor died down. She hated to be separated from Mamma, but this rumor was no trifle —it buzzed in every corner of the town, that all Jewish female children would be drowned in the river.

The peasant woman was kind, though well-paid. She had agreed to keep Sonya and tell her neighbors that the child was her niece, visiting her. That was no problem since Sonya looked Slavish and spoke Polish fluently. "But the name Simah!" The peasant woman had shook her head. Simah sounded too Jewish. It would easily arouse suspicion, argued the woman. It was then that Mamma had suggested that the woman call her Sonya. And so the name had remained.

"I'm leaving you with my Polish friend because I want you to live." Mamma had told her. "Utter not a word about your re-ligion to anybody. Keep up your courage—your *endurance,* my child. Fear nothing, fear no one. Fear Him only." These were Mamma's parting words.

The following morning a group of Polish youngsters had chased after her in the village, laughing, teasing, mimicking that she talked with her hands like a Jew did, and that she looked like one. Sonya's anger had spilled over. She rushed at them with her fists, forgetting her promise to Mamma, and burst out in a flood of curses: *"Psia krew! Cholera! Suki syns!* I am Jewish! What the hell of it?" She spat at them, kicked one, and scratched the face of another. The youngsters befell on her like a flock of hungry bees—they stretched her out in the gutter, sat on her head and legs, pounding away at her. Then the Polish woman appeared and led her away. She called her "little tiger," and warned her to stop fighting and talking about her religion if she wanted to be safe from the river. But Sonya had argued that she was to fear God only. Mamma had told her so.

"When you go up to the desk," Leah interrupted her thoughts, "ask the hunchman what I'm doing here?"

"What do you mean?" Sonya stared at her, puzzled.

"What chance have I got with *her* being what she is? That's what I mean."

"Your mother has nothing to do with this."

"Oh no. Wait and see if they'll accept the daughter of a—"

"Don't!" Sonya rushed a hand over Leah's mouth. "Please, don't call her that!" They stared at each other for a fierce second, then lowered their heads and silently waited for their names to be called.

IV

"Sonya Bronska Holland!'

She staggered back a step at the sound of the hunchman. "Why, tha-that's me," she stammered. "Holland is my real name, my—my father's name. It's beautiful, no?"

"So it is.' Leah replied sharply. "But why explain? Why waste time?"

The hunchman called a second time, louder than before.

"Why don't you go up to his desk? What's the matter with you anyway?"

"I want to, Leah. Honest."

"Ha-ha," the blond girl teased. "And she was going to tell him off. Sonya the *kozak*. Sonya the fearless. Ha-ha. Ha-ha."

"Oh, shut up," Leah hushed, raising a clenched hand. "Sonya's got the strength of a lion. What the hell d'you know about her, you *narrisher cupp*."

That's a laugh, thought Sonya. After waiting here all these hours, and now her feet were glued to the floor.

Again the humpbacked man shouted, beating his fist on the desk, seized by a violent coughing; he spat into his handkerchief, yelling and cursing: *"Zyd, cholera!* Come up here before I tear up your paper!"

"Go on," Leah nudged her angrily. "Look, he's turning purple with rage. Go on, go. Since when are you turning soft?"

"But you don't understand." Sonya half laughed, half cried. "It's my feet, they won't—"

"I don't care. Crawl, walk on your knees, but get up and get your paper. You may be the lucky one. Who knows. If he tears it, you'll never get another chance. You know that." She got behind Sonya and pushed her forward.

Sonya zigzagged across the room and after a minute regained her full balance. She straightened her shoulders and tossed back her braids. "Thanks, my friend," she said, glancing back at Leah. "I can make it to the desk. Get back in line. Hurry."

At the desk she gazed down at the frail little man with a touch of pity. He looked so small, so weak, sitting there with his head buried in one shoulder, like a bundle of wet rags.

"What took you this long?" he grumbled, without lifting his eyes from his book he was writing in.

Sonya shrugged and remained silent.

As he leaned back with his egg-shaped head on the tall chair-back, she grew less frightened as she looked at him. He was thin and gray, shrivelled like a November leaf. He breathed heavily, noisily, coughed from time to time; his knotted hand beat upon the desk feebly, like a child forcing a loud sound from his toy drum. A rattling noise came from his throat, as though the end had come for him at last. Yet when he shouted in his deep bari-tone, the students in line trembled. The walls, the ceiling, even the kerosene lamp seemed to tremble at his sound.

"You—you're a sick man, Pan Principal." The words escaped her, surprising even her.

"So!" he grunted, staring at the ceiling.

"I'm sorry . . . I'm very sorry for you. Really I am."

"So?" He repeated with a twist of the mouth as though wanting to hear more, without moving his eyes from the ceiling.

"I had pneumonia when I was a child. It left me with a dread-ful cough for a long, long time. That's why I'm sorry, I guess. I don't know." She laughed a short hysterical laugh.

"Hach," he snorted and returned to his book.

Sonya studied him: the crooked fingers curling a yellow mus-tache; the blue lips hugging a clay pipe, sending forth little jets of smoke to mingle with the smell of dampness and hot kerosene. The smell stung her throat. She coughed, swallowed, and waited.

After a silence he reached for a printed slip in the pile on his desk and handed it to Sonya. She held back her hand.

"May I ask you something, Pan Principal?"

He stabbed her with a look of anger and said: "What's your question? I'm a busy man."

"Well," she tugged at her braid. "I've been thinking. You're a principal, right? A sick man with a sick temper, nevertheless, a principal, right?"

"I am an educator," he said, raising his sunken chest in a pompous manner.

"Exactly. I was hoping for you to say that—"

"Well then? What's your question? I'm a busy man!"

A busy man. She covered her smile with her hand. "Well, as an educator—do you think it's right for us to stand for so many hours, tired and hungry and . . . terrified, begging so desperately for an education?" She was eyeing the slip in his hand. He'll tear it and drop the pieces in the waste basket. But the yellow fingers held the paper gently, waving it as though it were a fan.

He turned to her with a curious frown. "You shouldn't ask such questions."

"I know—I shouldn't breathe, but I must, because I want to live." She avoided his stare. "We are as anxious to learn as they are," pointing to the side door.

"You talk too much! *Djabel!*" He pounded on the desk.

"I can't help it—oh, well, tear up the paper if you must—"

"Shut up! You—you, *Zydowka!* Here, take it, quick before—." He flung the paper at her.

She folded it into her blouse pocket. He watched her and said in a calmer tone. "Aren't you going to read it?"

"No. I'd rather not."

"But why? Why the hell not? Everybody does."

"I know. I've watched them. If I read what's written in the slip, I'd have to tell the students about it as I pass them on my way out."

"So? What of it?"

She fingered her blouse pocket in which the slip lay folded, hesitating. "If I told them that I was not accepted they would sigh, cry with pity for me. And *pity* is the thing I dread. I—"

"And if you were accepted?" The hunchman cast a curious glance at her, curling his yellow mustache.

"Oh, then it would be worse, much worse, Pan Principal, your honor."

The hunchman stuck his pen into the inkwell and leaned back in his high-backed chair; his lips parted with slight quiver as though he wanted to smile and couldn't. "What in the devil do you mean by worse?" He glared up from his chair, puffing on his clay pipe.

"It's simple," she replied with a shrug. "If I were accepted, I'd have to tell the students and my classmates the truth. That, I'm afraid, would make them sick with *envy*." The hunchman shook his head as he watched her hurry from the room.

V

Out in the hall and down the stairs the voices of the students in the line followed her: "Sonya—were you accepted, were you—? Tell us—please—please—te-l-l u-s...."

She walked rapidly toward the gate across a pebbled, tree-lined path, inhaling the aroma of mint leaves and green chestnuts. Pausing behind a birch tree, she looked around for a minute, then withdrew the slip from her pocket. "Catch, catch the ball...!" A shout interrupted. She glanced across the park at the white brick building with its white marblelike stairs, the tall white doors and brass knobs. "Ah, yes . . . yes. That's the Gymnasium, of course." A beautiful building, straight as a statue, not like the crooked little wooden house with its broken wooden stairs, the *Szkola Powszechna* she was attending. On the lawn near the Gymnasium, a group of girls was chasing after a ball. They were dressed in navy skirts and brass-buttoned jackets to match, small sailor-hats rested on their heads with the shiny letters, which Sonya could scarcely make out in the distance: G. O. B. Gymnasium of Bunionov. Their arguments and laughter and shouting made her heart flutter. She fingered the slip in her pocket, wondering....

Presently she hurried out of the park, then stopped abruptly. "Must read my slip and get it over with." She unfolded the paper and read:

Sonya Bronska Holland
Accepted in the Gymnasium of Bunionov
Call in September to take up studies.

Sonya's eyes widened. She pressed her fingers tight against her paper to keep them from trembling. "Must tell Mamma!" She ran with the paper in the air, ran across Warszawska Street past a hay wagon. "Greetings, Pan-na Sonya!" a voice shouted from the wagon.

"Look, Pan Stanislav!" She waved her paper. "I've been accepted in the Gymnasium. Look!"

"Can't hear a word. . . !" The wagon vanished in a gallop.

On Stodolna Street she ran into the farmer's milkmaid. "Hey, Franka. I'm going to attend the Gymnasium in September."

"*Ach, tak . . . tak.* What's Gymnasiu, Pan-na Sonya?"

"No! No! not Gymnasiu! Gymnasium. Say Gymnasium, Franka."

"Gymna-sim-"

"No! Here, read." She pushed the paper under the girl's nose.

"But . . . but . . ." Franka stared dumbly at the print.

"But what? Aren't you glad—?"

"*Tak,* sure. I'm so happy for you I could drop dead. Only, I can't read."

"Ah, Franka." Sonya laughed, caressing her shoulder. "I forgot. Honest. Come over during the week, when my stepfather's away on the road, and I'll teach you to read and write. Honest I will. I teach a number of people in town."

"Could I, really?" The peasant girl brightened.

"Sure. You needn't pay me!" She called to her as she ran. "Just bring us a chunk of freshly-whipped butter, or some eggs."

Sonya hummed and skipped across the lot, mad with excitement. A lark trilled in the orchard. "He's singing for me," she laughed. The sun hung low now between the trees. Bainish must've pulled in hours ago, and she was not present to write down the deliveries. What would he say? What would he do to her? Her heart skipped a beat, then her eyes fell on the slip in her hand, and in less than a minute she forgot about Bainish and his wagon and the deliveries. She skipped again, hummed again, her unbraided hair flying in the wind, her blouse half-buttoned, hanging slovenly over her skirt.

"Stop jumping like a wild goat! You'll fall!" A voice called after her as she neared the house.

Sonya smiled and slowed down. She knew the kind, warm voice of Berel, the shoemaker. She turned to him quickly. "Reb Berel, I've been accepted in the Gymnasium. Isn't it a miracle?"

"Wha-what did you say? What?"

Sonya raised her voice, remembering that Berel was hard of hearing. "I said Reb Be—"

"Don't shout, child. You're deafening me." Berel lifted his rubbed-out coat-collar to his ear.

"Here, Reb Berel. It says so in this paper."

"Who can read *Goyish!* That's for them," pointing over his shoulder. The old shoemaker pulled at his earlobe with his blackened fingers and said: "Now tell it to me slowly and quietly."

"Reb Berel . . ."

"Yes. That I heard."

"In September I shall go to the Gymnasium."

"Wha—what—to an *unyiddishe szhkoleh* and write on *Shabbes!*"

"I need not go to school on Sabbath. I am excused."

"No?" The old man frowned, scratching his scraggly beard. "But it's a sin all the same."

"Of course not, Reb Berel. It's not a sin to get an education. I'm going to learn science and history and literature and everything."

"You think so? You really do?" The old man's narrow eyes widened. "After I had finished with the cheder . . ." scratching his beard, "I had mentioned to my father that I wanted to go to school, and d'you know what he did to me?"

"I can imagine." Her smile vanished, and she was serious again.

"Yes . . . he beat me," Berel said with a sigh. "My father, God rest his soul, used to say that it was a sin to even think of going to school." He touched the paper with one finger in Sonya's hand, as though it held a hidden power for him. "Maybe if I had gone to school, I wouldn't be sitting and patching shoes. Maybe, huh? Berel, the shoepatcher, that's what they call me. And I can't blame them, for I never made a *new* pair in my life. Look at these swollen black hands, full of cuts. Day in and day out I sit and patch, never make a *new* pair. . . ."

Sonya patted the leathery hand. "Don't think of the past, Reb Berel. The future is all that counts."

"Wha—what did you say?"

"Will explain another time. I've got to run and tell my mother." She wetted his palm with a kiss and hurried away.

"Don't run like a wild goat!" She heard his warm shout and giggled. "You will fall, God forbid . . ." the voice trailed after her as she leapt up the steps.

VI

Sonya threw open the door; flashing her paper before Miriam, she shouted: "Mamma! Mammusha! Look, I've made it!"

At once Miriam rushed up and covered Sonya's mouth with her hand. "Shhha. Oh, dear God . . . what am I to do. . . "

Sonya froze at the sight of her stepfather. He sat at the table with a look of violence.

"Eat . . . eat." Miriam smoothed his shoulder.

Bainish pushed his plate aside and jumped up from his chair. He rushed at the trembling girl with his heavy leather belt. "Why the hell didn't you show up at Rynek and write down the deliveries? I don't remember a single thing! I'm a ruined man!" He lashed her across the back and neck and arms. "That'll teach you to show up when I need you! That'll teach you to run around with that *tailor-jung,* and with the whore's daughter. A *cholerya* should catch them!"

Sonya bit her thumb, swallowing her tears. No, she would not cry and upset Mamma. The paper slipped out of her hand. At last she snatched up the white printed slip, blackened by Bainish's boots, and ran into her alcove.

A Matter of Principle

BY ALVIN JOHNSON

IT WAS a hot day in early summer of 1880, hot even for north-eastern Nebraska. A Saturday, and as usual my parents had driven to town, to market butter and eggs and buy sugar, coffee, and whatever else nourishes and glads the heart of man. My parents had taken my sister Edith, two years my senior, to get her some new shoes. They had also taken my baby brother John. The farm was left in charge of my halfsister Mary, age fifteen, and my halfsister Laura, age twelve. I was five and a half, but being the eldest son, considered myself far on the way to manhood.

I had been reading the *Child's History of the Bible* in the pleasant shade of the box elder trees. When I was three I had found that my mother was teaching my sister Edith, at five, to read. To me that was outrageous discrimination against the male sex. I made a terrible fuss, and my mother promised to teach me, too. She thought I'd soon get tired of it. I didn't.

You who remember your three-year-old birthday and the dreary "What can I do?" feeling will understand how the horizon lifted when I discovered that those neat little shapes on the page could say "The cat has got a rat" or "See the boy run." I testify that though I have had literary experiences since, there has been none so blindingly brilliant as "Hear the cock crow" on the white pages of book and mind, at three.

But that was long ago, for me. I was reading and rereading the *Child's History of the Bible*, four hundred pages with long words syllabled off like Ne-bu-chad-nez-zar.

For my sins I had to reread it. When I was four and my sister Edith six we set out in a competition to read the *Child's History* through.

We had to use the same book. Edith could read faster than I could, and her bookmark was far ahead of my place in the text.

I scamped. If the text had Zer-u-bab-el I just said Bbl-bbl. And when everybody begat everybody I said to myself in my childish way, "Begat be darned."

Always when I surrendered the book I put my bookmark well ahead of Edith's. The poor child had to work her eyes out to pass me, which she did honestly. But my bookmark would pass hers again. To quote Goethe's formula for the march to the House of the Devil:

> *Wie sie doch sich eilen kann,*
> *Mit einem Sprunge macht's der Mann.*

I won. Edith accepted my victory. But at five conscience still troubles you. I had scamped a victory. My soul was troubled, and for penance I decided to read the whole *Child's History of the Bible* honestly. I did, and found it wondrously interesting. I'd talk Bible until my parents needed to pack cotton in their ears.

To return to the hot summer day. A troop of men on horseback came cantering down our lane. The leader jumped off his saddle.

"Little boy, who's home?"

"Mary and Laura," I said.

"We're starved to death. Got to have something to eat. Where's Mary and Laura?"

"I'll get them." I soon found Mary and Laura, in the flower garden. "Mary, five men are here, say they've got to have something to eat."

"Good gracious! We ate up about everything there is in the house. Not a speck of meat of any kind left."

"We could catch some spring chickens," said Laura.

"We'd have to pick them and dress them and it would take an hour to get up a meal. I'll have to go out and tell them, they'd better move on."

"Spring chickens!" said the apparent chief. "Sure we'll wait an hour for them. Go ahead and git 'em. We'll pay for 'em."

With the aid of the dog, four young cockerels were caught. They were beheaded, scalded, plucked, dressed, and while the frying pan was heating the girls made up a corn meal batter, to be johnnycake. They brought up pickles and preserved plums from the cellar, made a huge pot of coffee, filled a big pitcher with cream.

Seeing that the dinner was progressing well, I felt it my duty to go out and entertain the strangers, who were sitting on our long bench in the shade, carrying on a lively tobacco juice competition. It wasn't merely who could shoot the brown juice farthest, but who could make the highest arc. The horses, tethered to trees near by, were fighting flies.

"Your horses have been awfully hot," I said. "They're just soaked with sweat."

"Yes," said the chief. "We been riding since before sun-up. About all horses can stand. They been drinkin' dry every trough on the road."

"In the Bible times they rode on camels. My father says camels don't sweat. So they don't need much water."

"I seen camels in the zoo. They didn't look as if they could go far."

"Joseph's brothers rode their camels way down into Egypt, from Beersheba."

"What's that you say, kid?" The humorist of the gang sat up. "Sheba's beer. Wish we had some of it here."

"Shut your dirty mouth," said the chief. Biblical material wasn't right for humor. "Little boy, did you ever ride a horse?"

"No."

"Like to?"

"Yes."

"Well, come on, I'll put you on my horse."

The horse was beautiful, but very tall and big around. The chief put me on the saddle. I knew I ought to grip the horse's sides with my legs, but they were too short and stuck straight out. But there was a beautiful pommel I could hold on with.

The chief led the horse up the lane a hundred yards, and back. Two hundred yards of pure bliss, over the gently rocking motion of the horse.

The chief lifted me off to terra firma. "Now you can tell us some more about Joseph."

"He was about the youngest son and his father Jacob made a

pet of him. The older brothers didn't like that. You see, Joseph
was a blowhard. He'd dream that each of them had a star, and
their stars all bowed down to his star. So they sold him down
into Egypt."

I saw that my technique of storytelling was acceptable, and so
went on to David and Goliath, and I had got Daniel into the
lion's den when Laura announced that the dinner was ready. The
men rushed in and ate like wolves. Not a shred was left of those
cockerels; the guests even broke the drumstick bones and drew
out the marrow with their jackknives. Not a crumb of johnnycake
was left, nor a gill of coffee, nor a spoonful of cream. The men
rose.

"Young lady," said the chief to Mary, "that was the best dinner
we ever et. I want to give you a little memento." He put his hand
into his pocket and brought out a quarter. Mary saw it and
would have accepted it thankfully. "No," he said, "this is for
your young man. If the preacher told such good Bible stories I'd
go to church." He handed me the quarter.

Again his hand fished around in his pocket and brought out
the most beautiful of coins, a five dollar gold piece. He dropped
it into Mary's hand. She blushed.

In a minute the guests were astride their horses, trotting up
our lane to the county road. I watched them follow it for a
quarter of a mile. Then they turned to a road leading over a hill
to the Indian Reservation.

In an hour our parents returned. We gave an excited account
of our guests. My father was most impressed when he saw the
five dollar gold piece. He didn't see the quarter, for, at whatever
age, a professional is shy about showing his honorarium.

"Who were they?" my father asked. "Did you get their names?"

None of us had thought of asking for names.

My father stroked his beard. "I heard about something in town.
That may be it. Maybe."

It *was* it. In an hour another group of men on horseback came
down our lane. My father went out to meet them.

"Hello, Sheriff Blackwell," he said. "What now?"

"We heard at the courthouse, the Younger gang had robbed a
bank in South Dakota. They were riding down through this

county headed for their hangout somewhere near the Kansas line. I got together a posse to intercept them. I heard they were coming along the road here. Seen anything of them?"

"Well, yes," my father said. "My wife and I were in town but my daughters tell me, five men came here and demanded dinner. The girls made them a dinner, and they went on."

"I reckon they're the gang we're looking for. It was one of the Younger brothers himself who led the gang, and killed the cashier. A smooth fellow with a scar in front of his left ear."

(My friend the chief! I had seen that scar.)

"They say," the sheriff continued, "the cashier was all ready to skip out for Canada with all the bank's assets collected in a flour sack. Two hundred thousand dollars. When the Younger gang broke into the bank that cashier tried to shoot it out with them. He'd never have done it for the bank, but for his own money. He had stolen it, what better title? But nobody had better shoot it out with the Youngers. Their aim is infallible. Well, which way did they go?"

I piped up: "They went along the county road to the side road to the Reservation."

"Well, then, they are out of our jurisdiction," said the sheriff with relief. And one could be certain that, in the dozen counties the Younger gang would cross, sheriffs and their posses would always be too late to intercept them. It's not lucky to intercept five dead shots.

The sheriff and posse were gone. Mary came to my father with the five dollar gold piece on a paper in her hand.

"Papa, what shall we do with this money? We can't keep it. It is blood money. That brigand killed the cashier to get it."

My father stroked his beard. "Yes, the money may be blood money. If there is blood on it, it is the blood of a thief. The cashier was stealing the bank's money. The Younger gang took it away from him.

"Now I'll tell you what we can do. You give me that gold piece and I'll give you five silver dollars. There is no question, you and Laura earned it. And I will give the gold piece to that poor widow Mrs. Wilkins. When Wilkins died he left nothing at all to his wife and her two little children. That five dollars will pay for a hundred quarts of milk. And I'll give another five dollar gold piece, for flour and bacon."

Mary handed over the five dollar gold piece, her conscience wholly appeased.

I did nothing about my 25 cent honorarium. It was the first quarter I ever earned. I had a vague but authentic anticipation of the papal rule, "The crime does not stick to the cash."

Spanish Scene

EXCERPT FROM A NOVEL BY BARBARA ANN GREVER

TIMIA PUSHED open the double oaken doors and stepped onto the terrace. With dusk, the heat had lifted. At the far end of the farmyard, under a stunted fig tree, a chicken pecked in the dust. The angry sunset filled all space but for the flat dried-out fields. She locked the doors, dropped the iron key into her empty wicker basket and walked very slowly down the path.

She climbed over the gray-board gate and jumped down onto the dirt-packed road. The red sandstone walls on either side of the road seemed to enclose her like a tunnel. To her left was a field of grapevines bathed in color, sprinkled over with fine dust. Beyond, in a reflection of pale rose silver, lay the Mediterranean Sea. Over the silent fields hung the burning sunset.

At the turn in the roadway, she came upon a man in olive drab uniform, standing in a donkey cart.

"Buenas," said this man in the nasal inflection of the island. He lifted his cap with an insinuating smile, like a pervert glimpsing under a child's petticoat.

She had never seen this man in the village. She stared back at him without speaking. After a moment, she went around the cart. She heard the cart move behind her, but she hurried on without looking back. She passed the white stucco house of Raquel the physician, and the long yellow stucco schoolhouse, and the chalk house of the village fisherman. Finally she came to the bakery, closed for two days in preparation for the Fiesta of San Francisco.

She became gradually aware of many voices in a deep low murmur of sound. The fact that a crowd waited in the village square seemed suddenly fearsome to her. In all her months on the island, she could not remember having seen more than six people together except in the bus.

A spotted pig lay in dung outside the army barracks. The pig was too fat to move. He had urinated among the dung, to set up a powerful stench. A soldier leaned against the barracks, oblivious of this smell. Beyond the barracks gate, a woman in a short blue skirt hurried into a darkened doorway.

As Timia approached the village square, the voices became more intense. She was suddenly overwhelmed with the idea that because she was a foreigner, the villagers would all stop speaking and stare at her when she entered the square.

However, as she came into the square and turned her head to look among the crowd, she found this not to be true. The square before the church of San Francisco was crowded with Spaniards. They strolled about in their finery, nodding to one another and talking with unaccustomed ceremonial gesture. Not all were native to Formentera.

The young girls wore long white starched dresses. They stood about in careful poses, as though their dresses were made of tissue paper. The young men, too, were unaccustomedly suited. They seemed to stance, rather than to stand. As the young men talked among themselves, they offered one another Spanish cigarettes.

The married women, as was their custom, stood apart. Today they had covered over their dark skirts with long festive aprons of bright color silks, in stripes and floral embroidery, which brushed the earth. Above the aprons they still wore their severe black-button jackets as tight as penguins' skin. While the men stood together, talking of larger matters, of crops, wars, and governments, the women whispered in low voices, of babies, courtship, embroidery, their neighbors, and the like.

The young children did not know what to do. They stood apart even from one another, watching their elders, and carefully preserving their elegant dress. Some of the older already parroted their parents, they stood in self-conscious postures spouting younger adult thoughts with over-confidence which, when overheard, made their elders smile.

The red sunset diffused upon the great white stucco wall of the village church. The black and white garbed figures, relieved only by the long silken aprons of the women, seemed arranged in miniature before the immense wall upon which reflected the red glow of the setting sun.

The foreigners were absent. But for Timia, they were all together, crowded into the Blue Inn of the Two Sisters, at the base of the ravine road. Today, Timia did not want to be one of them. But neither did she belong among Spaniards. She understood that from the faces of several now watching her.

A little girl in long white batiste knocked her pretty flower-and-lace headdress off her head; the girl, running, called happily to an old woman who held out her arms. With an intense longing, Timia watched the child and the old woman embrace. It was a glimpse into a life she had never known, of a life which she sensed she would, by the nature of her circumstances, also be prevented from creating for her own children.

Thus thinking, the empty market basket swinging behind her shoulder, her head still low, she walked slowly up a path to pause before the low stucco house of the grocer. She pulled aside the doorway covering of strings of bamboo and stepped into the airless, darkened room. The glaring sunset sifted through the bamboo beads upon the earthen floor.

The room was empty. "Buenas, Senora," she called in the island's high nasal.

The old woman proprietor came through the door which led from her living quarters. She still wore her cotton work apron. On the old woman's face was the expression of merchants everywhere. For some interval, Timia and the old woman stared at one another. For the first time, Timia realized this old peasant woman was as remote from the villagers as she herself was. Though no word was said between them, she felt that they had at this moment spoken to one another.

Timia looked away from the old woman, down among the

hempen sacks upon the earth floor. Today there was no fruit, or any vegetable. There were only tomatoes and onions.

"Un media kilo tomatoes," Timia said, pointing to the basket. "Un media kilo cabellas," she said pointing to the onion sack. She then slipped the basket from her shoulder and placed it on the counter. As always, she wished she could say something to this person. It was the village custom and therefore polite to chatter. Only when she went to the miller's grocery above the windmill could she comfortably talk. The miller's wife dressed like a city woman; she was sloppy and had seen something of life.

Timia watched the old woman dump onions onto one pan of the swinging brass scales. She chose carefully from a group of small weights, finally selecting two which then swung the scale into balance. Only then did Timia turn away, for though the old woman set her own prices, it was considered proper to watch the weighing.

Lacking language, they exchanged smiles.

Timia stepped over a sack of potatoes. She stood between a sack of grain and one of noodles to take four white candles from a paper bundle on the almost empty shelf. On the shelf below were a tin of shoe polish, several chunks of home-made soap, a pot of honey, a few pencils, and three cans of sardines. Timia took one can of sardines and stepped back across the sack of noodles. She was the only person who bought sardines from the old woman. This was because she was afraid of the fresh meat. The butcher strung up his old goat for several days at a time, until it was covered with flies.

The old woman nodded with satisfaction while Timia put the candles and the can of sardines beside the tomatoes and onions. Again, she looked up to smile. "Quanto es?" she asked in her simple Spanish. As always, in the never-deviating pattern of two people who do not communicate beyond bare essentials, the woman wrote numbers on a scrap of newspaper, at the same time adding aloud for the benefit of both. Timia stood beside her, knowing the old woman"s addition, like her weighing, was always accurate, but that did not matter, for the old woman had the only shop in the village, and set her own prices.

There was the sound of many people walking. The old woman

paused, "Momento, momento, Senora." An unexpected radiance came upon her sharp face. She raised her hand, palm to Timia. "Momento," she repeated, staring past Timia.

Timia turned slowly, her eyes not wishing to depart from the old woman's radiant face. Timia's eyes skimmed the darkness of the room, to the door hung with dried bamboo and wooden beads, behind which now passed a single line of young girls in long white communion dresses, white-veiled; before their breasts their hands clasped rosaries. It was white of innocence. Behind the innocence, the flaming backdrop of the setting sun touched the ridge of the hill of San Francisco.

On and on the white figures flickered past the bamboo screen.

The girls in white walked silently before the flaming sky. Island women followed, dressed in their fiesta dress, thin braids hung narrow down their backs. Their heads were covered with lace, or smaller silken handkerchiefs sewn with large silken flowers. The colors in their shining aprons caught reflection from the sunset, bringing flashes of deep green and wine.

Following the girls, and more conscious of the look of watchers, walked a group of women incongruous to the island, dressed in modern black silk but yet long-sleeved and high-necked, in Spanish custom. They wore black lace mantillas over short curled hair, and appeared to be the patronesses of native celebration. Though conscious of religious devotion, it could be seen they had other lesser devotions.

On they passed beyond the bamboo screen, and all from the smallest child to the eldest woman held their hands clasped at their breasts, and bowed their heads, as they walked forward up the hill toward the Church of San Francisco de Javier.

Behind the women was an empty interval, then the young men and boys appeared. Shuffling somewhat apart from the manner of the women, they held their heads down, hands clasped behind their backs, their bodies angled, almost slanting at the earth.

Four black-garbed men bore a statue of Saint Francis stretched flat upon a wooden platform, as though the saintly figure rested upon a coffin. Behind the first four men came four others, all supporting the statue of Saint Francis on heavy wooden planks.

After them walked more men carrying the statue of another saint who sat upright in wooden immobility upon a gilded chair.

There was an empty distance, only bamboo beads and flaming sky, until the old village priest walked by, his tattered frock covered by a white linen robe. He wore a scarlet satin surplice and a narrow black hat, and behind him walked a strong young man who bore aloft a heavy golden cross. Then came four elders with a giant statue of the Virgin Mary.

All held upon their faces this still expectant light, as though in the course of miracles one might most easily occur upon this day. Finally, it was the end of the procession, a solitary man passed the bamboo screen and then went on, his head cut against the tiny window at the end of the shop.

The old peasant woman waited still another moment until she turned to Timia, on her face again the expression of all merchants. It seemed the woman was about to rattle off in rapid dialect, as a foreigner sometimes unconsciously will, forgetting that a sympathetic friend does not understand his words.

The old woman remembered. Lacking words beyond the ones of business, they again exchanged smiles. Again, Timia felt this woman, beyond the role of merchant, might be to some degree her friend.

She paid her, pulled aside the beaded curtain, and stepped out into the road. To her left, the procession moved quietly up the hill, the statues held high above the heads of the people. She was the only spectator. She turned onto a narrow path behind the cafe which sold bitter coffee. She walked quickly until she was parallel to the procession, though on another path. It seemed right to her that she should do this.

And she walked silently as they did, thought not amongst them, until the procession turned away from her, trailing across the deserted village square toward the Church of St. Francis, whose giant wooden doors which reached three stories high were, for the first time in her memory, swung open. The procession shuffled forward, swallowed into the darkness beyond the open doors, until the village square was empty, the deeper dusk edged into darkness, and from inside the church the voices rose and fell in chat, fell and rose again in the religious verbal pattern of the faith, as aspirations sought a dwelling place.

A hound sniffed his way across the deserted square, in search of crumbs which had fallen from the sweet cakes of the children. It was as it had been, when she arrived in the village months before, except for the voices in ritual within the church.

Timia crossed the square and hurried down the ravine road toward the Blue Inn of the Two Sisters. She passed the patisseria where Cabello made the yerbats, and stopped before the tailor's house. Across the way, the Blue Inn was shuttered. The deserted patio tables held food and unfinished wine. She could hear from within the inn the voices of the foreigners, of which she was one. They had then been forcibly prevented from witnessing the procession.

She waited until the doors of the Blue Inn might open. And waiting, the voices of the foreigners from within the Inn grew louder than the chanting from the Church of Saint Francis.

Timia slipped the basket off her shoulder and set it down before the tailor's shop. She stepped back into the darkened entrance hall. A nude child with a dirty belly sat in silence on the dirt floor. She stared at this lonely child for some interval of time. She made the sign of the cross over her heart for the two of them. Yet her heart was heavy.

4. Scars That Vanish and Scars That Stay

Persephone Lost

BY MILDRED MESURAC JEFFREY

A CHILLY spring gust blew a crumpled paper against the wall of Junior High School 957, the Bronx, and incinerator ash swirled suddenly downward, settling along the stained gray window sills. Three teachers coming out of the building squinted and turned their faces away from the gritty wind-slap.

"Uh!" The tallest woman frowned at a wafer of chewing gum on her black pump. She scuffed the sole impatiently against the step, watching the gum turn to a rubbery smear on the cement while she spoke to the woman at her elbow. "And you won't do a bit of good, Mag."

"Just file a truant slip and forget it," said the third woman. She jabbed a hat pin deeper into her straw skimmer.

"I can't," Margaret Wand said. The brown eyes that dominated her thin face seemed to grow larger.

"It's absolutely crazy to go into one of those tenements alone."

"Right. What difference does one more day make?"

"She's been on the hook for a week already." The black shoe sole took a final scrape. "Anyhow, you don't know enough Spanish."

"I'm sorry," Margaret said, pulling white gloves from her coat pocket. "I suppose I sound ridiculous."

"At least think it over."

"I did. I've reached a point where I have to settle it one way or another. When she first told me about her mother's being a prostitute, I just couldn't believe it. But thinking about it, now I—"

"Honestly, Mag!"

"She was a good student, El. In spite of being locked out half the night. Something must have happened to change her."

"Look. We simply can't take another cut in our course or we'd come with you."

"I wish you'd wait."

Margaret hesitated.

A portly fellow-teacher brushed past, twittering.

Margaret shook her head. "Sorry. But thanks for the offer."

One of her companions shrugged. "Okay, if you're as set as all that."

"Please be careful," the other added.

"I will," Margaret said, smiling. "I'm not going very far, you know. It's only around the corner. See you tomorrow." She turned to start briskly up the block of tenements, their dark windows clotted with bedclothes.

Once she had put the school and the neighboring elevated tracks out of sight, her walk slowed. She stared down an unfamiliar street. Three wooly-pated boys flickered in and out of a doorway, then darted into the street past an oncoming truck. It swerved, banged the fender of a parked car, picked up speed and roared around the corner. Two floors above, hoarse unintelligible oaths sounded through an open window, and a fist beat the air in the direction of the vanished truck. Bunched pages of a newspaper flew out the window. The sheets, half-opening in midair, fluttered toward the sidewalk like huge stricken moths.

Margaret hurried toward the building where Natividad Perez, her truant pupil, lived. A dog with massive haunches, snuffling and pawing at a tipped carton of garbage, growled at Margaret's approach, and she hastily detoured into the street. Two Negro women who had been heaving with laughter grew silent as she passed. She could feel the sharp glances of their shiny eyes like pins in her back. Was it her imagination or were there other eyes watching, too? She felt like a tourist who had blundered into a native quarter. Tomorrow it would be all over school that Mrs. Wand had been to Natividad's house. Miss McAllister, the principal, would hear of it and question her coldly. What was the attendance officer for, if not to make home visits?

Ah, the house. Margaret paused on the sidewalk between the cluster of trash cans spewing chicken bones and the gang of smudged urchins chalking the doorstep. Their rippling incomprehensible chatter halted as she stood in front of them. They stared at her. She studied them. Their black-chip eyes. Their pointed little-boy faces suddenly motionless.

"Does Natividad live here?" she asked finally, offering a smile like a new coin. "Natividad Perez? My friend. *Amigo*. Natividad."

Shaking their heads, they backed up. Muttering, they moved closer to one another. A five-year-old in sagging dungarees had flashed a grin at the word *amigo;* he had time to blurt out, *"Si, si,"* before the others whirled around to drench him in rapid Spanish and pound him with their fists. He ducked away and flattened himself against the pumice of the building. "No," he growled, "no Natividad."

A girl with high cheekbones and with hair tumbled by the wind peeped from the alley next to the building. She was chewing at a pomegranate, and scarlet juice streaked her chin.

Margaret waved, though she didn't know the girl. "Hello! Can you tell me—"

The youngster opened her mouth to drop a mass of blood-bright seeds, plat! on the gray sidewalk. Then her teeth dug greedily into the fruit again, and she disappeared back into the alley.

Margaret clutched her purse and plunged past the silent staring urchins into the dim vestibule. An inner door with a cracked glass pane. A knob that pulled at her glove. A heavy stench that hit her like a punch in the stomach. She recoiled. Nausea washed over her.

Wood, rotting in dank stair corners and under leaky sinks. Garbage, spongy and black with decaying plantain skins, apple cores, pork fat, lard-caked rice, sour with yesterday's vomit of the feverish child on the second floor. Roaches, heavily pungent, smashed under palms or shoesoles, trapped in grease-spattered ovens where they burned into small charred heaps. Human skin, itchy with grime and sweat in the stale warmth of unaired rooms. Feces, crusted on the ripped linoleum of hall toilets. The accumulated stench was heavy enough to have a texture and weight of its own.

Margaret raised a hand to her face. Catching a faint whiff of carnation scent, she put both gloves, tentlike, over her nose, and the sickness in her stomach gradually died down. She glanced angrily up into the gloom at the top of the stairs and turned back toward the door. Then she paused. The little boys were probably still out there. The girl in the alley—she'd be watching.

The kids outside—they lived in this smell. They came in and out of this stinking hall two or three times in an hour. . . .

Still breathing through her scented gloves, Margaret slowly turned around and looked up the staircase again. The gloom seemed to have lightened. She stepped tentatively up on the first stair, waited, climbed one more and one more and one more, until she found herself almost at the top, staring at the wood near her feet. It was dark and wet, reeking of urine.

A faint rustle. What was that? Paper in a draft? Something else—something alive down there along the baseboard? She kicked one shoe against the other, hurried past the stain, along the hall and up to the third floor.

Garlic, rich, rank, browned in hot olive oil. A trumpet spattered orange riffs from a radio. Behind a door at Margaret's back, a baby waa'ed suddenly and set off two feminine voices screeching at each other in the alien tongue. Margaret tapped at the gouged rear door. She rehearsed a smile. She readied a Hello for Natividad, a *Buenos Dias* for the mother. Rat-tat. No answer.

She waited. Knocked again. The wood panel stayed flat and blank before her.

Behind her a hinge squeaked and she spun around. A pair of eyes speared her.

"I—do you—I'm looking for Natividad, Natividad Perez—she's —"

The door slammed.

Voices came up the stairwell from the ground floor. Boys' voices, grown boys.

"My kid brother said she's in here. She's upstairs, I bet ya."

"Nah," the second voice said, "ya fulla crap. That's the nurse that goes to Louie's old lady in the back."

"In a fur coat?"

"Fur f—! I gotta see the Wop. Ya comin'?"

"Okay, okay. Don't get sore." A remote door crashed.

Filling her lungs with the thick air, Margaret breathed out

heavily, glanced around. The stairs she had climbed were deserted, the hall behind her empty, the steps to the next floor
—someone was crouching halfway up to the next landing. A
youth, hair patent-leather in the dingy light, watched her with
unblinking eyes.

She wrenched her glance down, pretending not to have seen.
She banged on Natividad's door again, called sternly, "Natividad!
It's Mrs. Wand. I want to—" Her voice turned plaintive and she
broke off. She wheeled to march up and down the hall, rapping on
every door; then like a toy with a broken spring, she came to a
stop in front of Natividad's again.

Silence. The radio had been snapped off, the baby quieted.
The quarreling women were still. Between the bannister posts
the face with the reptile eyes watched soundlessly. The air, pent
in the narrow hall, packed down the descending stairs, was charged
with silence.

Natividad's door opened.

Only a head emerged, a young man's head framed in smoke
curling from the cigarette in a thin mouth. The smoke spiraled
past the high cheekbones, circled the black frizzy hair.

Margaret's neck prickled.

His eyes narrowed. "Nobody here. Go away."

She flushed. "Now, look here, I know—"

"Beat it," the youth said flatly. "Nobody here."

Margaret frowned, but as he came across the threshold toward
her, the slitted eyes glinted like razors and she stepped back. He
loomed in front of her, so close his fetid breath hit her in the
face. "Beat it, lady!"

A faint brushing warned her as the watcher on the stairs rose
to his feet.

Wet fear funneled up and burst over her, rushing her along
the hall, down the stairs to the second floor. A flicked cigarette
butt hit her shoulder and she cried out. From above, a laugh
answered, hollow in the stairwell. She pelted down the remaining
steps to the street.

The afternoon was bright around her; the sidewalk firm beneath her feet as she fled down the block. She rounded the corner
and a sharp pain in her side pulled her up short. She gulped two

or three mouthfuls of chill air, and pressing her hand against the hard rib cage under her breast, walked rapidly down the long street toward the station. Three more blocks. Two more blocks. She broke into another little run, but the pain caught at her again. This last block was longer than the others, the cracks in the grainy sidewalk yards further apart.

The jumbled ash cans between the El pillars along the curb were piled higher than ever. The usual clank and roar of an uptown train now reverberated almost visibly between the walls of this gray canyon. Margaret plodded toward the staircase reaching up from the street corner to the station which jutted out from the tracks like an aerialist's platform. She seized the end of the round iron bannister, sagging against it with her eyes closed, breathing deeply for a few moments. Traffic lights flicked from green to red. Cars ground to a halt. Red to green. They roared off again. Finally she pulled herself up the stairs.

In the downtown express a throng of car-card faces surrounded her—staring, glaring, sneering—red print, black print barked at her—*Shop Subway! Alkalize! Use O-DO-RO-NO.* . . . Margaret closed her eyes, but the words stamped noisily around in her mind, brandishing their capital letters like convention-hall signs—*CalvertBVDChesterfieldTUMS.* . . . The train careened crazily on its way downtown, stopped now and then to jolt her to attention.

Thirty-Third Street at last. Margaret hurried to cross in front of a line of taxis and trucks stopped for a red light, and a peddler with white scarecrow hair fringing a wool cap shuffled off the opposite curb and came toward her. Suspended from a strap around his neck was a tray holding bunches of violets in a row of lopsided purple circles. As the traffic light changed, the cars lunged forward and Margaret dashed across the street. She bumped the old man's elbow and he swayed in a half-turn, spilling three nosegays. He bent down mumbling, heedless of the cars. The edge of his long overcoat dragged in the street.

"No! Wait—" Margaret seized his arm and pulled him back. "Don't—I'm so sorry—"

He wrenched himself away, still mumbling. She caught his sleeve. "Wait—"

A taxi skidded around the corner. Its rear wheel mashed purple violets into the asphalt. The two other bouquets lay, petals down, in the dank gutter. With a sudden gesture of rage the old man lifted his flower tray high above his head and hurled it out into the middle of the street among the turning wheels.

The Seed of a Giant

BY GWYNNETH FAIRE GROBIN

I WAS the third child of a tall father. My father stood two or three inches over six feet, and as a child it seemed to me as though from that towering height he could stretch out his arms and topple chimneys, and perhaps see around the curve of the world.

I

He stood at least a head above the other people, craning their necks like avid birds to see the floats and balloons of the R. H. Macy Thanksgiving Day parade. I was five, the youngest child, so he lifted me to his shoulder first, before he, in turn, hoisted up my brother and sister. From that great vantage point I could see all of Broadway before me; but I soon tired of looking at the never-ending stream of costumed paraders. I imagined the noses of the clowns were red from the cold, which crawled down my neck and stiffened my mittened hands. I stared instead at the face of my father, seeing it for the first time from above, a chiseled line of cheekbone and jaw, proud, aquiline nose above lips strangely soft for a man, brown eyes inflexible, for their pale, sparse lashes lent them no shade. My hands pressed hard against him, not from any fear of falling, but as though that link of touch could, like a great aorta, commingle our blood bond. I did not mind the long minutes during which he held my brother or sister aloft. The close-packed legs of the spectators formed a breakwater against the nipping wind, and I could look upward and see my father's face, its darkness silhouetted first against the golden whorl of my brother's hair, then matched against the deep brown eyes and hair of my sister. My hand kept firm hold to one trousered leg. Through the scratchiness of knitted mitten and worsted cloth, I could feel the rippling of his supple flesh.

After the parade was over, we walked to where the car was parked. He stopped and bought roasted chestnuts from the cart of a little man, the man's brown face wreathed with wrinkles, his body shrivelled under layers of raveled sweaters. The acrid smoke of the charcoal brazier stung my eyes as I stood close and let the fire's heat lick my cheeks. I did not eat my share of the chestnuts as we drove home, segments of gray afternoon sky shuttling through the car window, but held them tight in my fists until my fingers had drunk all their warmth.

II

I was six years old that June when my father returned from the first of his long stays in Washington. My brother, sister, and I were having supper at the round, white painted table in the sunny dining room of our apartment on the Bronx River Parkway. Supper consisted of graham crackers and warm milk, which we called mush. I mashed the graham crackers into the bowl with the back of my spoon, watching their brittle forms sop up the liquid, then mottle the whiteness as they crumbled into soggy defeat. Dickie, my brother, sat with his head resting pensively on one arm, elbow propped on the table, his heart-shaped face, finely moulded by illness, gazed intently downward as he solemnly and precisely pressed each graham cracker into his bowl of milk. Long finished with the preparations, my sister Barbara was rapidly downing her supper; a delicate milk mustache formed on her upper lip, an opalescent sheen against her olive skin. Even seated, her body seethed with fluid motion as though in a moment she would be running free through open fields, the tall grasses parting and kneeling before the gypsy child with the streaming mane of chestnut hair.

If I had not known my father was home, it would have been apparent from the infectious excitement of my mother's voice as she called from the living room, "If you children finish everything in your plates quickly, Daddy will walk with us down to the river to see the sunset."

My father, long-limbed and erect, walked slightly ahead with my mother; she, tiny and tremulous, clinging to his arm. We walked slowly, apace to my brother's hobbling gait, my sister and I picking buttercups and weaving them into stem-entwined chains; all of us pelting my father with eager words, stored during his absence. As we neared the river, my brother and sister, jubilant voices interrupting each other in their eagerness, were telling him:

"And we sent her around the corner—"

"It was my idea, Dickie, I thought of it—"

"Yes, and she went! I told her to go see if it was raining around the corner—"

"She went all the way around and she came back and told us it wasn't raining around the corner *either*!"

My sister's last words frothed out in a fountain of laughter, joined by my father's deep howls of delight, rushes of laughter from the others and the uneven tattoo of my giggles. Yes, I laughed too, although the story was about me; though I had not understood then, or now at the retelling, why they found this so funny. But I loved to see my father laugh, his head thrown back, his eyes softened; to hear the sound of his laughter rolling down to me like a warm, enveloping shawl entwining us in the hilarity of love.

My mother's face glowed in pleasure at our making him laugh. She nestled against him. Slight wisp against his body, she barely reached the height of his chest. But it was not to her nor to his other children, lovely in her image, that he turned, but to me, his changeling child. When he knelt beside me his shadow was no higher than mine. He withdrew from his pocket and fastened on my dress a gilded pin: one-half fashioned into a heart and joined by a slender chain to a key with the emblem: Memento of Washington, D.C. He whispered to me, "This is for my baby. This is the key to my heart."

III

In the impassive night air my sister's frightened breathing sounded like the tearing of corrugated paper. Our beds were but a few inches apart in the bedroom shared by us two, two years apart in age—she nine and I seven. For an instant I was not sure whether it was her breathing I heard or my own. I lay rigid and silent, fear spreading through me in undulating swells from the vortex in my belly, as I peered through the crack of open door, down the dim hallway, into the lighted dining room where my father stood tall in his rage above the shrinking form of my mother. His words were indistinguishable as they smashed into our bedroom, splintering like icicles into syllables of fury, underscored by the muffled throb of my mother's sobs. I quivered wildly at the sounds of glass and metal smashing and the violent slamming of a door. Then, like a blizzard blanketing all beneath it, there was only a suffocating silence. My sister's wails pierced the stillness and in a moment our bedroom door opened. My father stood in the doorway, a Colossus framed by light, his tone taut with control as he said to Barbara, "If you don't stop that snivelling, I'll give you something to cry about." He pulled the door shut as he left.

I heard a light, tapping sound at the window and I darted from my bed into the living room, crying, "Daddy, Daddy, there's a burglar!" I followed in the protecting wake of his long shape as he strode into our bedroom, turned on the light and flung the window open. There, crouched on the snow-laden fire escape, like a small, nocturnal animal, was my mother. I saw that her feet were bare.

IV

The flat leaves on the bushes bordering our house on the Bronx River Parkway were a patent-leather green, shining beetle-back leaves splayed out from skeleton finger branches. I plucked a leaf, its thick membrane coated with the hoarded warmth of the September sun, then tore it cleanly in half, along the dark line of its spine. Thin leaf ooze gummed on my index fingers and thumbs and I was ten years old and I had fingers and thumbs that smelled like a dank, palpitating frog.

She stood in front of me, my mother, and she mouthed a repetition of the words, "Your father isn't coming home to us any more," and her lips formed words which were not words but swabs of sound pressing in hard on my eardrums.

I stared at the fissuring cracks in the pavement, "Step on a crack and break your mother's back," at the telephone pole at the edge of the sidewalk: worn, splintered wood stretching to the sky, and finally I stared into my mother's eyes, saw her tears about to spill down her like molten drippings from a dwindling candle, and I was a pillar of fire—paling the sun, the park and houses postured against a bleached-out sky.

There had been blinding light like that before, years ago, that day at Far Rockaway Beach. I had tired of playing in the damp sand at the water's edge and turned, pail and shovel in hand, to march back to my family, and an alien wasteland stretched before me—as though the shifting sand had devoured my landmarks: beach umbrella gone, trash basket gone, leaving a wilderness of half-clothed bodies grouped within their hostile, blanket-boundaried enclaves. Behind me I heard the lapping tongues of water feeding back, in pulsating swells, to the bottomless maw of the ocean.

I wandered through the aisles of fiery sand, the soles of my feet scorched, stumbling on sun-whitened shells, the blanched remains of living things, and my ankles ached with panic as the sand sucked at my legs. The sun dazzled my searching eyes, seeping behind my eyeballs, searing their sockets. Another step and I was suddenly within the refuge of a pool of shadow and my father leaned down, then lifted me high in his arms.

Shadows formed now too, as my mother encircled me with her arms. I stood stone-still in her embrace. She took my hand and led me into the house. It was time for supper.

Late in the night I woke to the despairing sounds of my mother's grief, weeping alone in a room where no one heard, and I left my bed and went to her. She was seated in a corner of the couch, small hands palm-upward on her lap, blond hair matted with the tears which flowed down her backward tipped head, and I crawled on to her lap. Her tears stopped and the wind of the tears was her voice, "Leave me alone. Go back to bed. You're too big to be sitting on laps, anyway."

* * * *

I went back to my bed. I was ten years old and almost taller than my mother and finally the tears came.

Alex

BY JACK FIELDS

WHEN MRS. ZUCKER, the social worker, told me that Alex was coming to my foster home to live with me, I yelled, "Hot Diggety!" turned a somersault in the hall-way, grabbed my peggystick, and raced down Corliss Street. On the way I passed the stick along the bars of the iron fences, making a loud clattering sound. Boy, what news!

At the corner I squatted in front of Myers' delicatessen, where I could smell the sharp tang of hot pastrami, sour pickles, and smoked fish. I closed my eyes and thought about Alex. It was hard to remember what he looked like the first time I had seen him, five years back when I was six years old. That was in the summer, when my father used to visit me once in a while. He had come that Sunday afternoon to the house where I was living, and he had said, "Come on, Joey; we're going to Atlantic City to see your brother Alex."

I didn't understand. "Who is my brother Alex?" I asked Pop.

He said, "You won't remember him. You were separated when you were two years old and he was four. That's when your mother died. After that the Society has been taking care of you in the different homes."

146

Pop and I took a train at the North Philadelphia station, and a couple of hours later we were in Atlantic City. I don't remember much about that visit, except there was a whole gang of people on a big boardwalk, and the air smelled fresh and keen. I could feel the salt glaze on my cheeks. That was the first time I saw the blond sand beach and that terrific blue ocean, too.

Then we went to the house where Alex lived. A woman took us into the living room and introduced me to Alex. He was bigger than me. When Pop asked if he remembered me, Alex grinned and said, "Yes," and I liked him. While Pop talked with the woman, Alex and I went out in the back yard. He talked about Atlantic City and other stuff, but I didn't say much. I just listened.

When Pop called me and said it was time to go back, I didn't want to go. I wanted to stay with Alex, my big brother. I pulled at Pop's sleeve, complaining, but Pop made me go. He said I could see Alex again soon.

We did visit Alex a couple of times after that. Once, a year later in Ventnor, and then two years after in Millville, New Jersey, we went to see him. Each time I liked Alex better, and he liked me. We always asked to see each other and we wrote. But I guess we just couldn't see each other more.

The last time I saw him we made up a plot because we wanted to be together. I said I would pester my social worker about wanting to live with him and he should do the same thing. Maybe that way we could make it work.

Well, I kept pestering Mrs. Zucker about it. At first she said it wouldn't be a good idea. She said foster mothers didn't keep children a long time, and then when they decided to let them go, it would be very hard to place two brothers together. She said it was hard enough to find a home for one. And she said, "You've been used to being without Alex. But if you are brought together now, and then get separated, it will hurt you both very much."

But I didn't want to listen. I just wanted to be with Alex, and I kept pestering.

Now Mrs. Zucker had said he was coming. Oh boy! I felt so good.

The next day Alex came. Gee! he had gotten big. We shook hands and he gripped my shoulder and grinned a crooked grin on the right side of his mouth and said, "My kid brother." I

147

slapped him on the back, saying, "We'll never be separated now, will we, Alex?" He said, "No. We're gonna stick together from now on."

That day we stuck together all the time. He told me what he had been doing, and I told him all about myself. I couldn't take my eyes off him. It was so funny. He looked a lot like me, except he was bigger. He had black hair, brown eyes, and a big Adam's apple that wobbled up and down when he swallowed. When he grinned, his mouth would sort of curl up on the right side, giving a twist to his long, pointed nose. He talked slower than I did, in a deep voice, and I noticed he was kind of shy around Mrs. Wilson, our foster mother, and her two kids, Harold and Eleanor.

Harold was twelve and Eleanor was nine. Both of them tried to horn in when Alex came, but I wouldn't let them. They could stay with each other and high-hat me as much as they wanted to now, for all I cared. Alex and I were pals. We didn't need any favors from them.

That afternoon Alex and I hiked out to Fairmount Park. Near the Schuylkill River, where I liked to catch crayfish, we stretched out on the ground and looked up at the sky. We could hear the birds chirping and twittering all around us in the willow trees. The water slapped softly against the stone steps of the dock nearby. Alex put a blade of grass in his mouth, and I did too.

"How are the Wilsons?" he asked.

"They're okay," I said. "You get enough to eat. Mr. Wilson's kind of stern, Harold is a sissy, and Eleanor is a pain. But Mrs. Wilson is okay. All you gotta do is stay away from Mr. Wilson."

We chewed on our hunks of grass and looked up at the sky. I felt so good right there with Alex alongside me that I hoped it would never end. When it started to get dark, we went back home. At the table we sat right next to each other. When we went to sleep, Alex slept in my bed. We were real pals.

The last two weeks in August and the first two in September were great. Alex got to meet the gang, and we taught him how to play Ring-O-Levio, Hide the Stick, Kick the Can, and other games he didn't know about in New Jersey. Then, when school time rolled around, I learned that Alex was in 8-B, the same grade I was in. He said he had been left back a couple of times because he didn't like school. He said the people in the houses where he used to live would make him work and wouldn't let him do his homework, so it was no use even if he did like school. That was swell, because now we could be in the same class and wouldn't have to be separated. Things were sure working out fine.

After a while, though, Alex began to grumble about school. He didn't want to do his homework, and he asked me to do it for him. It was easy to do because we had the same classes, but when he was called on in class he didn't know the answers, and he would get goose-eggs. When I was called on, I did pretty well. Alex would make a face and call me a teacher's pet. He didn't like school at all. He kept getting us to play hookey, and we'd go off to Fairmount Park.

One day Mrs. LeFevre, our English teacher, assigned us to make a speech. When my turn came, I told a story about my visit to Alex in Atlantic City and what fun it had been. After I finished, Mrs. LeFevre said it was a very good speech. Then she called on Alex. He just sat without saying anything.

"Haven't you prepared your speech, Alex?" she said.

Alex looked sour and didn't answer.

"Do you realize that you're going to fail, if you continue coming to class unprepared?" Mrs. LeFevre said. "I can't see why you're not able to prepare your work, when your brother manages to do his so well."

Alex's mouth curled up on the right side, but it wasn't a smile this time. He turned and looked at me. It was a real dirty look, and it was the first time he had looked at me like that.

When we got out of school, he walked over and grabbed me by the arm. "Why'd you have to shoot your mouth off about me?" he said. His long fingers dug into my muscle and hurt. His mouth twisted again as he said, "You can stick around your teacher now, you little teacher's pet, but stay away from me. You hear? Just stay away from me." He shoved me against the red brick wall. Then he moved away in angry giant strides.

I couldn't figure out what he was so sore about. I hadn't done anything. All I did was give a little old speech about my visit to him. Holy smoke! What was he so sore about? In my speech I had told what a swell guy he was, and now he was acting as though I was his enemy. That sure took the cake.

Back home I found Alex in front of the house with Harold. They were putting on their skates. "You going skating?" I said. "Wait up. I'll put mine on."

"We're going alone," Alex said.

"Gosh, Alex," I said. "I don't know what you're so sore about. You know I'm not a teacher's pet. I don't like teachers."

He didn't say anything. He just got up without looking at me. "Let's go, Harold," he said. Their skates scraped and rolled over the concrete as they grated off.

That night at dinner Alex switched seats with Eleanor so that she sat beside me. He kept talking to Harold without looking at me. Harold made a crack about something that had happened while they were skating, and they both started to laugh. Harold pounded his hand on the table, whooping it up so loud that his mother had to warn him to shut up. I clinked my spoon in the soup plate, but I didn't feel like eating.

When we got to bed, he turned his back and slid over to the edge.

"Alex," I said.

He wouldn't answer.

Once, when I moved toward him, he gave me a sharp kick in the leg. "Stay on your side of the bed," he said.

I folded my hands behind my head and stared at the black shadows on the ceiling for a long time. Beside me I could hear Alex's steady, deep breathing.

The next day he played hookey again. After school when I found him with the gang, I came over to join. But as soon as I did so, he walked away. It was the same the day after and the next. Alex wouldn't talk to me, and I couldn't understand why.

One afternoon when I saw him walking out of the house, I followed him. He went to Fairmount Park to the same spot we had gone the first day. And just like on that day he stretched out on the ground, put a blade of grass in his mouth, and looked up at the blue sky.

I came over slowly.

"Alex," I said.

150

He turned around quickly. "What do you want?" he said. "Who told you to follow me?"

"Look, Alex," I said, "what are you so sore about? I didn't do anything to you."

He jumped up and grabbed me. "Listen, you little wise guy," he said. "You've been asking for this. I told you to stay away and you wouldn't listen. Well, maybe you'll listen to this." And he socked me in the mouth.

I could feel the blood coming out of my lip, and it kind of burned where the knuckle had caught the corner of my mouth, but I didn't mind that so much. What hurt was that Alex, my big brother, had hit me. We had been pals, and we had sworn that we'd always stick together. And now he was looking at me the way some of my foster fathers looked when they beat me. It hurt. I guess I must have cried a little. I stared at Alex. He was standing there with his fist clenched and his mouth twisted up and that hard look in his eyes.

"I guess we're not pals any more," I said. I walked home by myself.

The Hand of the Potter

EXCERPT FROM A NOVEL BY JOHN BURRESS

THE DARK CAME. It was like soft, invisible arms that wrapped themselves around him and held him close and secure.

This time, the dark was different from any he had known in his twelve years of life. The thing inside him that made sound—not the one that made sound when he breathed, but the one that made steady, thumping sound—began moving faster and faster until he was afraid the ones in the world below would hear.

Hope was an exciting thing.

The part of the floor that could be raised so Hard or Soft could come into his world with the feedings was not fastened. At last he could go into the other world and show them how smart he was. When they saw he had solved the puzzle of how to enter their world, they would approve of him and show him how to make the sounds with his lips so they could understand him when he spoke.

He waited until the dark was complete before he squatted and slid his fingers into the widest crack that marked the outline of the thing in the floor. He lifted cautiously and the thing moved. The excitement became so intense his fingers numbed suddenly and the thing fell back into place with a muffled thud. He rose and moved quickly away. The thing inside him sounded and felt like it was trying to come through his skin to the outside. If they heard that thud in the world-below-his-world, someone would come and make the clicking sound that meant the thing in the floor wouldn't move.

Holding his breath so he could listen for the sound of footsteps down below him, he moved the width of his eight-feet-by-ten-feet world until he came to the place where there was another doorway to the other world. This was a much smaller doorway, the size of a finger or of an eye. He put his finger through the doorway and felt the smooth, cool thing that was on the other side. Although the barrier his finger touched was solid, he knew he could see through it, for he often put his eye to this doorway and watched the little ones playing in the world below. Of course, he couldn't always see the little ones, even when they were there. If the soft stuff that hung against the blue way, way off wasn't thick enough to cover the bright thing that burned more fiercely than the candle Hard or Soft sometimes brought with them at the time of the feedings, the wet would come to his eyes and he couldn't look out. Then, all he could do would be to sit and listen to the sounds coming faintly to him through the wall that kept him from getting to the children.

Feeling the smooth with the tip of his finger calmed him and was a reminder he must go through the opening in the floor to get to the world below. He went back to the trap door.

He raised it slowly, listening for a sign that the people below heard. He released the trapdoor when it was all the way up, held in place by its hinges. Hesitantly he put his right foot down into darkness that was as deep as the darkness in which he stood. He could not actually see in the dark, but could sense objects another person would be unaware of. Because he had watched when they came up with his feedings, he knew there was a ladder. After a moment he found it and rested his foot on the top rung. He stood for a long time with his right foot through the doorway before he worked up the courage to lower his left leg after the right. It was much harder to keep his left foot on the rung, but he managed, and lowered his right foot again.

He had to open his mouth to breathe when he stood at last at the bottom of the ladder. He was in a world similar to the one he had just left, except that this one was not as wide as his. His fingers told him the things hanging from pegs along the wall were coats and hats. He had never worn a coat or a hat, but he had seen the others wear them and knew what they were. He also knew what a shirt was although that, too, was something he had never worn.

Disappointment became a heavy weight inside him when he found there was another door that must be opened before he could get into the world he sought. Faint light marked the outline of this new door. It was in the wall rather than the floor. He had no idea of how such a door would work.

Hard was no more than a dozen feet away, but was on the other side of the wall. The faint light that outlined the door was coming from the world in which Hard sat. All he had to do was find a way to get through the wall.

He found the latch by accident. He was exploring the door with his fingers when they touched something that made a clicking sound and the door started to swing open. As it moved, he let his mind quickly locate the four people who lived in this world. There was nothing supernatural about his ability to locate them. He had trained his sense of hearing until it, like his senses of touch, smell, and vision, was keen beyond that of the average person. He knew that the other big one—the one he thought of as "Soft"—was in a distant part of this new world he was about to explore. The two little ones were in the room with Hard. He thought of them as "little," although the one who wore pants, the way he did, was almost as big as he was. The other one, who had hair the color of the bright thing that made the wet come to his eyes, was smaller than either of them.

With a wide smile of self-admiration and satisfaction, he stepped out into this new world. How proud these people were going to be! He got no more than a glimpse of the room before he had to close his eyes against the glare. There was a thing in this world that was a miniature bright thing. The light from it made the wet come to his eyes. All the candles he had ever seen wouldn't have given this much light. He got an impression of space beyond his wildest imagination. As far as he was concerned, this world was as vast and endless as the world he saw through the small door when he looked out to watch the little ones play. The wall across from him was so distant he would have to take many steps to reach it.

As his eyes closed he saw that the things the people were sitting on were not beds, as he had assumed they would be, but were so small it was a wonder they didn't topple off them. In his world, the only piece of furniture was a bed, which also served as table and chair. There were holes in the walls of this world, bigger than the one in the floor of his own world. Some of them were like the doorway in which he stood, and the others, which were smaller, all had bright things in them. His impression of the room was too short-lived for him to see that the smaller holes were windows and the lights in them reflections of the lamp sitting on a table.

There was a crashing sound and he opened his eyes a split second, long enough to see that the chair in which Hard had been sitting had toppled to the floor. The man was staring at him with open mouth. He stepped back into the closet to get away from the glare of light that was making the wet drip from his eyes. He heard the footsteps as Hard came toward him, then the door slammed and he was in darkness again. He listened as Hard made the sounds that were words being spoken. He didn't understand what the man said, but could tell he was excited.

"Nancy!" the man shouted, "for God's sake, get in here!"

He followed the sound of Soft's footsteps as she came running into the room.

"What be the trouble, Farnam?"

"Take the youngsters and get them out of the house!"

"But what—?"

"Get them out, I tell ye!"

"Farnam, if you'd but tell me—"

"Aye, then, I'll tell ye!" There was savage anger in the man's voice.

"You left the trap door unlocked and the devil's loose!"

He heard the sudden intake of Soft's breath, then the sound of the little ones questioning, "What is it, Mama?" and Soft's voice going, "Sh! Sh!" over and over until that sound as well as the sound of footsteps faded and he knew the only person on the other side of the wall was Hard.

There was silence except for the beating sound inside him and the harsh breathing of the man on the other side of the door. As the door began to open, he knew he had made a mistake. Anger came pouring into the closet, almost as visible as the light from the lamp. He didn't know what the mistake was, but he knew he had done something to displease the people. He felt sad, for he had come down the ladder only because he wanted to please them and win their approval.

As the door opened wider, his lips spread in an apologetic smile. At least, that was what he intended it to be. Evidently the man did not see it as such. He did not smile in return. Instead, his brows drew together in a frown. Anger came from the man in waves.

"What in the name of God are you doing down here?"

He understood the questioning tone and the idea that it was a question, but he did not grasp the meaning of half the words. He made no attempt to answer. He sank to a crouch at the foot of the ladder and looked up at the man, waiting to see what was going to happen. As time stretched and the man just stood and stared and hated him, he tried to speak, to explain that all he wanted, now, was to climb the ladder back to his own world. He made sounds that resembled words, but they had no meaning for the man.

"Don't growl at me, you devil!" the man said.

He stopped trying to speak and looked up. The man towered over him like a giant, huge and menacing. He was looking up from a squatting position, which meant he was not seeing with the proper perspective, but the man looking down at him was a huge man. If he looked like a giant to the boy, he also looked that way to the crew of his fishing boat.

The man's hand reached out and clamped itself to the boy's naked shoulder. The grip was out of all proportion to necessity. As thin and underdeveloped as the boy was, it would have taken no more than thumb and forefinger to hold him. The muscles of the man's forearm were like ropes as his fingers dug in until the boy winced with pain.

When the man moved, he had no choice but to move with him. As he was pulled into the room he had to close his eyes against the glare of the bright thing. He stumbled now and then, and his left foot tapped against the bare boards of the floor like an oversized knuckle. He was led through another doorway and could open his eyes again, for the light from the lamp did not shine directly on him.

There was a bed in this world, but a bed easily twice as wide as the one in his world. There were other things he could not identify. One of these was a square thing sitting on the floor against the wall. There was another square thing above it which he thought was an opening to still another world, for he could see strange shapes in it, like the ones in the world where he stood. As Hard pulled him toward this seeming opening, he saw another man leading a creature toward him. Panic gripped him, for he didn't know there were other people in this world, besides the four he already knew about. He looked up at Hard. The man pointed to the wall.

"Look at yourself!"

He turned his head and looked. The first thing he noticed was that the man facing him looked very much like Hard. There was the same harsh, frowning face with the same fringe of hair along the jaw line. Then he looked at the creature the other man was holding by the shoulder. He felt a shudder go through his body, for the thing he saw was a monster. Long hair, so thick and matted it looked like black rope, hung to the thing's shoulders and fell partly across its face, but not far enough to hide the fact that the creature had a caricature of a mouth. The upper lip was split as though a piece had been cut from it. The lower lip was gross, the flesh from the upper seemingly used to fill the lower to overflowing. There was a greasy, dirty look to the thing's face as well as to its body and its pants—the only garment it wore.

He raised his hand to shove the hair out of his eyes so he could see better. The creature on the other side of the wall did the same. He paused with his hand on his head and the other one paused. He turned his head and the thing turned its head. He screamed, and the thing screamed with him. He put his arm over his face to cut out the sight. He had never seen a mirror before and knew nothing about reflections, but he knew without question that the monster he looked at was himself.

"Cry, and be damned to ye!" the man said between tight lips.

He did not cry. If he had ever been able to relieve his feelings by crying, it had been so long ago he had forgotten how to do it. All he could do was stand with his arm over his face so he wouldn't have to look at himself. He wanted to go back to his world at the top of the ladder so he could burrow into his nest and hide. As he tried to move, his weight rested on his left leg and he almost fell, for the curled knot at the end of that leg had no surface to grip the boards of the floor. As he stumbled, he jerked against the man's gripping fingers.

Until the man hit him, he had suffered more from anxiety than anything else. He had been slapped a few times when he had not been able to do exactly what Soft or Hard told him, because he hadn't fully understood the command. Those had been little more than blows that stung. The slap that landed on his face when he stumbled numbed the whole side of his face and knocked him to his knees. He would have fallen on to the floor except that the man still held his shoulder.

With the blow came fear; an unnamed, unreasonable fear that made him lose all control of his body. His kidneys contracted suddenly. The man saw the wet spot on the front of the boy's pants and the stream of urine darkening the floor. He started shaking the boy, but that made the flow increase. With a growl, he jerked the buckle of his belt open and pulled the leather strap from around his waist. Letting go of the boy's shoulder, he stepped back and brought the strap down with a powerful swing of his arm.

"Devil!" he said between clenched teeth, and each time the strap cut into the boy's back, it was accompanied by the word which could have been a name or a curse.

Terror shattered his senses. He seemed to see rather than feel the pain. If he had been able to cry out, to beg, or even to scream, the man might have stopped beating him, but he was unable to do anything except let his body stretch out on the floor until he lay flat on his belly with his fingers opening and closing slowly, grasping for something to hold onto, physically, as well as with his mind. When the man stopped hitting him at last, he did not know it.

The man stood, his great body heaving as he drew breath into his lungs in gulps. He was exhausted. He stood looking down at the bloody back of the thing on the floor with a wolfish grin on his face. The grin remained for a long time before it began to fade and the man raised his belt and looked at the dark stains on it. He opened his fingers and let it drop, then fell to his knees and rocked back and forth, whispering, "God forgive me! God forgive me!" until the words became a chant and lost all meaning.

Tenderly he slid his arms under the unconscious body and lifted it.

The Magician

EXCERPT FROM A NOVEL BY H. L. NEWBOLD

PERHAPS I would have been less frightened of boys if a strange man had not squeaked his truck to a stop at the curb near me one afternoon when I was five years old. I looked up from where I squatted making mud pies.

"Would you like to see my magic?" he asked. He was like my granddaddy, only his smile was nicer, held me in its arms and rocked me back and forth. His big face was decorated by a bushy gray mustache, like a walrus in my picture book.

He pushed open the truck door and held out a flat red stick which glistened in the sunlight.

"Touch the stick and it will turn blue."

I stood up and, afraid to let my mouth smile as much as it wanted to, walk over to the curb.

"Touch it," he urged. His smile rocked me back and forth, pulled out my finger. After I reached out with one finger and touched the smooth surface, he lifted the stick with a red whir and then held it out for me to see. Blue!

"Now touch it once more and it will be red again."

His smile rocked me and his bright eyes played across my face, up and down my body, like sunlight reflected from a pool of rippling water.

My finger touched the magic stick. He made a blue whir and then: red!

After the wondrous stick disappeared, he drew a golden tube from the inside pocket of his black coat and held it out in the sunlight for me to see. While I gazed at the magic tube, his glance passed me, played up and down the windows of the apartment house.

"Do you like this magic tube?" he asked. His eyes came back to me, brighter than before, while he moved the cylinder back and forth so points of sunlight skipped across it, hopped away and swam up and down the side of his black coat. While my eyes marveled, he drew a green silk handkerchief from his trouser pocket, fanned it back and forth until I felt the green wind cool my lips.

"Now, if you touch the magic tube, it will turn the handkerchief white."

The shimmering gold pulled my finger toward it.

"But you mustn't touch it while we are here in the street," he said as he pulled his magic away and made it disappear in the folds of his black coat.

My hand fell as if it had been slapped.

"Now," he said as his eyes passed over me again, flicked up and down the quiet street, "now you follow me around the corner to where I park. Then I'll make the magic tube turn the handkerchief white."

My tongue wet my lips and they smiled again.

He eased the door shut and rattled the truck slowly down the street. I skipped and ran, skipped and ran to keep from losing my magic man. He turned the corner and then guided the puffing truck down the alley until he reached a spot beside the closed doors of a garage where we would be hidden from the rear apartment windows. I ran up just as the engine gave its last choke and settled into place.

"Run around to the other side," he told me as he leaned over and opened the door. I stretched my foot up to the running board, stretched again to pull myself inside and then wiggled up beside him on the worn leather seat that smelled like oil. I was way, way up in the air.

"That's a good girl," he said and patted my bare knee, making my skin tingle everywhere as his smile rocked me back and forth.

"Now watch." His voice tightened and his fingers shook with happiness as he pulled the golden tube and the green handkerchief from his pocket. I felt happy and shaky too. His smile kept rocking me back and forth, sleepylike.

He held the golden tube toward me. The tip of my finger tingled when it touched the gold grains covering the magic tube.

"Now watch."

Carefully he guided the green silk into the tube, then reached inside with two fingers from below and teased out the silk handkerchief.

It was as white as a princess' gown!

My tongue played over my lips and I laughed. He patted my leg again. Happiness wiggled through my body from head to heel, leaving a quick tremor where it touched. I slipped my hips back on the seat where I could sit more solidly.

"Now, do you want to see another trick?"

I nodded my head and tucked my lower lip between my teeth.

"Now touch my cyclops and it will do a magic trick."

The brownish skin looked like the wrinkled neck of a half-sleeping turtle which had peered at me one Sunday afternoon at the aquarium.

I took a long breath in, locked my lips and stretched out my trembling finger.

Suddenly an open can of red paint turned upside down in my head, flowed down the edges of mind and frothed into the corners.

I screamed, threw open the door and fell to the ground. I could hear him laughing as I ran, stumbled and fell, ran again toward home.

Proud Words

BY EUGENE N. DOHERTY

J EFF WAS TALLER than I, but only half as broad, and not nearly so strong. He loved to whistle and he chattered endlessly, even when no one was near to listen. His lustrous brown eyes were soft, yet boldly candid, and his face was quick to wrinkle in a smile, which infected everyone he knew. All through high school and my two years of college he almost worshiped me. He kept a scrapbook of my basketball career, my football jersey and varsity letters decorated his wall, and it was he who cried the night I was eliminated from the Diamond Gloves competition. Sometimes I would complain to my father, "He follows me around like a puppy dog. Everywhere I go I expect to find him there, smiling at me and wagging his tail." Secretly I enjoyed his admiration and I was intensely fond of him. But I used proud words to him the last day of my furlough.

The night had been particularly well planned. I meant to leave a crimson stain on our little hamlet that would warm me through the long months overseas. I had showered and shaved with care; and, as I contemplated abandoning the forest greens in favor of a natty civilian suit, my brother dashed into my room. He was so excited the words gushed out, "I promised Mary and her mother that I'd take them to a shower, but let's meet somewhere and have a few drinks." As he spoke, he retrieved one of my shoes from under the bed.

I had plans for the evening that didn't include reminiscing

about the good old days with my seventeen-year-old brother. "Not tonight, Jeff. Wait up for me and we'll have a few when I get home."

A concerned look swept across his face and he seemed reluctant to talk. Finally he stammered, "When are you leaving?"

"As soon as I finish dressing."

"Gee, Euge, I promised Mary that I'd take them. They'll have fits if I don't show up!"

"Well, call 'em and tell 'em you can't."

"I can't do that. They're depending on me. I've got to have the car."

"You better call 'em. I'm using the car tonight."

I was more than a little surprised to hear him give up so easily, but he merely spun on his heel and retreated to his room, where I heard him making hasty preparations to go out. Happy that this incident didn't explode into unpleasantness and contented with the image surveying me from the mirror, I left my room and sauntered downstairs to make some parting remarks to my parents.

The coolness and smoothness of the banister rail thrilled. I felt strongly confident. This promised to be a great night that I would recall with pleasure while sweating out some far-flung hellhole of the Pacific. My reverie was suddenly interrupted by the impatient grinding of a starter, followed swiftly by the rasping grate of gears as the driver too hastily shifted into reverse. I sensed a shudder run through the house as a car raced down the driveway. Frantically I realized that my brother was escaping with the family car.

I bolted down the remaining steps, flung the front door open, leaped over the porch rail, and intercepted the car just as Jeff was manipulating his turn out of the driveway. The door handle jarred my hip as the car bucked forward, then stalled. The impact set off ripples of pain, which infuriated me. I tore the door open. My brother's eyes were wide with terror as I reached into the car to catch hold of him. He struggled to avoid my grasp and the loud rip of his suit coat startled us both. He stared at his rent coat, stunned and disbelieving, then he sprang from the car. His fists clenched and his arms flailing, he looked comically like a stum-

bling windmill that had somehow lost its foothold. A sob, more
like a groan, escaped his lips as he caught me with one hand and
struck me with the other. The crack of his fist against my cheek
enraged me, and with all my strength I returned his fury. I
didn't mean to hurt him, but rather only to impress him with
the futility of his laboring. My blow was aimed at his chest, but
in his frustration and confusion his feet became entangled and
he lunged forward. As soon as the punch landed, I knew the fight
was over. My fist had caught him flush in the mouth.

For a second his startled eyes met mine. He seemed surprised
that I would hit so hard in so uneven a contest. His idol had feet
of sand. I grabbed his arm and tried to explain that I meant only
to frighten him. The sight of his mouth appalled me. He seemed
to have three lips. Blood flooded his mouth and gushed from the
open, jagged wound. The scarlet stream poured down his chin
and dripped onto his torn lapel and stained his white shirt. His
teeth were blotched with crimson and I worried that some permanent damage had been done. His sobs came in gusts and his
whole body shuddered and shook from their intensity.

"I'm sorry, Jeff. Forgive me. I didn't mean—"

He writhed free of my grasp and raked me with his eyes. Blood
from his torn lip splattered my face as he screamed, "Get away
from me you—you bum!" He turned and ran toward the house.

My mother, who had observed the fracas, wrapped her arms
around him and led him through the doorway, then closed the
door behind them. She never said a word. She didn't even look
at me.

My last day at home lay in ruins. I backed up the car in front
of the house and then caught a bus into Elizabeth. I knew that
no amount of drinking nor dancing would erase the memory of
Jeff's frightened eyes or his tattered lip. I don't remember how
many places I visited nor how many times I reminded myself
that this was my last day at home, but the memory of his face
always sobered me and a great loneliness overwhelmed me.

It was very late when I returned, for I had missed the last bus,
and I had to walk most of the way home. My house was quiet
and comfortingly warm when I entered, but I felt like an intruder.
I'd be happy to get back to camp.

My brother's bedroom door was slightly ajar. Pausing there for a moment, I pressed my finger tip against its hard, cool surface. The opening widened silently and I edged into the room. I could see his shoes lying askew, his socks in the same position in which they tumbled from his feet, his shirt and trousers a dark shadow and a patch of white draped over the chair. Jeff's faint accent hung in the room like an invisible mist. I was about to retreat when a breeze pressed an overhanging bough away from the street light outside our house. Jeff's pale face was lit with a vague, inexpressible radiance. This reflection was marred only by the livid gash in his lip and a perceptible puffiness under his right eye, which had somehow been blackened. I yearned to wake him and to appeal once more for his forgiveness, but the unpredictability of his reaction held me motionless. I promised myself that I would speak to him in the morning . . . everything would be all right in the morning.

The warmth and brilliance of sunlight splashing across my face warned me it was already late when I awoke. I leaped from the bed carrying half the sheets and blankets with me, and raced downstairs. I was both embarrassed and ashamed that I had squandered my last morning at home indulging myself with sleep when I knew how very much my parents wanted to chat. My mother guessed that I wanted to "mend fences" with Jeff and answered my unspoken question. "Jeff went to Mary's. They took a taxi last night."

"Did he say anything before he left?"

"Only that he was sorry he spoiled your last night home."

I waited around the house longer than I should have. If my train hadn't been late, I would have been A.W.O.L. My farewells with my parents were repeated several times. Each time I heard a door slam or footsteps on the porch my pulse quickened and I felt a strange elation, but Jeff didn't come home until after I left.

I never saw my brother again. On some forgotten, unimportant slope in Okinawa a month before the war ended, my brother bled for the last time. "Proud words wear long boots and you can't call them back."

Wonder Is Not Precisely Knowing

BY ANN McGOVERN

> *Wonder is not precisely knowing,*
> *And not precisely knowing not,*
> *A beautiful but bleak condition*
> *He has not lived who has not felt.*
> —*Emily Dickinson*

JANE JABBED the outside bell of the gray stone house laced with fire escapes and strips of June sunshine. While she waited for the answering buzz that would open the door to sanctuary, she muttered angrily to her jumprope trailing the ground.

"I'll take you and wind you around Shirley's neck so tight her face will turn all purple. I'll show her she and her precious Dave can't leave me in the middle of Riverside Drive all the time."

Riverside Drive was a pastoral warring ground for Jane and her older sister, Shirley. There Jane fought and lost her battles against Shirley and her ally, Dave, a fattish boy who followed Shirley like a drooling puppy.

The buzzer droned and Jane walked into a dark hall smelling of summer caged in. Her sneakers made a squeaking sound on the tiled floor, and she rose tiptoe and walked soundlessly down the long narrow hall to the stairs. From behind the stairs she heard giggling. She edged against the brown stucco walls, her fingers tightening convulsively on the wooden handles of the rope.

"Hurry up," Dave was saying, his fourteen-year-old voice teetering between a squeak and a strange new depth. "Jerky Jane will be here in a minute."

Jane ground her heels into the wall and awarded an extra length of rope to encompass his neck, too. Outside a siren wailed thin and muted.

Shirley's voice was cool. "Boy, do I have to tell the whole world how to act? All you do is crouch down when I give the signal. Jane's so dumb she'll think we're playing leap frog or something."

Dumb. Dumb. Tiny drum beats. Dumb. Dumb. Her sister's favorite word. She called her dumb more than she called her Jane. But it hadn't always been that way.

A year ago when Jane was eleven and Shirly twelve, Jane had earned her sister's reluctant respect. Always on the alert for attack, Shirley had noticed that Jane spent too much time in the bathroom. She had run to their mother triumphantly to complain. "Jane's always reading and I can't get in. Tell her!" But for once her mother had not followed Shirley's orders. "Don't be silly. A girl who reads is smart. We should encourage." So for a few months Jane had been "smart," until her sister had probed Jane's literary tastes and found her reading books no library would ever house. "But they're about love," Jane had protested, standing under the naked glare of the white kitchen light while the water dripped, dripped, in helpless drones. In quieter moments her mother talked absently and hardly above a whisper. But now her mother's shouting outburst had been far worse than Shirley's jeers. "Love," she had screamed. "Love in the streets! Love behind stairs! Pushy, grabby, sweaty love. You don't know. You don't know."

Now Jane ran up three steps. Leaning over the banister, she peered down into the dim corner behind the stored baby carriages. Although little light filtered through, Jane saw her sister and Dave as though they were illuminated by a flashbulb. They were stooping down facing each other. Dave's dungarees were parted in the middle revealing something startlingly white and strange. Shirley's skirt was bunched into the elastic waist of her panties. Jane breathed in, trying to recapture the clean greenness of the park she had just left, but her nostrils filled with sour heat. She almost coughed with revulsion.

Tense and motionless, they looked at her as if she had commanded them to turn to stone. Jane dropped her jumprope: a broken whip. She screamed at their whiteness, "Wait till I tell. Wait till you get it."

"Tell what?" Shirley's voice was a sulk, and she pushed her skirt down while Dave zipped and snapped.

Jane ran up the stairs, shouting back, "That you're dirty, that's what. Dirty. Dirty," remembering the heat that had filled her long ago in the bathroom, remembering the girl in a story she had read, whose legs had slowly stretched toward those of the man she loved. Love?

The apartment was cool and quiet. Jane was vaguely surprised to see it looked the same. Her mother called out from somewhere. "Jane? That you? Wash the sweat off your face. Lie down. It's hot. Only take your shoes off first." Her voice trailed, like sky-writing. "And there's juice in the fridge."

Jane walked into the room she shared with her sister, a room the walls of which had once been papered in fresh green buds. Now they were stained brown in spots, from grim water fights.

She shared much with her sister—the absence of a father, the presence of a shadowy unhappy mother. They had one bike and one sled between them and had learned long ago that these possessions were not worth the fights. So the tires of the bike wore thin with time and no one wiped the rust from the sled.

Jane looked at herself in the closet mirror, half expecting to find tears. Her face and figure bore no promise of future distinction. The mouth was small, her nose a button, her straight hair as dull as the faded brown rug on the floor. Only her eyes were vivid. They were large and black, but she kept them half closed.

Jane opened the closet door and began to search for her favorite pink dress. Her fingers touched crisp organdy. She yanked the dress from the hanger. She threw her shorts and shirt on the floor and pulled on the dress that she was only allowed to wear for special occasions. Her pink socks sagged over her worn blue sneakers, but she was not concerned with her appearance. She was only aware of a tingling as the warm flush spread down over her body. Slowly she lifted up the dress and tucked it into her pants, never taking her eyes from the mirror. She felt the crisp cloth crease and crackle.

"Ooooh," she squealed, dancing and extending her legs. She thrust out her flat chest and wiggled her buttocks. As she pirouetted before the mirror, her large eyes gleamed; her mouth went dry.

"I love," she tittered, leering into the mirror. "I love, love." She had the dress over her head when Shirley walked in and with one swift glance digested the scene. As she flopped on Jane's bed a sly smile spread over her face. Purposefully she moved her feet around to leave shoe marks on the light green bedspread.

Jane opened her mouth to protest, but the look on Shirley's face left her mute.

"Did you tell?" Shirley asked lazily.

With sudden horror Jane knew it would be she who would suffer for her sister's mysteries behind the staircase.

At supper Shirley chatted brightly with their mother, who was almost pleased for the moment with her daughters. The elder so smart and gay, the younger quiet and manageable.

"It's your turn to do the dishes, Janie-Banie," Shirley said laughing. Jane knew it would do no good to complain. Their mother was blind to her children's injustices. The death of her husband was injustice incarnate; she moved in its shadows.

Much later, after their mother had called goodnight, Jane got out of bed and padded to where her sister slept.

"Shirley?" she pleaded.

"Hmmmm?" Shirley's eyes were closed.

"Shirley, are you in love with Dave?"

"What?" Shirley mumbled, hearing.

Jane plunged. "Shirley, do to me what Dave did to you. Please?" She waited. And could have died right there.

The laugh that filled the room was wide awake and wicked.

"Go play with your paper dolls," Shirley said. "You are the dumb-est . . ."

Jane reeled and threw herself on top of the covers. She lay on her stomach and thought *love,* thought of her doll patched tenderly with bandaids, thought of the taste of orange juice after roller-skating, thought love, legs, little questions moaning, love, love . . .

She turned her head and looked at the night through the narrow window above her sister's bed. She had never seen the sky like this before, never knew that the stars were tiny silver knives, falling through the night-black sky, falling closer until they almost touched her. She buried her head in the pillow. With her hand clenched near her mouth, she slept.

The Circle on the Grass

BY LILY PORITZ

THEY CAME rushing down the hill on that hot summer's day in December, the Cape Town children, their golden hair blowing with the mountain breeze, their blue eyes like crystal in the sun. They came in a crowd, their voices joined in unison, and caught me stumbling out of the bleak gray cubicle in the toilet rooms at the back of the schoolhouse.

> *We found her! We found her!*
> *We found the little Jew!*
> *Eating her lunch!*
> *In the toilet room!*

They were the girls and boys who sat in the big circle on the green grass under the sun eating their sandwiches, pomegranates, and avocado pears. They laughed at the wrinkled brown paper bag in my hands, and dancing around me to the echo of the school bell, they led me back to the classroom and the sharp eyes of Juffrou Van der Merwe.

> *We found her! We found her!*
> *We found the little Jew!*
> *Eating her lunch!*
> *In the toilet room!*

The long spiderlike woman rose tall on the platform, her eyes falling upon me like heavy weights.

"Is that true?"

The laughter and voices of the children subsided as they returned to their desks and the shadow of the woman fell darkly over me.

"Is it?"

"No!"

My hands tightened around the crumpled brown paper bag, but she saw me and asked:

"What did you have in that brown paper bag?"

The thin blue-veined hands of Juffrou Van der Merwe felt their way to the long metal-edged ruler on her desk and the skinny fingers ran over the cold metal blade.

"Come up here!"

Numb, immobile, the brown paper bag falling from my hands, my fingers tightened into small knots disappearing deep into my blazer pockets.

"Come up here!"

Her eyes held me, drew me onto the platform, tearing my knuckles from the pockets, spreading my hands out flat on the wooden desk, the fingers frail and naked. The teeth of the children bit deep into their lips to the slashing of metal into bone. Blood formed on my own as blackness overshadowed me.

"Now go! Go!"

Blue, puffy swelling fattening my hands, I followed the sword-like finger pointing away, from the other children to the old wooden desk at the back of the classroom—the desk that stood isolated from all the others.

The desk was not always apart. It once stood in the middle where there was now an empty space. It once stood with Janet Strombok, Marie Gerhard, Uta deVilliers and Wendy—my best friend, Wendy van Hutenbek. Nobody cared then—not until the day Juffrou Van der Merwe found out the truth about me.

She was my first teacher. I was six the year I met her, the year we moved to the Ronderbosch section of Cape Town and I was sent off to school. She was a long, spidery woman with a hollow space where her breasts should have been. She had razor-blade eyes behind steel-rimmed glasses, lips as sharp and straight as her metal-edged ruler, hair the color of the barbed-wire fence around the bull pen in the field across the road from our house. I met her the year we moved away from the three-room flat above our factory in Cape Town, where my brother Barry and I were born to the grinding of machines. It was here, the time of the First World War, that my parents settled when they immigrated from Europe. But when Barry was eight and I six, my father bought that big white house in Ronderbosch. And our Indian, Malay and half-caste friends, with whom we played in the gutters in front of our factory on Keerom Street, faded in our minds as we met the sun-kissed children with the light blue eyes. We forgot, too, the shrill and shrieking sounds of trolleys, buses, the hammering of giant machines, the slashing of knives. Our rhythm became the wind, the river, the trees.

From the very first days at the schoolhouse I learned that the blue tunic had to be carefully pressed, the white shirt sparkling at the collar and cuffs, the black-laced shoes polished like mirrors. I learned that my hair was to be combed out of sight from my face, that my nails were open for inspection each day, and that the leather satchel worn on my back was to straighten my shoulders. But there was one thing I did not learn: I did not learn to hide the truth about me.

My mother had warned me once, both Barry and me, before sending us off to school.

"In this place, if they ask what you are, it is better not to say."

"Ask what?"

"About being Jewish—better don't say nothing."

"Why?"

"It is better not."

"But what if they do ask?"

"So they do ask! Listen, kill you they won't for it!"

It was not until the third day of school that Juffrou Van der Merwe paused at my name as she called the roll.

"Julie Cantor!" Her head lifted from the register. "Kindly rise!"

The classroom lay hushed in the minutes that followed, all heads turning to me as the naked eyes of the teacher revealed themselves, peering from beneath the steel-rimmed spectacles.

"Remain behind after class this afternoon."

Long after the children were gone, I sat quietly among the

vacant wooden desks, listening to the laughter fading from the playground out into the homeward streets. Juffrou Van der Merwe's white face did not lift from the desk until the last voice was muffled in the passing traffic. She rose, then descending the tall platform, and walked with folded arms to the door. Her long neck reached into the dim corridors, then quietly she drew the door closed, never suspecting that from outside in the playground, hunched beneath the classroom window, they listened.

"Cantor!" A strange quivering smile formed on her lips as she pronounced the name, and a long finger bade me rise from my desk and entreat her on the platform.

"Cantor!" she repeated, now looking down at the frightened gaze I could not release from her. "What sort of a name is that?"

The frail uncertainty of my mother's voice whirled around me. About being Jewish—better don't say nothing . . .

"Church?" The bones in Juffrou Van der Merwe's neck swelled and contorted, her voice bellowing like an angry rooster. "What church d'you belong?"

The wish for darkness, for obscurity, encompassed me. As I lowered my head, my dark curls fell over my face. But I felt her shadow draw close, and I saw the cold, blue-veined hands.

"Push your ugly hair out of your face and answer me!"

Tremors ran over her thin lips, and as I looked up, unable to conceal the horror in my eyes, the menacing smile returned on her stained teeth.

"On Sundays—what church does your mother take you to—Protestant?"

"Yes."

"Protestant?" Her mouth widened and saliva oozed through her uneven teeth.

"I don't remember."

"Catholic?"

The distant echo of my mother's voice, the chanting of the rabbi rose like giant pillars around me.

"I'm Jewish."

My desk was pulled away from the others. My friends caught me in the playground the next day, and they danced around me.

We know! We know!
We know all about you!
Who told us? Who told us?
Who told us all about you?

Who do you think was
under the window?
Listening, listening,
listening all the time?

But Wendy didn't laugh like the other children.

"Ouma says I can't play with Jews," she whispered when the children were gone. "What's a Jew?"

"I don't know."

"Maybe you isn't even a Jew. Jews smell funny. Can I smell you?"

"I don't know . . ."

"You don't stink. Ouma says Jews stink. You think maybe you isn't a Jew?"

"Maybe."

"If you isn't, then we can still be friends—you and me. Okay?"

But Wendy ran away to the children with the light blue eyes and sun-colored hair—the children who laughed and played hopscotch and ate their lunch in the big circle on the green grass under the sun.

Sometimes I followed my friend. But the other children watched, and she never turned around. And she never found out where I ate my lunch—not until the day they all came rushing down the hill, the day I came home with the puffy blue hands.

"Everything to you must happen!" my mother said, ignoring the puffy fingers. "From a school from maybe hundreds of children, everything to you must happen!"

"Look!" I displayed my hands in rage.

"Ugh!" she said. "It's not like you make out. Every child gets sometimes a little the strap."

As my mother turned back to the sink, splashing the hot soapy water over the dishes and mumbling to herself, I removed from

173

my back my brown leather satchel and flung it across the kitchen floor.

"I'm a Jew! You hear me!"

"Shuh!"

Fiercely averting my eyes, my mother waved a wet soapy hand toward the satchel. "Pick up from the floor!"

"A dirty Jew!"

"The neighbors!"

"A dirty, dirty Jew!"

Clutching my burning hands, I bounced heavily on the leather satchel with my ugly shoes, repeating the phrase over and over again until there came the slap of the damp dish towel against my face and before me were the horror-stricken eyes of my mother.

"Devil! Your mouth I will wash out with a strong soap!"

I never went back to the old gray cubicle in the toilet rooms at the back of the schoolhouse. I hid against the trunks of tall, thick trees or sometimes behind the tool shed where the grass grew high over my head. I longed to go out in the street—outside the stone walls and the big, iron gate, where there were buses, trolleys, shops, and people. A boy once did—a wild boy with long gold bangs jumped from the bough of a tall tree on to the stone wall and over into the street. Wendy told me he's in the detention house now.

Sometimes on rainy days I stood in the cloakroom behind the coats and hats. Then one day my brother found me.

"What are you always hiding about? Cry baby!"

"Who's a cry baby?"

"Look at your eyes! No wonder you don't have friends!"

"I have friends!"

But they passed me by, the children, laughing in a group on the way to the playground.

"If you'll dry your eyes, then maybe we can go outside," my brother said. "It's not like it's raining any more!"

He led me out into the playground, marching straight towards the hill. The rain had stopped. The sun was coming out. And soon we could see, near the top of the hill, the big circle on the green grass. And there they were—the children with the sun-kissed hair and laughing eyes, eating their sandwiches, pome-granates and avocado pears. And as we drew closer, a hand was waving. We walked towards it, and the figure of Wendy rose from the big circle and ran to meet us.

5. Sons and Daughters

The Quiet Block

BY JULIET TOUBIN SAUNDERS

DAVID HAD FORGOTTEN how still the street could be. It was very early on a March morning, a Saturday. He supposed that the families were the same old families, their children now no longer toddlers out on tricycles but teenagers sleeping late on a school day off. The block never changed much. The gardens were well cultivated, small neat squares of lawn fronting each brick house, separated from each other by the narrow driveways leading to a garage and a small neat square backyard. The trees along the sidewalk had grown fuller, lush in the damp Maryland climate, but not enough to disguise the orderly progression of their original planting.

Stretching now, David got out of the car, yawning nervously and watching the front windows of his parents' home. Perhaps he should have gone straight to Marilyn's house—but he had wanted to wash up, get really slicked up first. He stood, hesitating. The white curtains were drawn . . . they gleamed in their immaculate brilliance, their folds wondrously symmetrical. In a sudden, spasmodic movement, he lifted a long, blue-jeaned leg and thrust it, slamming shut the car door.

The outside of the old Chevy quivered, loose chips of brown paint falling to the ground like dead leaves. Inside the car, crowding the back seat, the pots and pans clattered busily against each other. He bent over and peered worriedly in at his merchandise, snorting a little as he felt the mucous pile up inside his nose, opening his mouth to breathe. A colorful sticker, emblazoning the window with University of Arizona, obstructed his view. He studied it, then dug viciously at its edges until they peeled up and he could tear the insignia away, leaving only a few bits of glued paper which would have to be washed off.

Turning around, David stared at the white glass curtains,

rubbing the back of his neck with one hand and snorting noisily. He was just not used to the dampness here. Of course the morning dew must be part of it. He would feel better inside. He would be all right. He waited, watching for a movement, unable to move to the front door himself, caged out here in this quiet air. The long drive across country had given him a dozen kinks; his body twitched, muscles pulling at each other. He watched the curtains, then, wheeling, spat at the paper sticking to the car window, and began in erratic movements to rub off the wet fragments with his shirt sleeve.

II

His mother's voice hissed from the doorway. "You're home? David, you're home?"

He jerked around; they gazed at each other across the front lawn. She was wearing a gold brocade housecoat, her hair blacker than he had ever seen it, with a gleam of rust that years of dyeing had given it. Even in the sharp morning light she looked very well preserved, beautiful. He stepped toward her and she cried out, "Henry! Henry, he's home! It's David all the way from school in the middle of the semester!"

He walked quickly, wanting somehow to reach her before his father came out. But he was only at the bottom of the front steps when the big man appeared, shaving lather along half of his face, a razor in his hand. "What's the matter?" his father asked, amazed. "Didn't the registrar get the check? I was a little late, I admit. But I finally scraped it together and I sent it. Airmail!"

"Look," said David, backing out into the street. His heart was pounding, his throat constricting and he felt he must shout to get the words out. "Look, I got it back. But I had to spend some of it to get here, didn't I? Besides a car's not a bad investment. I didn't throw the money away on plane travel. And I had some debts to clear up."

His father looked at his mother. "What's the kid talking about? Helen, do you know what the kid's talking about?"

"Come inside," she pleaded in her soft hiss. "We can't stay out here yelling. The neighbors—"

"Helen, do you now what it sounds like, what this kid is talking about?"

"Please . . ." she said, her teeth clenched. "David, get up here, get inside."

Somehow David could only move backwards, settling against his car and gesturing at it pridefully. "I'm too old to go to school. I've been in every school in the country. I'm over twenty-one. It's time. I mean, it's *time!*" The mucous swelled in his sinuses, and the last words came out thick, syrupy, garbled.

"You know what catching cold will do for your asthma, in this climate," his mother said resignedly. "Now will you come in. How you could leave Arizona—"

"And I've got to get to work," said his father, turning away through the doorway. "*That* car's an *investment?* I've got to make money so your son can throw it away."

"Fuck the hellos," David said suddenly.

They both stopped for a moment, his mother's eyes skittering across the street at each of the houses, his father's hand reaching up absently to touch his cheek, wiping away the lather which had lost its fluff and was leaking down into his neck. Then silently all three of them went into the house.

His mother disappeared into the kitchen to prepare breakfast, his father to the bathroom to finish shaving. David stood for a moment in the living room, trying to find something familiar, but there had been another complete redecorating job.

"What's this called?" he yelled to his mother.

"Italian provincial. Isn't it stunning?"

"Not bad, not bad." He began to send talk her way, loudly, pontificating about furniture, the apartment he had had in Tucson at the university. The words came out in erratic snatches, forced enthusiasms, as he paced up and down among the new things, his body taut and strained. He could not sit down, he felt rootless, the emptiness an ache inside. He stopped for a moment, finding old framed photographs. There was a picture of his grandmother. David hardly remembered her; she had died shortly after the war was over and his father had come home. But he always liked the picture, liked to touch it. He turned from it to a photograph of his mother and father when they had been engaged—he in a football outfit, she in the formal worn as queen of homecoming. His father looked as large now without the pads as he had then with them. His mother never seemed to grow fatter.

III

David went on into the kitchen to grab a glass of orange juice as it was being set on the table. In deep gulps he drank it; then, still standing, wolfed down one roll, two.

"Couldn't you have washed up first?" His mother's voice was not castigating, but there were the familiar puckering lines of disgust around her lips.

"I will before I go over to see Marilyn."

"Did she know you were coming?" Her face brightened, became more purposeful. "Did *she* put you up to this . . . this quitting school business?"

"A thousand miles apart is for the birds. She loves me. What good am I to her a thousand miles away?" David grabbed another roll.

"Only since Christmas vacation—" His mother's penciled brown eyes looked at him almost impersonally; yet he felt exposed. "She's only known you that little while. How can she . . ."

"What do you mean by that crack? Do you think it's impossible somebody might?" The third roll stuck in his throat and he began to wheeze. "We're going to get married," he said, chokingly. "What do you think of that?"

"A man gets married," his father said, coming into the kitchen. "Not a boy. You don't think I'm going to support a married boy? Have you ever really worked in your life, can you hold a job?"

His mother's thin delicate fingers flew between them. Startled, they both looked at her. Her face so unusually contorted, the lines of age were suddenly evident, her lips thinner, drawn back. "What are you talking about—a job? He's going back to school. He'll stay here a few days, all right. But he'll go back, we'll arrange it, he can get back in. Henry, you'll arrange it, he can go back."

"No," said his father, settling down in a captain's chair, dominating the table with his bulk. "I've tried as much as I can with this boy. Spent more money than any other father would dream of. Why he's been in private *pay* schools ever since the trouble started in junior high. Let's face it. He's not college material. I'm not talking just about grades. He hasn't even entered into the campus life . . . even sub on one of the teams, at least that. I'm through. He's got his room here. Maybe he can get a job."

"Dad—I've got a proposition already. Pots and pans, door to door. I got them on consignment, very cheap. They're the finest merchandise. In the car, want to see? I knew a fella out in Tucson made a great start, I figured why not here as well as there, where I can be near Marilyn—"

His father groaned. "Pots and pans. I can take only so much at a time. You'll have to wait til I get home tonight. Helen, let me have my coffee, I'm already late. And I may be late tonight."

The coffee spilled from its pot as she served it. She was crying, no tears falling but eyes full of them, hard knots in her cheeks. David put his hand over his stomach, over the knotting inside. Her face was so tight, the words came out in a flat whine. "That's right, it's easy for you, go to the office, while I've got to stay—" She stopped, swallowing hard.

The coffee flowed over the cup into the saucer as David got up. Patiently his father folded a napkin and put it into the wet, drying off the bottom of the cup before he drank what was left. David sensed his own stance, hands hanging low, apelike. He walked with studied insolence over to the refrigerator, found at the far end inside a line of soft drinks. At least it was the same refrigerator, with a bottle opener built into the door. And maybe the same shocker to open coke at breakfast time. He drank some, swilling it, belched, then took the bottle with him upstairs to the extension telephone.

"Who is this?" Marilyn's mother asked in her imperious manner, putting him off.

David's hands sweating, the receiver slipped a little. "Marilyn. I said I want to talk to Marilyn." He waited while her voice trailed off calling Marilyn, adding clearly enough for him to hear, *it couldn't be who I think it is.* And then finally her voice, cute and sugary, giving him the vision of lips shaped like a kewpie doll's.

"It's what we talked about Christmas, remember?" he said. "What we wrote each other about. This is too big for us to let it wait. The way we've got it." His voice dropped and he was giggling nervously, snorting again. "Remember that night, baby? I mean, how can we go wrong?"

"Is that nasty asthma bothering you?" she asked solicitously. "You sound kind of choked up."

He chortled. "Choked up is right. You're funny, really funny, sweetie. You've got a good way of putting things with the old lady listening. Is that it, is she listening? Don't answer that. I'll be right over. You still have that red sweater, wear it for me, huh?"

She giggled, too, and then he hung up, wiping his palms along his pant legs. How she had *let* him finally, that last night of Christmas vacation. After that, he would never let her down; she had loved him completely, he would never hurt her; he'd work for her, give her everything she wanted. He had not meant to come at her animal-like the way he had that night. But she had let him, she had understood, she had wanted him. He would be easier next time, he wouldn't feel so desperate, he *knew* now.

IV

Excitedly he went into the bathroom. Downstairs in the kitchen, right below him, came the sound of the captain's chair scraping back. David quickly turned on both faucets in the tub, let the shower shoot out loudly. The noise and the bathroom door locked —his father would have to leave without words to him. But in a minute he found himself shutting off the water, waiting. The house was still, except for his father's step near the coat closet and finally the slam of the front door. David could picture the office, could almost smell the cigar smoke.

To hell with the office, he'd make his own way. "Lady," he said to the shower nozzle. "Lady, these pots are the finest, have a pot, lady, a pan, a pot, lady, lady?"

He came out of the water shivering, drying his tall skinny body, flicking the towel at his legs in slaps, as he moved his feet in the dance he had seen fighters do before entering the ring. He caught sight of himself in the mirror and stopped, hunching his shoulders, bringing the muscles up in small shiny mounds. Some girls like a hairless chest on a man. Plenty of hair on his head though. He fastened his eyes on his hair, thick, black, glistening, pointing down in back and at the sides. From a shelf David picked up his father's hair brushes and glared at their ivory clarity. When he was through with them, they were each filmed with oil. He grinned at himself in the mirror, then sneezing violently, realized he was still naked. He grabbed a wad of toilet paper and harshly rubbed his nose, his mouth drooping open—that look of stupidity. . . . He rushed away from his face into his room and dressed hurriedly in tightly fitting black pants and a red flannel shirt.

Downstairs he hesitated near the front door, realizing his mother was probably lingering over coffee without toast. Why had he brought the empty coke bottle down with him? He stepped toward the kitchen. "I'm going over to Marilyn's! Maybe I'll be back for lunch, maybe I'll bring her back with me, huh?"

"David, there's a luncheon uptown I've got to—" she called back tiredly. "I didn't expect you, I can't just—"

He let the coke bottle slip wetly out of his hand, to bang and reel along the pale antiqued wood of an end table, as he left the house.

When the car would not start David grew panicky. He sweated profusely in fear, and then was furious at spoiling his shower, the preparations he had taken. Flooding the car with his curses and violent pumps on the accelerator, he blessed it as fervently when suddenly the motor turned over. But the brief failure filled him somehow with foreboding and he made superstitious signs to himself all the way over to Marilyn's house to prevent anything else going wrong. He *expected* her not to be out on the front stoop waiting for him. And before getting out of the car he sat for a moment, passing his hands over his hair and peering up at her bedroom window. The venetian blind flipped as if to shut out the sun. David made the sign of a cross from his forehead to his chest, intoning prayerfully, "New York, New Haven, Hartford, Connecticut." Then he flung himself out, the pots and pans making the sound of crashing cymbals.

V

Marilyn's mother was a large uncomfortable presence in the small parlor, where she made him sit down, she wanted to talk to him.

"Listen," she said in her heavy man's voice. "I know you're a rich kid, but where do you think quitting school is going to get you, anyway? Yeah, Marilyn told me, she tells me everything and what she doesn't—I can guess."

David's face grew hot. He stood up, feet twitching, wishing crazily he was back in the car where he could pound at the accelerator, pump, pump, pump. "Look," he said, restraint muffling his words. "Look, if you want to know something, I'm a businessman now, and I'll personally be able to support Marilyn." It was so close in here, the overstuffed furniture crowding in on him—he began to wheeze. He pulled a handkerchief out of his pocket and honked angrily to get clear.

"So I see," she said knowingly. "Not even Arizona helped you with the asthma. I see, I see."

"I'm home because I want to marry Marilyn!" He turned and strode away toward the staircase. Marilyn was trapped up there, he knew it now. Her mother had locked her in her room, that was it. They thought they could lock everything away, in schools, in rooms.

"Just a minute, my fine young man." The hand was heavy on his shoulder, pushing him back. He leaned against the weight, yearning upward. With a start he saw Marilyn sitting quietly at the head of the stairs, her face turned away, listening. "My fine young man," said her mother. "In such a hurry to fix yourself up with a girl who hardly knows you. She's a friendly girl, my Marilyn. Maybe she gave you a few ideas she shouldn't have. But maybe you forced her a little, too. She doesn't know her own sweetness sometimes. It gets her in trouble. But she's only eighteen; marrying is something else. It's not so easy getting out of a mistake like that. And with a sick boy. . . ."

The heavy voice seemed to go on and on, piling up into sledge-hammer strength, pounding inside his head. He leaned and looked up, Marilyn's red-sweatered breasts like flames sweeping upward into the stairwell. David pushed, freed himself and stumbled up the steps, reaching Marilyn as she scrambled up quickly. He grabbed out at her, wanting to hold her, kiss her sweetness that was only for him, for him alone.

"Mama!" she cried, backing away. "See, that's the way it was! You see how he acts!"

David slid along the railing, almost falling. "Marilyn," he half-whispered. "You don't have to talk that way. Don't be afraid of her." At the softness of his tone, she quieted and pursed her lips, as if she were sucking a lollipop. She kissed that way, that was the way she kissed. "I wish I could care for you, David. But I believe a girl ought to change around often at my age, I believe that's the way a girl my age finds out what the real thing is, finally, I mean. I wish I could, I mean, but I don't." She sighed and raised her arms to her hair, the red sweater stretching taut.

"What about—" he started to say, but his throat had closed up, viselike. He struggled to speak; he had to yell, he always had to yell; it was the only way. "You love me, goddamn you bitch, you love me, you love me, you love me!"

Marilyn turned and ran up to the rest of the stairs. He heard her door slam, and he was there, banging on it as inside she turned the lock. Then her mother was there, and he wanted to hit her mother, who seemed all shoulders, a tackling pressure keeping him away from the feminine softness of the red sweater, the lollipop lips. He wanted to hit her, but began to wheeze and found himself instead hanging onto the shoulders, gasping for strength, for breath.

"You'd better get home," the deep voice said. "You must have a spray there for that asthma. You'd better get home, go on now, go home."

VI

He went home. He got in his car and went home, the pots and pans jangling, the engine sputtering loudly, making a racket on the quiet street, the white curtains parting a bare inch and his mother peering out to see.

"What's the matter?" she said, as he came inside. She was

187

dressed to go out, her suit a tapestry silk, like the draperies, the handbag an import, probably Italian to fit with the current house décor. She always liked things to match, never a jarring note. He stood between her and the door as she looked anxiously at her watch, saying not asking, "What's the matter?"

"Nothing. Nothing!"

"You don't have to shout."

He pushed by her. "Go ahead. You'll miss your party."

"There's some leftover roast in the refrigerator, you can make yourself lunch. Or if you'd rather, here's a couple of dollars, go out and eat."

"Go ahead. Go ahead. I'll get along by myself."

"If you expect me to feel sorry for you, you're sadly mistaken. You bring these things on yourself."

"*What* things, what do *you* know, *what* things!"

"I can imagine. A boy who quits school doesn't make the best impression on a girl." Looking at her wristwatch, she came into the living room.

"Leave me alone!"

"All right . . . ." She seemed to linger, her face, in the shadow of the curtained room, strangely soft and brooding. "Look—they're not the best people anyway. That mother—the lowest class. Don't feel too bad."

David stared at her. He wanted to cry, he wanted her hands on his hair. He could not speak, *help me*. Didn't she know that's what he was thinking, couldn't say it? Why didn't she come closer, closer? Why did she wait for him to pull her through to him? Why was it *his* responsibility? But try, *try*. . . . In her nervous habit, she looked down again at her watch. The pleading words reeled back in his mouth as his lips turned sour with a thousand past moments of bitterness. He spat scornfully. "What's the matter? You worried or something? Afraid no one will have me and you'll be stuck with me? You worried or something?"

Her body stiffened. She put her hands on her hips and smoothed down the skirt that was already immaculately fitted. "Why, I ought to kick you out altogether. I see now your father's *smart* not to think of taking you into the office. You have no respect, you only know how to take, take, take. I ought finally just to say well go ahead, be on your own, move out altogether." She balled up her gloved hand and tapped her chest. "I just don't have it *in* me to do a thing like that. But I ought to, for your **own** good, I ought to tell you goodbye and good riddance."

The tears came to his eyes; he could never survive her habits of reprimand; she could never see through his. "Fuck the good-byes!" He exploded, turning quickly from her, thinking, *Marilyn, Marilyn.*

VII

Upstairs in the study the blinds were all drawn. His eyes so flooded and the room so dark—David could barely see to the telephone. Blindly he yanked at the window cords. The venetians slid up in shrieks, sun streaming in over the room, making dizzy-ing patterns of light. The zigzags seemed to invade his brain; he felt all head, with the mad rushes of light pulling up away from his neck until finally his head would blow off, disintegrate in hot flashes. He sank down, eyes painfully squinting at the dial as he picked out Marilyn's number.

"Hello" demanded her mother.

"Listen, I apologize for my behavior, okay? I've got to speak to Marilyn."

"It's no use. Don't try any more. It's all over, if there ever was anything."

"Listen, I just want to talk to—"

But she had hung up. David dropped the receiver into its cradle, for a moment watched it rest smugly there. Then, grab-bing the phone, he threw it on the floor, the receiver flying off.

"David . . . David . . ." He thought it Marilyn's voice he was hearing and he sprang towards the sound, falling on his hands and knees. But it was his mother's voice from the downstairs telephone; she had been listening in. David blasted out, "Go to your goddamn luncheon, what're you waiting for!" and, jumping up, slammed shut the door of the study, rushed to yank at all the cords at all the windows, the blinds shuddering closed again.

The room was a dark jail; he had made himself a nice dark jail. He wanted bars now, bars he could shake and shout through.

He flung himself around the room like a clumsy dancer, looking for things to lay his hands on, things to bend, things to throw against the walls, making himself know and hear and feel the trap he was in. The room was full of sport trophies. They made huge, crashing sounds as David hurled them from one wall to the other. He ripped banners down and broke glass with silver loving cups until the only things left intact were the clothes on his own back, his own flesh and if this was ripped away there would still be the tiny core of himself that no good riddance could get rid of.

He sat down in the middle of the rubble and put his fingers over his face, gazing through them. From under his leg, a small child's football gleamed forward, white into the dark room. Here it was, after all these years, in good condition. Why not? It had never really been used. His father had bought the ball the day he had come home from the service. David was seven then, *all grown up,* his father had said, staring down at him from a great uniformed bulk. David remembered clinging to his grandmother's hips while she whispered to him, "Go ahead, take it."

Shyly David had come close to his father's offering, reaching at the ball. A quick movement and the ball had eluded him, then another reach and he had missed it again. "Come on, come on," his father had teased. "Get it, get it, first thing you got to learn, I'm feigning the pass, you got to catch me at it." And they went on like that, his father laughing, teasing, and David reaching, missing. He had not *wanted* to cry then; he wanted to be laughing too. His grandmother had begun to scold his father and there had been a lot of shouting suddenly, his mother coming from upstairs where she had been dressing. She had worn long earrings and a necklace of pearls and a dress David imagined to be made of gold thread, taken out of the stories his grandmother had read to him.

"This is a day for celebration, not shouting," she had said sweetly, hushing them, cupping her hands delicately over her hair as if the ugly sounds would disarray the wave. "After all, mother has been so good to us! She's been someone to take care of us while you were away, Henry. I don't know how I'd ever have managed otherwise. Besides no time for fighting. I'm all ready for the celebration you promised first night home."

His father pushed the ball into David's hand, mumbling angrily, "It's become a woman's world here, I can see that."

His mother, walking up to his father, had tucked her arm through his, eyes slanting. "Well, I for one am glad a man is back."

Later his grandmother had read to David quietly, warm and close on her lap. But he had been able to sleep only fitfully that night, had heard his parents come back to talk loudly in their bedroom.

"What do you mean sickly—" his father was demanding.

"He's that kind of boy, I guess," his mother had answered. "Frail. I don't understand it but there it is. I mean, neither of us was ever that way. I was always healthy. And you—you—" Her laughter was low and then the voices went low, disappearing. David had stayed on in his bed without closing his eyes, the still blackness like a prison.

Here in the darkened study, David held the ball, a white, rubbery, yielding substance in his hands. He held Marilyn's breasts, felt himself swell, rising, bringing himself into her and she gasping her joy with him. Even if it were just one more time, if he could only see her, have one more time, she would remember how good it was, how she loved him.

VIII

David got up, swayed out of the study and down the stairs. His mother had her hat on, her eyes frightened. He brushed past her and into the street. Rapping on the car for good luck, he kissed its hood and climbed into the front seat, seeing himself with Marilyn, seeing the chance he had.

One brief flare and then the motor died. Another chance— he pumped the accelerator—another chance and another, but nothing. Not even another start. He stayed with it, stopping regularly to bang his forehead on the rim of the steering wheel, cursing. Crack, crack. Pump, pump. The motor was as silent as the air that hung over this street, this quiet block.

Finally David got out and opened the hood, staring in at the motor, staring and waiting as if some part of the machinery would suddenly assume meaning and answer. He tightened whatever would tighten and pulled out the oil gauge and studied it. He could see himself as the American boy who must have the mechanical know-how. Why then didn't it come to him, why—? He banged down the hood, the pots and pans inside the car sounding a dozen punctuations.

"David," hissed his mother from the doorway. "Where do you want to go? Come inside, you know you can't fix that wreck."

"Mind your own goddamn business." He picked up the hood and let it slam again.

"David—please—"

"How would you understand where I've got to go? Now, NOW." He picked up and dropped the hood.

She came into the street, close to him, looking anxiously about at the houses. "David, you've got to calm yourself. Your father should be here any minute. I called him. He'll get a mechanic. Just come in now, have something warm to drink. The whole street doesn't have to know."

David wheeled at the idea of his father and saw him suddenly, coming down the street. He ran around and once more got into the car, pounded the accelerator. He could see his father come closer and his heart knocked with longing to get the car started, to leave like a man and come to Marilyn. It was his car, his own car, he must get it to go. His father came along the street, the bulk of his shoulders increasing, pressuring, closer. David began to whimper a little. He slammed out of the car, attacked the hood, threw it up, banged it down, the pots and pans constant echoes of his movements. His lips felt wizened with frustration. He brought his fists down thundering on the immovable hulk, pounding the paint off, yelling as his father got to him, "Everything—everything I touch turns to shit!"

His mother gasped. "Out here . . . out here. . . ."

His father grabbed him, trying to pull him into the house. Bracing his feet, David could feel all at once how strong his fury made him. And they were afraid of him out here. Inside, the house was his trap, out here was theirs. In one burst he pulled away from his father, luring them to stay with him. "Why in hell haven't you even seen my pots, my pans? I want you to see them!"

One by one he picked them out, flourishing them in the air. His mother's eyes stared over the street, the drawn draperies everywhere. David brandished his pots. "Look at them, mother, look at me!" She was whispering to his father. "Look at me! Mom, look!" And he flung the first pot across the street where it smashed a window, where the curtains flew open. His mother screamed. He threw another, a three-quart saucepan, heavy, taking all his strength to make it to a glass door he had spotted. His father fell upon him from behind, trying to drag him down, but David got away and threw a skillet, a dutch oven—first the bigger ones, then the smaller ones which did not make such a crash but were easier to aim. There were shouts from inside the houses but no one came out, until the patrol cars rode in, their sirens screeching. Two policemen were able to hold David securely, though he heaved in their arms, his legs kicking at their legs. Then the people in the houses came out, all the people in all the houses. They swarmed over the street, looking at him.

His mother was sobbing, her makeup smeared with the wet of tears, her hat listing sloppily over one eye. She wobbled drunkenly toward him like a street walker. "Why do you want to do this to us? What did we ever . . . ?"

David could feel the phlegm come up through his throat into his nose, choking him, and he snorted, moving violently enough to free one hand from the policeman's hold. He slapped his mother's face once, then something struck him and he slumped.

Later, even after he heard and felt again, he could not seem to open his eyes. He sensed the movement of a car beneath him, heard the sobbing, his mother's presence hovering over him, within his reach. But every part of him was bound, straps digging into his flesh. There was the touch of hands on his hair, caressing, and the voice asking if he was all right, he must be all right, *it must have been that girl, because of that girl.*

He was wrapped too tightly to answer and any energy gradually coursed inward, flooding his own voice, blocking out all sound or touch or care.

Knifed with a Black Shadow

BY SALLY WEINRAUB

FROM WHERE Gloria knelt by the half-filled suitcase, fumbling with shoes, steadying the lid that sagged back against rusty hinges, heaping the rapidly growing pile of discarded clothes neatly against the wall, she could hear a clock chanting evenly-spaced minutes into oblivion. It was time to go.

The door, caught in the August afternoon breeze, wavered, not open and not closed, a green, swinging slab of wood knifed with black shadow and finished off with a round brass eye of a handle and a scratched brass teardrop of a keyhole. It was past six; time to throw it open and say goodbye to the little girl's room with frilly organdy curtains and spread, long outgrown, but which she had never had the energy or the will to put away.

There was not much that she wanted to take . . . a few blouses and skirts . . . some cotton dresses . . . the green silk evening gown because that had been part of it, part of the beginning. Her glance skimmed about the room, flickering over the painted white furniture with shadows in front where her brother Gerry had tried to paint over the decals; the oval mirror in its carved pink and white frame, reflecting crystal feathers that concealed the light bulbs, coming to rest on the vanity with the bottles of cologne and the black china horse.

She got up, her stockinged feet soundless on the white wool rug, hearing only the creak of her straightening knees, and took the ornament in her hand. All these years a black horse galloping across her dainty, frivolous vanity! She had almost forgotten it was there. She had bought it right after Nina and Tina had moved when they lived in the old house. She had watched them leaving from the front porch. When the moving people had packed everything into the truck and had been about to leave, she had run down, across the street, crying, "You forgot the horse!

Nina, tell them they forgot the horse!" And then the men had gone back and brought the big, black rocking horse out from under the tree and put it into the van, and they had all gone away.

That had been sixteen years ago when she was only ten years old, but she remembered it because she had longed for them to forget the rocking horse. She had saved up to buy the china one instead.

She hesitated, and then wrapped it up in a handkerchief and tucked it into the fold of a sweater. She put in the comb and brush set that she had got for graduation. Her mother would be hurt if she left it behind.

II

She heard the refrigerator door slam shut in the kitchen. She must go soon. She could not wait much longer or the door would open, the brass knob clicking and scratching, and the vast form of her mother would confront her, crowding into the small bedroom. She glanced at the mirror, at her own slight frame, pale face and large eyes, at her dark hair pushed back from her deep forehead and the drops of sweat at her hairline.

The afternoon had been cool; the late August sun lacking in intensity. There was no reason for sweat. She wiped her forehead with a tissue, dropping it into the white fluted wastebasket with a teddybear still dancing on the front.

Goodbye teddybear! The suitcases were finished. It was time to go. She touched the hard wood at the end of the bed. She should be sad. Under its frilly coverlet, the bed had been a sturdy friend to her. Right up until last night when she had woken up gripping the posts after dreaming of suffocating telephone booths and blank dials, and high voices crying, "What number are you calling?"

No one was ever at the other end of the wire in her dreams.

III

The front door opened and shut and the heavy voice of her father rumbled in through the keyhole and under the green door.

They were both home now. Both her parents, both waiting to see if she had really meant it when she said she was going today. All three of them waiting to see.

She gasped, pressing her hands into her ribs, comforting herself with the assurance of her own presence. She turned again to the mirror, to the dark, questioning eyes, and muttered, "Don't listen, just close your ears and don't listen. No one can stop you if you really want to go."

If I really want to go. But what will I have there? Not even bedposts to cling to—just a studio bed that looks like a couch in the daytime. There would be Rosemarie, too. Rosemarie her roommate. But Rosemarie had stood in the doorway of her apartment, her dark ballerina eyes fluttering like the wings of a bird in flight, and she had said quite clearly, "A roommate is a roommate." The words flew back to Gloria now, "Not a husband, nor a best friend, and certainly not an analyst. You understand what I mean, of course."

Yes, she had understood and it had seemed right. That was what she needed, she had told herself . . . absolute privacy. But absolute indifference? Would she be able to cope with that?

In the mirror, she saw her eyes shifting. Fearful, she steadied them. "Be brave," she muttered, "for once in your craven life, have a little courage. Could it be much worse than this? You could always come back to this!"

She could always come back to her comfortless nest; to the shrunken, hardened womb that battered and cramped her limbs even as she sought oblivion in it. And if they should threaten her with the loss of that, with the closing off of this tepid refuge, what then?

She darted scorn into the still fearful eyes, and walked over to the window.

"Look out there," she told herself. "Isn't it this that you are leaving, after all? This outside, and this inside—nothing but this?"

Two half-drawn shades of symmetrically perfect windows stared back blankly from the house opposite. Up and down Adams Street, symmetry, conquering nature, had decreed squatting square boxes of white shingle and gray roof, each roof decorated by a red candle of a chimney. In front of these, scrawny treelets, encircled and staked like drab maypoles, marked off thirty-pace intervals with proper precision.

Perhaps if it had been the other house, the big, shabby house in the shaded old neighborhood of Port Chester where they used to live before Melody and Gerry married and Mrs. Gesell complained that they were rattling around like marbles in a great barn, then she might have been sad to leave the house and the garden and the painted wooden front porch. But who could feel sentimental about this brand new started-from-scratch section of the same town, this naked, straight aisle of white squares and uniform green shutters?

Through the thin walls percolated new sounds, the clatter of pot lids and the tinny ping of the bell that timed the oven. The smell of roasting chickens drifted in. What was she waiting for? It was many years past time to go.

She pushed open the green door that was too thin to be a shield to privacy and dragged her suitcases to the head of the stairs.

The hall was empty. The murmur of voices came from the living room at the left. There was no door to the living room, just an arch. Architects believed less and less in doors these days, so that houses were becoming like beehives, arches leading into chambers and more arches. It was lucky that Americans were still puritan in their habits. You could be alone in the bathroom. Bathrooms even had locks so that you could be safe in your solitude.

Which was a way of saying that there was no way past those murmuring voices off through the arch to the left. If their last wave of protest were too much it might engulf her, drowning her forever.

IV

Her arms had no strength in them, so she turned one of her suitcases over on its side, and standing below it slid it down to the bottom. She hurried up for the other one as her father's voice called, "Gloria!"

"Just a minute!" She pulled it down beside the other one, so that the two of them stood close together by the front door, and walked into the living room.

Her father was standing in the center of the room, his feet embedded in the blue flowered rug. He wore a dark suit and tie. He never took off his jacket unless he was in the privacy of his bedroom. His hands, with the black hairs shadowing the knuckles, hung straight down as he looked out of the open window.

He barely turned his head as Gloria walked in. There was the slightest movement of the heavy ruddy cheeks, a changing highlight in the round, silver-rimmed lenses, a deeper visible expanse of the bushy mustache, and that was all.

Gloria, watching, waiting for him to speak, was suddenly shocked. The mustache had always been black and fierce and awesome. The mouth under it had spoken and not been defied. When had it turned gray? How had it happened without her noticing it? Gray, too, was his head and his heavy eyebrows. Only from the nostrils of his nose the black hairs still sprang, curling up over the gray of his mustache.

In the silence that was commanded by the stern gaze, she became aware of her mother, sitting upright on the couch to his right, watching him with a curious mixture of awe and derision. The awe was for him for she never crossed him, but obeyed with a self-deriding irony. Sometimes when his imperious voice would summon her, she would turn and say, "Ach! The king is calling. We'll have to hurry so as not to annoy his majesty." Gloria never quite knew whether her mother resented or enjoyed his dominance. Her big body moved swiftly, and the momentary flicker in the yellow eyes, so much like Gloria's, was gone.

Now she jerked her head up at her daughter as if to say, "Wait now! You haven't had the last word yet. He'll tell you a thing or two."

Gloria turned away, following her father's gaze to the window, neat in its brown silk drapes, swathed and flounced on top, and fringed down the sides. The drapes did not draw across the window. They were tacked to the floor at the sides because it was neater and they held their shape better that way. There were venetian blinds that could be drawn when it was dark, but it was not quite time for that yet.

198

SALLY WEINRAUB

Without looking round, her father spoke, "So you're going!"

"I just finished packing, Dad," she answered, almost choking as she swallowed down deep into the dryness of her throat.

He did not answer, but the color began to deepen in his heavy cheeks. His eyes, framed in the round, familiar lenses, turned to her, full of the anger she dreaded.

And she shivered with the old, unreasoning fear, feeling the force of his rage sweeping over her. What if he should slap her, knock her down? Would she run upstairs crying, creep into her room like a mouse into its hold? Maybe they were right, it was a silly whim, and she was better off home. What was she going to? Further emptiness . . . a multiplication of the loneliness she had come to dread? Not only alone, but without the sheltering warmth of a home.

Above the brocade sofa, the old framed wedding portraits of her brother and sister smiled out from the harmony of light brown walls, their gaze resting eternally on the blue china lamp settled on its gleaming wood table top. The andirons, straddling their brass pole near the fireplace, glowed with the cheerful reflection of their morning's rubdown.

The andirons are too big, she thought desperately; they belonged in the other house. They are out of place here.

"I told you it was today, Dad." She met his gaze finally. "I am going."

Oh, she thought bitterly, if he ever said something kind, I'd fling myself into his arms, even now. I'd stay.

"You don't need me here," she said almost pleadingly.

"What has that to do with it?" And his eyes were bits of blue ice.

"All right, then," she thought finally. "Then he can't stop me."

It had all been said . . . yesterday, the day before . . . the day before that. She had endured it. He's getting old, she thought, cruelly. He can't stop me now.

She looked strongly up at him, forcing him now to see her, to see that there was no fear in her anymore.

"I'm going to call the cab," she said deliberately.

But when it happened, when his eyes meeting hers saw what

199

she was telling him, and when fury was joined by bafflement, she was overwhelmed by guilt.

"I'm sorry," she mumbled, "I'm sorry, Dad."

"Don't call me Dad,' he said. He turned his back and walked out of the room.

She watched him go and wanted to hurl herself after him, shouting, "Daddy, Daddy! Please love me. I promise I'll be good!" Would he have consoled her, and stroked her hair as he had once when she had been small?

That had been long ago when she was only three. Her mother had decided that they would take a walk one sunny afternoon. People said you couldn't remember that far back, but she remembered it clearly.

"We have a long way to go," her mother had said. "You must ride in the carriage."

"No, no! I'm a big girl," she had cried, "I won't go in the carriage."

"It's too far for you to walk. Come, you can take your dolly with you."

"No, I won't. I want to walk."

She remembered stamping her foot, and more than that the humiliation she had felt at the thought of being wheeled in a carriage when she was so big. "Get in, now," her mother had insisted, and she had cried and screamed. And then her father had come out and carried her into the house and smacked her. She had been terrified by his angry voice and by his bigness, and while he was hitting her she had sobbed, "Please, please, Daddy, I'll be good!" And even now she remembered the shame she had felt.

But he had held her in his arms and smoothed back her hair and kissed her and told her to be a good girl. And then he had carried her out and put her in the carriage. That was the only time she remembered him holding her and hugging her.

V

She became conscious of her mother's accusing gaze, and she said shakily, "Mother!"

"You've upset him," Mrs. Gesell grated. "Go and tell him you're sorry and you didn't mean it."

"Oh God!' she said, suddenly weary, tired of the game they were playing, she and her mother. Her mother was shrewd. She should have known by this time that it was too late. Did she think that she would still change her mind?

Warily Gloria watched the young-looking face incongruously joined to the heavy body. She saw the yellow-brown eyes, long-lashed like her own, ungiving, skirting about, looking for a point of entrance. Unwillingly she admired the solid core of the woman standing before her, brushing back her smooth brown and white hair into its neat bun, stroking her long white nose with her fingers while those ever-watchful eyes sought for an opening of attack.

"And she never needs to ask why," she thought. "My mother, at least, knows who she is."

"What are you rushing about?" Mrs. Gesell said more softly. "Stay and have some dinner. It's getting dark. Tomorrow is another day."

She has Gerry and Melody and the grandchildren. Does she really care whether I stay or go?

Outside the light was fading. Through the open window came the swishing of the sprinklers in a whirling fugue of spinning metal, soaring jets of water and patterned drops falling heavily upon the dry earth.

"There isn't anything different about tomorrow, Mother." A door upstairs whined and banged, and Mrs. Gesell started, her head turning toward the sound, casting her face in shadow.

"It's the king, then," thought Gloria. "The queen is trying to save the glory of the king."

She wondered whether it was from habit that her mother struggled to keep the worn patterns of their lives from splitting. Was it possible that she loved her stern husband? It was strange, but she had never thought of love, in the romantic sense, between her mother and father.

But she could think about that later. There was so much she would have to think about later.

She went to the telephone and dialed the taxi.

"You really are going."

Her mother sighed and took one of Gloria's hands in her own.

"Look at you," she said mockingly, "Not an ounce of flesh on you. You'll be sick in no time. It's not that easy, girl, to manage a home and cook and work at the same time. Ah! You'll be glad to come home in a few weeks."

Gloria extricated her hand. "There isn't any use going on about it."

"Would you like a glass of milk or something?"

"No."

They sat down uncomfortably, waiting.

Gloria said, "Of course, I'll come and see you."

"Yes, of course."

"The cab should be here soon," Gloria jumped up and rummaged in her bag for a comb.

"It needs setting," her mother said critically, looking at her hair.

"Doesn't it always?" She tried to smile.

The gentle throbbing of a motor touched her ears, and from the corner of her eye she saw the reflection of headlights as the cab turned into the driveway.

"Here's the taxi, Mother. I have to go now."

Her mother gave her a quick squeeze, pressing her cheek to hers guiltily with a half smile as though laughing at herself.

Gloria opened the door and picked up one of the suitcases. Halfway to the cab, the driver jumped out and took it from her.

She stood in the driveway waiting for him, looking back through the half-open door at her mother.

"Why am I going?" she thought suddenly. "I don't even want to."

"Goodbye, Mother," she called.

She stumbled into the taxi quickly, so that she would not turn and run back into the house, into her own little girl's room. It was quite dark now. There were no lights, only the beam of the headlights. They drove straight into black emptiness with only the twin headlights cutting out a path. If you went to the right or to the left of the lights, you would be lost in darkness.

The Evening Paper

BY WILLIAM M. SHEPPARD

FROM THE SUNLIT drawing room of his London home, young Adam could hear his father's key turn in the front door lock. He sighed thankfully. He never did like algebra. He would rather listen to sparrows and starlings twittering through the French windows or watch the dying leaves of that bloodstained September afternoon pattern the wall with shadowed dreams. Now his father was home to help.

Towheaded Adam threw his pencil on to the desk excitedly, pushed back the three-cornered chair in which he'd been sitting, and ran across the parquet floor toward the stooping shadow in the hall.

"Is that you, Adam?" asked a middle-aged voice.

"Yes, Daddy, I was doing my homework. How was the army today?"

"Tiring, my boy, tiring, but it's the Home Guard, not the army," said his father, placing his steel helmet on a wooden rack and smoothing his bald head as though he had hair. "Where's your Mother?"

"She had a call from the hospital," replied Adam. "They hit Woolworth's about an hour ago and a lot of people were hurt. She just left."

"I suppose she won't be back for quite a while."

"She said I was to tell you not to wait supper."

As they walked back beneath the hall stairs in the direction of the living room, Adam could see the exhaustion in his father's face. Gone was the morning twinkle in the blue eyes, gone too, were the usual straight shoulders; his tanned skin had darkened in the dust of day.

"All this senseless bombing!" said his father, unbuttoning an ill-fitting battledress. "Do the Jerries really think we'll give in, just by making London a pile of rubble?" He paused.

"Have you had tea yet?"

"Mother put the kettle on, but there was no gas."

"Must have hit a main again, oh well, and on our twentieth wedding anniversary, too! It doesn't seem like twenty years."

Adam waited for his father to collapse into the wing chair by the netted windows; then he stood in front of him with his back turned to help pull off the boots. The feet were hot and stale, the socks had worn holes in their toes from drilling in the autumnal sun.

"How was school today, Adam?" his father yawned, stretching the scar on his left cheek and placing his hairy hand in front of his mouth.

"Oh, we didn't get much done, Daddy. The siren went nine times but it didn't stop Miss Perkins from giving us homework—algebra, too!"

"Don't tell me a boy of eleven can't do his homework?"

"Well, I just don't think I have a mathematical mind. I'd rather paint and draw and do things like that."

"Did the evening paper come?"

"No, I'm afraid not."

"I'll tell you what, Adam!" he said. "If you'll go round to the newsagent and buy me a paper and some baccy for me pipe, I'll take a hot bath in the meantime. Then we'll see what can be done about your algebra."

Adam knew his father would help him. He knew deep down inside that there was no father in the world like his own. His father had taught him how to swim and how to fish; he'd taught him how to box and defend himself against the boys in school; he'd taught him how to save money and how to spend it wisely—he'd even bought him a brand new bicycle for his birthday. With his father he'd learned how to use an air gun too, and best of all he was the only person he could beat at a game of Monopoly."

Adam marveled at his father's patience, at the way in which he would shut himself up in his book-lined study for hours at a time and later emerge with a design for a house. He had seen whole houses rise from pieces of paper, big tall houses with twin Elizabethan chimneys, square apartment blocks, and country houses with nooks and crannies to explore.

"Why don't you make houses any more, Daddy?" he enquired.

"Because there's a war on, and when there's war everybody stops what they're doing to fight the enemy. That's why you have to grow vegetables at school and knit scarves for soldiers to wear next winter."

Adam's father had also been in the First World War, and been given a medal by King George V. Adam knew his father was a brave man because he had gone over the top in the trenches in France.

"Go and get the paper, there's a good lad. Here's a shilling. I want the change back. Hurry now."

Adam ran up the street in the early autumnal sunlight. The blue sky above was still holed with drifting puffs of gunfire, distorted now. There were white streaks of battle entwined with the sooty clouds like holes being darned with thread on his mother's lap. Tiring for want of breath, Adam slowed to a walk, hopping occasionally between the concrete squares on the pavement. He could hear the distant clatter of an ambulance and thought of his mother caring for the wounded at the hospital. At the corner he turned away from tree-lined Drayton Gardens to the Fulham Road, a more commercial thoroughfare lined with endless four-story dwellings, stuck together since Victorian days like soldiers marching in monotonous rows.

He pulled the bright shilling from his grey flannel shorts, bouncing it in and out of his tiny hands as he walked past sand-bagged windows and others that had splintered into a thousand pieces on the pavement. A uniformed group of people pointed skywards at a barrage balloon; it had escaped from its moorings, gleaming all puppy-fat silver with a rusty church weather vane caught on its wire.

The street Adam had intended to enter was roped off with a painted sign which read: "Danger! Unexploded bomb." Adam knew that if he walked on for about five minutes, there would be another paper shop past the big gray church on the corner. The street was filled with fire trucks, hoses, and shopkeepers sweeping up glass. A second ambulance streaked past. He wanted to walk on anyway, he could see a crater belching flames from the middle of a side street.

"That's probably the gas main," he thought.

Suddenly the unwholesome bass voice of the siren moaned wailfully as though squeezing its way out of the brickwork in melancholy forebodance. Again they were coming, and probably again and again. Adam decided to walk on. He would hear the guns if the gerries were near. His father had promised to help with his homework if he brought home a paper, and Adam wasn't about to let the Luftwaffe interfere with his plans.

The street was deserted now, except for the breathless shriek of a warden's whistle. He walked on as far as the Protestant church. Then a fat man in a blue battledress ran up to him as the "crump" of anti-aircraft artillery disturbed the distance. The warden's face was pink and sweaty beneath the weight of his steel hat.

"'ere son! You ought not to be out in this," he said in broad cockney dialect. "Yer'll get 'it by shrapnel and that's red 'ot steel! Go down in the crypt 'til the All Clear sounds, there's a good lad."

Adam had heard shrapnel falling in the street at night. It made a tinkling noise on the pavement but he'd not realized it would be red hot. The side door of the church led down a chill staircase. Adam could feel the drop in temperature as he held on to the damp Norman walls leading in circles to the crypt below. The stairs were steep; they smelled musty. Above him, the sound of gunfire grew louder and louder.

The crypt was barely lit by an open grill, high near the ceiling that looked on to the graves around the church. The late sun threw soft shafts of orange light that timidly circled the pillars arching the edifice above them. Between the pillars lay long gray tombs sleeping ignorantly in the peace of stone, untouched by time and German bombs. Adam's shilling twiddled between the fingers in his trouser pocket. He could see sheltering people in the shadows, but they said nothing. It was not a time to say anything. There was a sudden screech from the skies above, a high-pitched whistle, a rush, a momentary silence followed by a deafening explosion, then another and another. Adam could feel the blast of hot air through the tiny window. And another and another still, yet another! The guns barked loud crescendo at the enemy, fire bells clanged across the streets above, shrapnel fell like sharpened raindrops in a hurtling staccato.

His tongue between his lips, Adam crouched behind a concrete catafalque, his heart beating quickening thuds in the ethereal gloom about him. A sharper, more frightening screech, a second, a third and others too, the rush of air, the high explosions, the sound of crumpling brick and masonry; beneath him the bouncing earth to shake the sleeping dead; outside the screams of helpless people trapped in wreckage. He could smell an ether, an incense from another life—he thought it must be death.

Suddenly there was stillness.

After a little while, the boy drew himself up to a standing position. His pulse was quieter now, but he could still feel fear pumping through his veins. He licked his dried lips and swallowed. His knees trembled. He held on to a tomb for support. The concrete figures above him continued to sleep serenely, their hands clasped in prayer.

"If there is a God," thought Adam, "why does he let all these people get killed. I wonder if there really is a God?"

The ochre sun-rays were diffused now, distorted by twisting smoke drifting on an early autumn breeze that brought the smell of burning flesh from the dying to the dead.

Adam walked between the solid pillars to the staircase door, avoiding flat metaled graves in the floor as he walked. Other people, silent still, were crossing the uneven floor. The quietness seemed unnatural, as though everyone above were dead and had forgotten to let them out. Slowly, one by one, Adam climbed the twisting steps. He could smell air again at that low level, smell the churchyard grass, but he could not hear the birds. And then— strong, solid, shrill and loud—at last came the All Clear.

Adam ran out of the church to the pavement wall. The four-story building from which he had emerged lay spilled across the street in mauve haze and curled black smoke. Part of a splintered store sign lay shattered against a grave which read "Rest in Peace" beneath a blanket of disturbed green moss. Bricks, wood, thick dust and pieces of clothing lay all over the pavement.

Adam turned out of the iron church gate left hanging on one decorated hinge, and ran back in the direction of his home. All around the boy lay flaming pieces of house, broken glass, hose pipes waiting for water from broken mains; people ran in every direction, rescue workers with tired granite faces, firemen, ambulance drivers and frightened or maimed animals.

Adam ran as he had never run before, back up the commercial thoroughfare to the safety of his father and the green-leaved street on which he lived—but this was no longer the street. An agonized tree lay uprooted in a smoking crater's edge; red-eyed rats scampered in confused disturbance. More bricks lay splattered across the road and piles of steaming wreckage erupted before his eyes. A policeman, seeing the boy, went after him, missed him, and almost caught him.

"Son, you come back 'ere!" he shouted, "you come back this minute!"

Adam did not hear the policeman's words; already climbing the mountainous wreck of his home, he coughed in the unsettled dust.

"Daddy?" he cried, "Daddy!"

Morning in the Sun

BY MARGARET DRURY

KITTY MATTHEWS closed the glass door behind her and stepped out onto the side porch of the shingle and stucco house that had been her childhood home. Holding her coffee cup stiffly in front of her to avoid spilling, she stood there in the sunshine, threw back her head, and took a long, deep breath. Though she had already been outside for three hours that morning on the drive from her own home to her father's, she felt once more that the whole of springtime had gathered into this sparkling May day, and that joyously it was absorbing her into itself. "Middle-aged or not," she thought, "at such a time as this I'd like to burst out crying from sheer youth—" and immediately she smiled.

The quick delight of the smile broke up the girlish placidity of Kitty's face. Thin V lines spread from the corners of her dark brown eyes to the edges of her dark brown hair, and deep V's cut into her cheeks at the corners of her lips. She walked forward toward the top of the porch steps, and under her navy print dress she carried her body with strength and energy. Pausing at the steps, she looked down onto a flagstone patio where the sun shone, in captured warmth, between a barberry hedge and the ivy-covered stucco of the house. There, in a cushioned garden chair, her father rested back, awake or asleep she could not tell. A newspaper, neatly folded, lay on the stone at the side of the chair. Kitty took her first step down carefully, to balance the coffee, and her father's head turned slowly on the cushion. "Hello, Dad," she called. "Here I come."

Her father blinked his half-dozing eyes as if his attention had been caught by some unfamiliar sound. Seeing her then, he lifted his head, and his face, dulled by the heavy-hanging folds of age and relaxation, drew itself together into a countenance of compact features, angled lines, and quiet blue eyes.

"Hello! Oh, hello there, Kitty," he said. He pulled at the chair arms and shoved himself upward on unsteady legs as if not quite sure which way he should move.

"Sit down, Dad," Kitty said. "Heavens, don't get up for me." But her father was already on his feet, still holding onto the arm of the chair.

Even when he stooped he was tall. His hair was thin and white, and his blue sweater hung from his shoulders as if it had been intended for a larger person. "Well, nice to see you," he said. "I guess it's been two or three months."

Kitty set the coffee upon a little metal table and kissed her father on the cheek. How stubbly his beard felt, she thought, as if it, like the rest of him, had grown stiff. "Yes," she answered smiling. "Two whole months, and you're looking even better than usual." The easy cheer of her voice sounded as pleasantly a part of the day as the breeze rustling the pages of the newspaper.

"Come on," he said. "I'm not getting any younger, you know." He half-smiled, looking at her from the corner of his eye.

"Nor older, either," she answered, nodding firmly.

He stepped backward to sit down again, and waved his hand to another chair facing his own. "There you are, Kitty," he said. "Make yourself comfortable." His chair creaked as he settled himself into it, relaxing his back, his legs, and finally his arms, but Kitty continued to stand where she was, watching him. Overhead in the ivy leaves a sparrow scratched and twittered. Kitty glanced up as a tiny avalanche of bark and leaf mold poured down the vines, but her glance swept again to her father's face.

"Pretty good, pretty darn good," she was saying to herself. "Color better, and he's added a little weight," and she thought of the letters she would write tomorrow to her sister and brother, one West, the other South. "Dad is fine," she would say. "Maybe he's no kid, but for a man of eighty-one—I hope I'm doing half as well when I'm his age."

She sat down then and picked up her cup, but without tasting the coffee she put it down with a little clink. "Say, Dad, what about some coffee for you?" she asked, and she pushed herself up from her chair. "Who am I to be drinking your coffee and not offering you any?"

"No, Kitty," he said, "Just keep on sitting."

"Indeed I won't," she said. "That perfect housekeeper of yours has the coffee put on the stove. I'll be back in two minutes or know I'm slipping." Glancing back as she walked up the steps, she saw he had closed his eyes again.

When she returned, he looked up at her, smiling. "You're as bossy as ever," he said.

She set his coffee down and shoved the table closer to him. "Sure I am," she said. "That's my terrible secret, but you don't expect me to drink alone, do you?"

They sat for awhile in the quiet of buzzing bees and the far-off cry of a mourning dove, sounding like an echo of itself. From time to time a fragment of conversation passed between them: "The boys—they must be getting big now." "Oh, so big. Hardly boys any more." Kitty would be there until evening and talk would grow when it was ready. Meanwhile she felt the sun soak like warm rain through her clothing to her skin. Behind the house she glimpsed the tulip bed that edged the driveway, and to her half-closed eyes its yellows, purples, and whites ran together blearily. Beautiful, she thought, and opened her eyes to see the colors separate again. Putting down her coffee, she pushed herself out of her chair. "As if my own gardening isn't enough," she said, stamping each foot on the flat stones like someone preparing for work, "those tulips of yours really get my gardener's blood up. Have you a place for me to spade? Is there any transplanting I can do?"

"Say, relax," he said. "I pay to have my spading done. I don't wait around for my children to come and do it. What have you been doing with yourself lately, besides spading?"

"Oh, what haven't I?" she answered, sitting down again. She took a pack of cigarettes and matches from her pocket, and struck a match. "Church, art classes, garden club, little theater, to say nothing of making cookies for those two kids of mine away at school." She laughed and lit her cigarette. "And being a companion to Ralph in the evening, too. Life is just a madhouse, as usual."

"You seem to thrive on it," he said.

She smiled as if in agreement, and looked out over the yard. Nothing had changed here, she thought. The roses and perennials still grew together in one garden; annuals and vegetables in the other. Even the bees that hummed around a clump of iris would be descendants of those bees that were here when she left to get married, twenty-five years ago. She laid her head back against the cushions of her chair, and the humming of the bees seemed, even several yards distant, to become louder and louder. She jerked her head up. "This sun is a menace," she said. "I'd better go down and look at the tulips before I fall sound asleep."

II

She stood up, smoothed out the wrinkles from her dress, and walked across the lawn toward the tulip bed. On her way she stooped twice to pull up bunches of onion grass, blue-green against the fresher green of the lawn, and she held the bunches in her hand, the earth dropping from the roots as she walked along. She carried the onion grass to a trash barrel near the back porch and dropped it in. Then, brushing her hands together, she went onto the tulip bed which stretched down the driveway between this yard and that of their longtime neighbors, the Thompsons. In massed color the tulips marched straight on to the garage below. Yellow, white, purple; parrot, peony, Darwin; and she stopped and let her gaze drift along the row. Yes, they were just the way they used to be, even to the bright red clumps on either side of the garage doors. Perhaps some day she would have time to whip her own tulips into shape like this; would do it in the fall, in fact; her project for October.

She walked back to the patio intending to ask her father what feeding he gave his tulips and where he bought his bulbs, but when she sat down she saw that he was looking at her, his face turned slightly sideways, and she held back her questions. Her father had always said whatever he wished to say bluntly, without hedging, but now she felt he had drawn a breath and was waiting for just the right moment to speak. She lit another cigarette. Her father cleared his throat and let the words out, strained but clear. "Did you hear," he said, "that Mr. Thompson died?"

Kitty sat upright in her chair. "Mr. Thompson?" she said. "You mean—?" and her hand fell forward in a gesture toward the house across the driveway.

"That's right," he said. "Jim Thompson. Died two weeks ago. I've known him for over fifty years."

"Oh my goodness," she said. "I'm so sorry. Of course I knew he had been sick but . . ." She turned her eyes away from her father. Mr. Thompson had been his best friend through all those years. What could she say? She had had so little experience with death. Of all those close to her only her grandparents had died, and her mother after an automobile accident fifteen years before. "How old was Mr. Thompson?"—as unimaginative a question, she thought, as "How are you?" to someone already sick, but it brought the conversation to the safe level of facts.

"Eighty-five," her father answered. "Eighty-five years old."

"Oh," she said. "A neighbor for so long."

"Yes," he said. "Moved into that house when he was about thirty."

"Good Lord!" Kitty said. "Just think of that." She pressed her fingers on the metal arms of her chair. She possessed no handy store of words to draw on when the circumstance was death. So many of her father's friends had died in recent years. "I'm so sorry," she said again, helplessly.

She relaxed her hands and closed her eyes. The sun was very warm for May. It must be almost noon by now, and from the house she smelled cooking. Might it be chicken? Yes, her father had always liked chicken. She opened her eyes drowsily, saw ahead of her the tulips and the garage, and closed them again. The brown and buttery smell of chicken, wafting on its own little breeze out of the house, mingled with the new grass and lilac smells of spring; but today should be Sunday instead of Wednesday, and there should be a little dark-haired girl in pink dotted Swiss and socks, and patent-leather party shoes, shiny as fresh-poured tar. And she should be running down the driveway by the tulips calling, "Daddy . . ."

She opened her eyes and smiled toward her father. "Do you remember Mr. Thompson and yourself working together Sunday mornings on that first car of ours, an Overland I think it was, down in the garage?"

Her father looked at her as if she had awakened him out of a sleep. "What? What's that?" he asked.

"You remember?" she said. "You and Mr. Thompson stretched out on the floor of the garage on Sunday mornings, cursing at that car." She laughed sleepily. Two grown men and that wonderful man-sized toy. "Our first car," she repeated.

Her father's eyes blinked as if, in catching at wakefulness, he had forgotten what she had said. But how could he have forgotten? Those Sunday mornings, the two friends, their overalls splattered with oil, stretched out on the garage floor. "Hey, Jim, hand me the screwdriver." "Say, where the devil's the monkey wrench?" And over all the smell of chicken, wafting down from the kitchen. "He does not remember what I will never forget," she thought, and then her sleepy gaze tightened, firm and still,

213

on her father's face. Her father was sitting up, erect in his chair. His hands, which until a moment ago had rested inertly on the metal arms, were holding them in a steady grip; his shoulders seemed to have widened, and his eyes looked straight ahead.

Kitty watched, unaware now of the humming of the bees or the comfort of the cushions around her. All her intensity, hidden beneath the lids of her half-closed eyes, centered on her father's face. She did not move. She hardly breathed. Her father's eyes had opened from their sleepiness: how blue they were she had forgotten; the deep lines around his mouth had vanished into his face; his pale, tired cheeks were full again, and color spread over them like a faint wash. And then her father laughed, a small and distant laugh. Kitty felt herself lean forward toward him, her fingers hard against her lips. Her father was looking, not at her, but far away at something over her shoulder, and a tingling weakness poured through her, from her shoulders down through her thighs and knees. The hand with which she clutched the chair arm pinched in pain. This was her father as he had been all those years ago. This was the young face she had forgotten in the face of the old man.

As if withdrawing his eyes from what he saw behind her, her father looked at her and smiled, and it was the wide, free smile she had also forgotten.

"Sure I remember," he said, and his voice was clear, as if he had suddenly stepped out from behind a curtain. "Jim and I had quite a time together. My golly, how we used to work at that darn thing, and every Sunday morning, too."

"Yes," she said, "and I would come home from Sunday school . . ." and then she stopped speaking, to remember more: the sizzle of roasting chicken when her mother, bending over the open stove, her white apron dangling to the floor, basted it with butter; the shouting of the Thompson children, already changed from their Sunday clothes into their play clothes, as they romped in the next door yard; and she herself, still in her dotted Swiss, running down the driveway, "Daddy, Daddy. Mama says dinner in half an hour."

She took a deep breath. All those things. Did he remember? But now her father's eyes were closed and his large-veined hands rested, without strength, on the arms of the chair. Kitty felt a tingling in her cheekbones and a pressure in her throat as if she were going to suffocate. She shoved herself from her chair and stood unsteadily. She had to get away for a moment by herself, to know what had been the meaning for her of that sight of her father's young face. "Excuse me, Dad," she said. "Think I'll take another look at the garden."

"Sure," he said, without opening his eyes. "And pick yourself a bunch of tulips to take home. As many as you want."

III

Slowly she walked across the lawn, stumbling over an outcropping of stones, but she righted herself without seeming to know that the stones were there. Slowly she crossed the driveway to the tulip bed and she stood, gazing down at a planting of yellow tulips. Best that she had stopped when she had, not spoken any more about those Sunday mornings forty years ago. Best for her father to glimpse only that one scrap of the past and then perhaps to forget.

But for herself, forgetting did not come like that. Her father was old. The one split moment of youth in his face had come by grace of one quick memory, revealing him to her not as younger but, by contrast, many years older than before, and that much closer to death. Her eyes felt hot, and her throat ached as if in a muscle cramp. Her father was dying, not of sheer accident like her mother—an accident might happen to anyone, even to the young—but because after so many well-lived years death was ready for him, today, next week, another year or two, but always ready. She must try to face this fact, that even the best of men must die, her father as well as his friend, and suddenly, under the warm sun blanketing her shoulders, she shivered. She had thought that nothing had changed here at her father's house, but she was wrong. Time had changed. Forty whole years had passed since that little girl in dotted Swiss had darted down the driveway to her father, and that little girl could not return again, even in the spring.

She took a few steps along the tulip bed. Why was it, she

thought, that death for another, no matter how sad, could seem to have about it grandeur and even beauty, but death for oneself was nothing, nothing at all but an absence of life. Her steps dragged as she walked, and beneath her feet she felt the crunch of gravel. Her father had told her to pick tulips, as many as she wanted. She would do that later, to please him. But for now, slowly she bent over the flower bed and parted the clump of red tulips carefully with both hands. Stretching down until she touched the lumpy earth, she snapped a stem and slowly raised herself again. In her hand she held a tiny tulip, dwarfed and hidden by the rest. She laid it across her hand, feeling on her palm the sheen of its still unopened petals. Now, amid this very burst of growth and life, she knew what her father's look had really meant to her: that glimpse of past youth on his tired face had touched not only him, but herself as well, with greater age and closer death. Spring would come, unlocking the earth at its appointed time each year, and it would never even know when she had ceased to greet it.

She looked down at the single tulip in her hand, at the glisten of sap on its broken stem and the smooth fit of the petals, one across the other. Then, turning the tulip over and over in her hand as if she had never seen a flower before, she walked up the driveway and across the lawn, soberly and heavily, to where her father sat.

Carousel

BY RAMONA ROBINSON

ONE AFTERNOON in July, Carmelita Maria Gonzalez walked along a wide gravel path in Central Park, stopping now and then to lift one foot above the ground, dislodging a pebble that had worked its way into her soiled white sandal. She was carrying a pocket book of shiny red plastic, and lightly holding the small brown hand of her five-year-old son.

"Look, Julio," she said, letting his hand drop to point across the grass. "Another squirrel. See how he looks at us?"

Julio stood still, his enormous brown eyes fixed upon the little animal. "His nose wiggles," he said. Julio's mouth was open and moving slightly, as if he were about to smile, but was so caught up in what he was about to do that he didn't want to take the time. Suddenly he ran a few steps toward the squirrel, his arms outstretched. He stopped when the squirrel scampered away, and when he turned to his mother, his mouth was drawn down at the corners, and a scowl had settled in his forehead.

"Silly!" she laughed, her fingers softly touching the lustrous mop of black curls that covered his head. "You should know by now that you can't catch a squirrel!"

"Someday I catch a skerl and take him home. I let him sleep with me!"

Carmelita's smile disappeared as she thought of the room with the soiled dark green walls and the torn red flowered paper curtains, where on a sagging, lumpy bed, Julio slept with his two older brothers. But when she looked at his face, he was smiling. His dark, heavily fringed eyes seemed to be casting off little gleams of sunlight, and once more she was caught and held for a moment by the beauty of her son.

"Come, Julio," she said. "We walked too far today. Better go fast. It's time for supper."

She didn't really want to go home. Almost every day in the summer, she brought Julio to the park, and every time she hated to leave it. She loved the deep brown of the tree trunks against the vibrant green, and the way the sun shown so brightly through the leaves that it spilled over underneath and took away their shapes, leaving only a dazzling, crazily spotted pattern of yellow and green.

Julio loved it too. He liked to run up and down the small hills, and climb among the massive grey rocks. Sometimes he would toss small pebbles down for her to catch, and she would miss them, pretending dismay, to make him laugh.

Often, he would choose a leaf to keep. He would carry it tenderly home, and put it away with the others. He kept them in a two-year-old copy of Woman's Day, which lay on a small, scarred end table, covering the place where an obscene word had once been carved with a knife.

Today, they had come a little earlier than usual, and taken an unfamiliar path that led them far below the Eighty-First Street entrance. They were approaching an open place, and Carmelita frowned as she recognized the whining music of the Carousel.

"What's that?" asked Julio. "What's that music?"

"It's nothing," his mother said.

They passed a big clump of trees, and then Julio saw the Carousel, and the laughing children rotating slowly around its center on the backs of the gaily painted horses.

Carmelita walked faster, tugging Julio along beside her.

"Come on, Julio," she said. "We came the wrong way—I mean we should not have come so far. It's supper time."

"Look!" he shrieked. "Those children are riding the horses! Look!"

"Yes, Julio, I see," she said. "Let's hurry. Papa and Mario and Carlo will be hungry."

"Mama! Mama! I want to ride too."

"They're only make-believe horses, Julio."

"I don't care. I want to ride one. Can I?"

Carmelita felt the quarter and three pennies in the pocket of her cotton dress—enough for one quart of milk. "No," she said.

Julio looked at the children, bobbing up and down with excitement, some holding balloons of red or blue or yellow, who formed a ragged line that led to the ticket window. There was a large white sign that said "Twenty Cents."

"Please, Mama!" he cried.

"No," she said, this time a little louder.

"Those children get to ride on the horses! Why can't I?"

"Because you can't, Julio."

She walked faster, pulling Julio along with her. Behind them, there was some giggling and a sound of running feet. A boy and girl, a little older than Julio, ran past them, red-cheeked and panting.

"Last one in line's a rotten egg!" called the boy, as the girl scrambled to catch up with him. Julio watched them for a moment, and then he began to cry. At first he cried silently, looking down at his toes where they showed through his sandals, and wiping away the tears with his brown fists. Then he abandoned himself to a loud wail, and opened his hands out flat, pressing them hard into his face.

"I want to ride on the horses! I want to! I want to!" he choked. I don't ever get nothing!"

"SHUT UP! SHUT UP! SHUT UP!" she screamed.

A young man and woman, passing them on the gravel path, turned to stare.

Julio looked up at her, astounded. His face was red from crying, and there were smears of dirt mixed with the tears. He turned away and walked a few steps ahead of her, down the path. His head was bowed again, and his hands were clasped behind him, over the big tuck she had taken in the worn jeans that had been Mario's. A spot of amber-colored skin showed through the little tear in the shoulder of his red-striped T shirt.

He didn't speak again, but once or twice he looked over his right shoulder, toward the music from the Carousel.

They were almost out of the park, now. They would walk up Central Park West and turn on Eighty-Second Street, she decided, passing the Groceria on Columbus, where she would buy the milk.

Julio stopped suddenly in front of her on the path. He was staring at something on the grass. She looked and saw a small, grey squirrel, sitting erect. Its luxurious tail was thin from summer moulting, and you could see light coming through.

Julio unlocked his hands from behind his back. His eyes brightened, and he stood poised for a moment, the familiar half-smile playing around his lips. The squirrel was perfectly still. Then Julio turned away and walked on down the path toward the street. He was looking down again, and his hands hung loosely at his sides. The backs of his bare heels brushed against the deep folds in the bottom of his jeans.

"Julio! Wait!" Carmelita heard herself say.

He turned to look at her, blankly.

She took him by the hand, and they turned back the way they had come. Then they cut across the grass, walking at first, then running, toward the Carousel.

6. Fathers Look Homeward

Fiddler's Bow

EXCERPT FROM A NOVEL BY CLAUDE F. KOCH

I
T WAS his birthday. One preferred not to make too much of
birthdays at fifty, but there it was. A fact whose truth was
hidden, as was the truth in most facts. He paused on the
bridge at Fiddler's Run and shifted his book bag upon the ledge of
a weathered stone pilaster. Fifty or not, it was still a brisk two
miles from the college at St. Praeds to the old house at Fiddler's
Bow; the black water still made a fuss all out of keeping with its
volume through the snow-edged stones, as it had for winters beyond
memory; and still the trees that receded here in the sweeping arc
(giving the house its name) drew his eyes from the creek and the
road—back, back with them in an obvious gesture of invitation
that he could scarcely resist, even now when the snow was knee-
high and his boots had been forgotten in the faculty room at St.
Praeds. There were other facts to be confronted with their ac-
companying mysteries, and he awaited them—lifting his head as
if the delicious fragrance of that importuning troop of pines grew
more full the higher one stretched. He knew what was coming,
and to that purpose he has worn his derby. He presumed not to
notice the first snowballs, lobbed in feeble arcs from the other
end of the bridge. They fell like puff balls at his feet upon the
packed snow of the roadway. He thought, still looking far over
the pines toward a sky opaque as antique plate, that he could
date the children's history by the compactness of the balls and
the angle of their flight. He knew the next move, and he swung
around, counterfeiting a fierce surprise.

The child was out in the roadway now, all the expectancy of
the game glowing beyond any mere adult's comprehension in eyes
as dark as a squirrel's; her legs elastic as pipe cleaners; red boots
flaring out at the loose tops like smudged heelwings of Mercury.

And the laughter, could it have come from her, or was it the imagined voice of all the harmonious air—the approval of man, earth, and sky—of such an old dodge, such a ritual gesture? He growled in imitation of bear or bison (one no more remote than the other from Fiddler's Bow) and took a gargantuan step toward her—and then she ran, head back and stomach out and spindly knees as high as a kite, up the whole laughing road that formed the draw string of the hollow of Fiddler's Bow. Lassiter Narbeth swung the bookbag over his shoulder again and followed her, smiling. He would wish all families such a latecomer—to startle them awake when they reached that stage when there would likely be shocks, but no surprises. The sound of her was gone, and he listened with a new attention to the muffled impact of his shoes on the powdered snow—a dry, unechoing sound, like the laconic break of wood against wood. He took a sensuous pleasure in snow crystals that were picking up light from somewhere (hardly the sky, that hung behind the white trees with a dresden indifference); his mind was as free of thought as though he glanced across the familiar stars; and so the other child, the boy, who stood at the bend of the road into the trees spoke twice before he was heard.

"Dad. *They're* here!"

Narbeth stopped a yard from him and raised his head. This one balanced forward on his toes, skittish as a hare, as though one movement in this strange and unanticipated world could send him bounding; his face had the stricken fragility of young adolesence.

"Who got you up?" Narbeth asked.

"This is Dennis' jacket," the boy poked a hand out, smothered in sleeve.

"I can see that."

"But they're *your* socks."

Lassiter Narbeth held out an arm, and the boy lurched forward and swung around in its curve so that his shoulders in the outsize jacket were just under its arc. "Your orders are here, Dad," he said. "They're to Quantico and you've got a week."

"It's a federal offense to rifle the mails, Paul."

"Is it? Mom's in dutch then. I was just passing by."

"I see."

"It says to Captain Narbeth. I didn't know you were a captain."

"I hardly know it myself, Paul. Do you think I ought to hold out for more? Colonel?"

The child had a trick of tilting his head and angling glances from the sides of eyes pulled in an almost oriental manner at the corners; and in the days before the sudden stringing out of his being in a weedy adolescence, when he was a round, grinning, irish-potato-headed sort of chap (those pulled eyes with a look of earthy, sly perception), Narbeth had often the odd feeling that he was being watched by an intelligence older than himself, hidden away in the form of a rakish and disorderly small wanderer.

"What did you do today?" He tilted up the boy's chin with his forefinger, a gesture that he had known for some time that the youth was outgrowing. They were at the dead center of the Bow, where the short cut led up the hill through the pines to the old house, cutting off two hundred yards of road that turned abruptly in the trees and made a hazardous climbing bend up by the gate. This was Paul's Place in the geography of the Bow. Six years before, a noncommital functionary of the State Forestry Service had posted his yellow *Deer Crossing* sign here; for reasons, Natalie had said, known more surely to the Department than to the deer. And Paul had become a watcher here.

"What did you do today, son?" Narbeth asked again, listening for his wife's intonation in the boy's reply.

"I wrote to Dennis, and Cathie walked on the letter. Right over it. I had to use the floor; she had her Tribes on the table."

Natalie had said that he would do that—watch patiently for deer that never came—it was his nature. And, as usual with Lea's offhanded observations that shook Narbeth to his boots, he knew that she was right.

He swung around for a long look at the line of trees, the bending sky, and the road: could one at Fiddler's Bow, in the Academic Year 1942-1943, imagine violence? No birds seemed to move in that slight valley. The sporadic drone of a plane declined far beyond the trees.

"Up with you," he said; his hand in the small of Paul's back boosting him over the split-pine fence. Cathie had gone under; he saw the half-tunnel her body had made. He was over himself and knee-deep before he remembered his boots. "Oh, well," he said. "So she had her Tribes on the table again?"

"She's queer. Most girls play with dolls. Why does *she* have to have Indians?" Paul's pique was conventional. His back was straight as he labored up the hill.

They met the road again at the crest—two prolonged wheel ruts in the drifted snow—crossed it, and pushed open the black, intricately twisted and shaped gates with their outlined fiddling minstrel in wrought iron—a humorously imposing facade for the arabesques of the carpenter's Gothic gate house, set fifty yards down the path. The mansion had gone long ago, long before Lassiter and Natalie had come twenty-five years before to find a home. Its cellar hole, hidden now under layers of sumac and snow, was of such sizable dimensions that one sensed the impressive hold the dream of tenantry had along these Pennsylvania hills in post-colonial days.

And now, Lassiter thought, dropping the brass knocker against its base on the colonial half-door, the whole pattern of life had gone, and there seemed little enough stability in the world beyond the hills 150 years later. Perhaps that explained Lea's Romanism. Waiting there with expectation, even now, after twenty-five years, Narbeth pressed the child's head against his coat. He was thinking, not of the boy, but of the persistent half-joke, half-serious turn to all conversation pointing to a block or dead end: it was Lea's "Romanism." A capital joke between themselves—yet one (and here Narbeth dropped the knocker again in good-humored impatience) whose point he could never fully see. It was Lea's "Romanism" that had chosen Fiddler's Bow, that had insisted on the living room on the second floor, that had decided them on Dennis and the Marine Corps . . . It was the charmed, private name for their most cherished, illogical agreement—as it had been the name for their one major divergence, minutely compounded over the years. *Here I teach at St. Praeds and resist the pit, and you're snatched from my very arms* . . . that was the wry joke of it. He heard her steps.

Because it was his birthday, and because the orders were in that would introduce one more "retread" to the Corps, and because there should be mild drama in the air, Lassiter Narbeth held his pose on the top step, shoulders slightly round and chin thrust slightly forward, a tall man stooped to smile at the level of his wife's eyes. Paul had whirled under her outstretched arm holding the door, picking up amazing speed from a dead halt, like a dog that has discovered a can at its tail.

"I forgot my key."

Natalie sighed: "Come in, Ulysses," she said.

"That boy's talents are wasted on a human being." Narbeth stepped up and kissed his wife's head. "I hear they're in." Her hair had gone gray more quickly than his own.

"On the table—I spread them out to get used to them." She walked ahead of him to touch with her wedding band the papers on the marble-topped table at the end of the hall. She tapped the band gently against them, and turned to face him, her eyes raised no higher than his scarf.

"A week," she said. "I didn't really think they'd come." She reached up to loosen the scarf from around his neck. "What will they ever do at the college?" Her voice was musing, and not to the point, for they had discussed all this.

"They'll get some young, unmarried, female graduate student —and when I come back we'll have to sell the old place, put the children out to pasture, and go on the town."

"There was a time," she slipped an arm through his, and they entered the dining room, moving by long practice toward the sounds of internecine war in the kitchen, "when you thought differently about young, unmarried female graduate students."

"But you've taught me their power, my dear."

"Oh, now, *that's* talk."

The ceiling was high, and around the rim of it, in the generous manner of certain old homes, white crown moulding, filleted ledge upon ledge, satisfied the eye. Narbeth followed its wavy, off-white creamy surface, settling his gaze with pleasure on the place he had patched, the precise line where paint met patterned paper; they had almost brought it back, he thought, to what it might have been a hundred years ago. A tree's roots, he had heard somewhere, would not outreach its widest branches; and, pausing in the center of the dining room under candelabra they had made by dismantling a hideous hanging electric light, he thought: that was it—everything went deep at Fiddler's Bow, and if that one branch, Dennis, had not swept in his unruly, unpredictable way out, the roots would yet scarcely strive beyond the hills of the Bow. A nice fancy. Natalie had subdued the quarrel in the kitchen, and was standing at the door, her eyebrows raised. Was it in recognition of his thought?

"Well?" she said, and crossed in front of him, to fold her fingers at the window.

"That's a tidy job," he pointed to the molding, congratulating himself—it was one of the steady pleasures of the house, this continual source of self-congratulation at cabinets made, pictures hung, plants nursed. But he saw she was shaking her head and laughing, and he realized that she saw through him, and laughed himself.

"I was about to pontificate about roots, but I've changed my mind."

What was it that formed the essence of a house? Here, the full-length windows that one could step through with ease opened upon Natalie's garden: hollyhawk and alder, boysenberry, barberry, and rose—odd, padded shapes in the snow. Here, in the past spring of this very year, they had sat with the long windows swung outwards, a gesture to bring the garden in through the eyes of the house and the eyes of the mind: shape and odor and color conspiring with memory in the moments when one almost realized what it meant to say that the year was young. Through the windows, toward evening, cutting across fields and over hills from the very high school they had themselves attended, Dennis would step—some passion of the day upon him, as unsettled and unsettling, as refreshing and quixotic as the quirks of April weather in the hills. The frost on the closed pane took definite form to his sight, and Narbeth knew he had been staring past his wife's averted head. He lifted his hands, then dropped them helplessly.

The quarrel had begun again in the kitchen. It was one of the familiar sounds of the house. *Some* people have mice in the walls, Natalie would say, or a familiar ghost. Catherine's voice was pitched two tones higher than the human ear could bear: "My tribe!" she wailed, "It's a mortal sin! You did it, old Paul; Dennis'll chop you when he comes home, he'll chop you!"

"Indians in the jelly! Indians in the jelly! Sticky Indians!" Paul's voice had not the pitch; his compensation was in volume. "It sounds," Natalie came away from the window and fully into his sight and his mind, "like an ancient hawker's cry, doesn't it? *Indians in the jellies, Sang the bells of Saint Nellie's.*" She had the tilt of the head that marked Paul, but none of the children's eyes were so surely communicative.

He shot a glance quickly over his shoulder as they went into the kitchen; to catch, perhaps, a familiar movement in the snow. Down by the white, wind-laced brick wall, the figure of the garden saint, voluminously hooded in stone and capped in snow, extended a compassionate hand, reaching with the other for a stone bird perched on its shoulder.

A vine ticked against the window. Narbeth closed his hand over hers. He felt the house as turned in upon itself, withdrawn, a receding of power: of blood in the body, chlorophyll in the surrounding trees, fire in the hearth. But not, of course, of the voices of the children; they stumped the philosopher and jerked the carpet from under the poet.

"For the love of mud," he said, "let us have peace."

II

"Romanism," Lassiter Narbeth said.

"I know. But it's the only answer." The car ran best in the snow. It could always be started by the long run in gear down the hill under the tree from the gate of Fiddler's Bow, so that by the time it shot out into the clear and over Fiddler's Run, it had caught in the coldest weather. And on the occasion when the right front wheel had unaccountably become detached, it had coasted comfortably along the snow bank on the side—a much smoother ride than usual, they had all agreed. Natalie worked her chin into her muffler: "I just cannot leave the house. We'll get a dog for nights."

The sudden absence of sound in the rear seat, the alarming withholding of breath, was a distressing affirmation; and Narbeth twisted toward the children: "Now, don't get ideas—"

"The road, Las!"

"I see it," the car rocked off a snowbank. "You know I can't tolerate dogs in the house—they make me sneeze."

"Yes, but you'll be in Popocatepetl, or some other obscure place by then, and—"

"I'll sneeze if you *write* about it. And how do you know where I'll be? We don't—" but he left the phrase at that, wrestling ostentatiously with the wheel, *we don't even know where Dennis is* he would have said; but with a common reticence based upon a common regard, they could hardly speak of Dennis, except indirectly, under guises—as, to protect the eyes, one watched an eclipse from behind smoked glass. "Ah, well, if you must . . ." The breath expelled behind him; the continuing silence—this time, somehow, ecstatic—held as they came over the last hill. The town, hill- and snow-locked there, seen at the height of steeples, with the white smoke of her chimneys a gauze over brick—*no rose-red city half as old as time, perhaps, and yet a place to linger in the mind.*

The union soldier upon his pedestal in Market Square, perennially frozen in his southward stride, was a formidable, whiskered object for snowballing in the long life of the town: and Narbeth reached over his seat without a second thought to release the children to that end. The lights of the square, bulbous and cross-treed with a Victorian grotesqueness, were already on; though the sky arched, oddly luminous, through wisps of smoke with the flushed dullness of a reflected fire across pewter. As they sat, subdued by inarticulate memory, glass snapped like ice breaking; a light went out, and the traffic policeman at the far corner blew musically on his whistle.

"That's my signal," Natalie sighed. "I'll meet you at the market in an hour."

"Lea," Lassiter Narbeth laid his hand on her muff. Her wrist beneath it lacked dimension; only her watch was firm under his fingers—a hard pellet. He felt a severing chill. Her eyes widened;

she shook her head. He stepped from the car and walked around to open her door: it seemed an irrevocable act.

III

The union soldier's right arm was swung out in the direction of his bold step, and the loosely clenched hand was a gesture of rakish insouciance. Narbeth threw the car in gear: he should have been years younger. Through the rearview mirror he saw Natalie in conversation with the policeman: a firm emblem in their youth, now simply an old man in uniform directing traffic. He halted at the light, turning the mirror slightly to hold her still. The children watched at her side, like figures in a triptych. He saw her hands move; fine, deft hands; with, paradoxically, the most awkard of gestures. Hands for subtle movements among slender stems, but gestures leading to cracked plates, dented fenders. In the mirror he saw years decline to that anomaly; his breath caught. There it was: in matters within hands' reach she never blundered. Reluctantly, he drew away.

The streets were the landscape of his mind; against them Crete was measured, and the walls of Troy. Seven years at the university in Philadelphia; one year as a Johnny-come-lately lieutenant at Quantico in 1918 (he skidded at the corner of Cedar and Lime —it was late to be traveling). A freight blocked the intersection at the junction, the engine hacking, belling, a fussy steaming moment in a placid afternoon. The locomotive ground backwards. He waved to the engineer. The gates went up. Why, he hadn't actually journeyed much more in his time than the iron man on his pedestal.

Two hundred yards beyond the crossing, the entryway to the campus of The College of Saint Praeds was uncleared for wheeled traffic. A path a few feet wide, tramped down by day students, would remain between snowbanks until the thaw—but Reverend Mother President had never, since her appointment to that post five years before, permitted automobiles up the wide sweeping drive that encircled motherhouse and chapel, and touched the fronts of library, classroom buildings, and residence halls. Little at the college surprised him. It had its predictable tradition of crochets. The previous president had staked goats before Main. He drove a hundred yards farther on and came to the parking area by the hockey field. It was a ten minute walk to the President's office in Clair.

There Reverend Mother President was alone, not at her desk, but sitting in a ladder-backed chair by the bay window, facing the door, as though awaiting his coming. It was growing dark in Clair, and her wimple shone on the edge of the lone light from her desk lamp. Her face was as anonymously alive in the shadows as that of a figure in a Dutch renaissance canvas.

"So," she said, "Dr. Narbeth. I knew someone would come."

IV

She gestured to a shadowy armchair, her large hand swinging out of the sleeve of her habit like a sudden dim dove in flight, settling at rest on her lap. He sat, gingerly adjusting his damp trouser legs.

"I'm sorry to track this in, Reverend Mother," he sighed. "Six years ago I could have stepped right off there at the door."

She inclined her head: "Offer it up."

He smiled. It was the reply he wanted. The lights went on in the corridors beyond the open door off to his left. He heard many quick steps on the stairs, voices moving up the scale, and then a counterpoint of laughter—the most familiar association of sounds at St. Praeds. They sat for the moment in silence. She was a great, knobbly woman, treelike, he always thought—wherever she sat or stood she seemed to root; her black habit fixed like a giant bole, she had the resistance to outside influences of an old plane tree. Her grace did not lie in her physical appearance, but in her detached, unhurried, limitless capacity to attend and to advise in a curiously soft, coaltown brogue. For her few friends (Narbeth had come to know) she had no advice except that one laconic phrase. Among her friends, her humility was sounded.

"What do you mean, you knew someone would come?" he asked.

She leaned forward again, rigidly erect from the waist: "I have a feeling for journeys, Dr. Narbeth."

It was a slight and touching deception; when had Lea phoned?

"Well, there you are. My orders are in. Though we didn't really believe they would come. The Marine Corps must be desperate."

"Then you haven't heard from Dennis?"

How quickly she got to the heart of it. "No," Narbeth waited while steps hesitated at the office door, then passed on, "but the Corps is such a small organization. I'll surely be in touch with him, sooner or later."

"And Natalie?" Her eyes were half-closed, her ungainly face pinched distressfully in the wimple. There was a slight accusation in her voice: "All of the male professors will be leaving, sooner or later. It will be a bland pudding here. All the salt gone."

"No one to keep the Faith."

It did not rest lightly between them, as old banter should. Against the black immobility of her body, the nun's hands lay upon her beads with so hesitant a movement of thumb and forefinger over them as to seem an absent gesture. In a moment of wretched quiet, Lassiter Narbeth raised his chin from his clasped hands and saw the indefinitely shadowed, blending lines of her unprepossessing face: a face long taken for granted, now a face strange to him. She had taught his wife before their marriage, and had encouraged him to come to St. Praeds as a young instructor after it; she had certainly been an instrument toward his wife's Catholicism (reversion, as they said between themselves); and had, no doubt, thought long of himself in that respect—though he could not be sure of that, so successfully did she maintain her reticence.

Yet these matters seemed, as he thought of them now, to bear not at all upon what was unplumbed in the stream of their acquaintanceship—but to touch it obliquely, oddly, as long-legged flies crease a standing pool. How her face, like her body, seemed indifferent to design, to the details by which one took pride in distinguishing oneself. It came to him with the urgency of cock-crow, like a third warning, demanding his denial for his own survival, that she strove to obliterate herself and indeed had done so for as long as he could remember, though he had not suspected before the way of it. It was not self-sacrifice in an ordinary sense, nor even charity, but a lack of self-regard such as one might assign to the arc of firs, to the spring road, to Fiddler's Bow itself.

While a battering freight clamored into the junction fifty yards beyond the bay window, shaking the shade of the desk lamp to a nervous disturbance of the light and jarring the small wooden statue of St. Praed on the desk, he rubbed his hand across his eyes like a sleeper awakening. The anonymity of the face was no illusion then. How much of what might have shown there had he taken to himself? Was this one of the conditions upon which the harmony of his life depended? For the space of a breath he was frightened; he had never thought of himself as unduly demanding.

"We will take care of Natalie," she said, as though Natalie were her charge as an undergraduate still, "and the children. Your leaving . . . well, we must simply offer it up."

"I will not attempt to thank you." He thrust himself to his feet.

She lifted a deprecating hand and he took it between his own, resisting the ridiculous impulse to raise it to his lips, and gave instead a purposeful, uncharacteristic handshake. Another train shattered the decorum of the moment, and he overcarefully steadied the statue of St. Praed before he left the room.

They were crossing the bridge at Fiddler's Run when Natalie, in her most indirect manner, made her comment on his silence:

"She's a dangerous woman, isn't she?"

"What? Who?" He was sternly obtuse.

"You know very well. She's one of God's spies."

"Now what kind of nonsense is that?"

"No nonsense, dear. She makes me see myself. She's one of God's spies."

"Romanism." Lassiter Narbeth's voice could not possibly disturb the children dozing in the back seat.

Dougherty

BY VINCENT PATRICK

DOUGHERTY stepped out of the mid-morning sun into Hogan's and settled himself on a stool halfway down the deserted bar. Hogan's was cool and dim, silent but for the slurping sounds of Fat Timothy, hunched over his morning coffee at the corner table. Dougherty extracted his handkerchief and searched for a clean spot, then closed his eyes and softly patted his brow and neck until the dizziness wore off. It would be best to spend the noon hour indoors, he thought; an old man didn't belong on the streets of New York in August. He shifted his stool carefully until his elbows lay comfortably on the bar. Perhaps the afternoon too should be spent away from the sun, and if he was sure to get home before the girls he could sleep through the evening; they shouldn't be so angry as to wake him. Even in the morning, he thought, he could feign sleep until they left for work. Oh, it would work out well. They would push and tug at him in the morning, but it would be easy enough to snore and bury his head in the pillow. By tomorrow evening they would have calmed down and the whole matter of his little spree blown over. The Social Security check was half gone and that was that; women of forty must realize that their shouting wouldn't bring it back. He relaxed; the day would work out well.

Timothy rapped the bar and leaned close to Dougherty's face. "Are you looking right through me, John?" he asked. "Or are you dreaming?"

Dougherty stared for a moment, then saw that it was Timothy and said, "I've been deciding what to have. Pour me a bit of bar rye, Timothy, with a little water on the side." He gulped the shot down without tasting it. "It's a nice bar whiskey you serve, Timothy," he said, and nodded toward the bottle for another. He sipped at the drink. "Even before your time, when Hogan was here, he always served a nice, mild bar whiskey. He'd permit nothing else."

Timothy nodded. "Looking at your eyes I'd guess you've been on a binge, John," he said.

"Are me eyes that bad?" Dougherty asked. He massaged them with his fingers—too hard, for the dizziness returned and with it a hum in his ears so that Timothy's voice seemed distant.

"Look at yourself in the mirror, John. You'd do better with something to eat and a long sleep."

Dougherty stared at the blur of bottles that covered the mirror. Each one slowly took form and wobbled on its base to a standstill. He studied the face that appeared between the rows of bottles. Drawn and nearly toothless, hair gray and uncombed, but every bit of it there, the nose that had been broken so long ago in this very bar now swollen and infected with uncut hairs protruding from the nostrils. He rubbed his palm across the stubble of his cheek and watched the hand in the mirror shift, cover first the mouth and then fall to pinch the loose skin on the neck. Something droned. He thought that it must be Timothy's voice, but couldn't concentrate, for the hand in the mirror had his attention. It was his hand, of course, but not his *own* hand; it belonged with the old face that nestled in behind the bottles. He didn't know where the hand would move, surprised when it felt at the nose and brushed back the thick hair. The hand disappeared. Dougherty squinted for a moment, confused, then looked down at the bar and saw his hand wrapped around the shot glass. He avoided looking at Timothy, who now stared at Dougherty, silent, his heavy arms hanging limply against his apron. "He has been talking to me," thought Dougherty, "and I've given him no response."

"Are you all right, John?" Timothy asked softly.

Dougherty looked into the round face. "Of course I'm all right," he said, and swallowed the last of his whiskey. "I'd thank you to fill my glass, Timothy. I get enough worrying and nagging at home."

"Have the girls been at you, John?" Timothy asked. He filled the glass and brushed back the money with his hand.

A free drink? Could this, then, be his third shot? Dougherty tried to go over his actions since he had entered Hogan's but couldn't recall the number of drinks. Timothy had asked about the girls; he had better answer this time or he would likely be refused service and sent home. "Ah, they treat me like an infant," Dougherty said. "The two of 'em without husbands and only me to nag at all day. Anne never would have put up with it."

II

Never. Anne would remind them of their duty to him—were she here. Were Anne only here to shout as she had when the girls were very young. They would listen now as they had thirty-five years ago when Anne raised her voice and wagged her finger in their faces. Jesus, he was entitled to some pleasure and freedom now, though the girls didn't think so. Nor, for that matter, did the young new priests who seemed to hear a man's confession without listening and didn't use a man's first name when giving a penance. "Ten Hail Mary's and ten Our Father's," they mumble, like reading something from a book. Father Scanlon now—when he was alive a man walked out of confession feeling light on his feet. Dougherty breathed deeply and remembered the long-gone confessions to Father Scanlon, remembered the smell of pipe tobacco on the old priest's cassock. When the girls were very small and very sweet . . . He folded his hands on the bar and leaned forward; he could hear the old priest's soft voice again.

"You say you've been fightin', John?"

"Aye, Father. Just last night in Hogan's. You may have heard the paddy wagon clanging by the rectory."

The confessional grew quiet but for the slow wheezing of the priest. Dougherty shifted his weight on to one knee. The wooden platform squeaked.

"It's every Friday night yer fighting and drinking, John."

"Aye, Father," he mumbled, and bent his head a bit lower.

"Did they lock you up, John?" the priest asked.

"Just for the night, Father. I'm on me way home now."

The priest wheezed. "And thinkin' of what you'll tell Anne, no doubt. I expect she'll be by to see me this afternoon to have me talk to you. What is it I should say to her, John?"

237

Dougherty shook his head at the dark screen. "I don't know, Father," he said, thinking, "Doesn't he know how me head hurts? I should have slept first and then made the confession." The priest finally spoke and Dougherty sighed. "You've got a fine wife," Father Scanlon said, "and the girls aren't infants any longer. They're eight and nine years old, grown enough to understand you've been out drinkin' and fightin'. I want you to say five rosaries, John. Kneel and look at the altar and say the Sorrowful Mysteries, and think of how Christ suffered for you without once striking out at his tormentors. Now give me a good Act of Contrition and spend this evening with yer family."

Dougherty lowered his head and spoke slowly. "Oh, my God, I am heartily sorry for having offended Thee . . ."

Timothy shook his shoulder. Dougherty looked up, confused. He saw the white apron and the huge, ornate cash register surrounded by bottles. "Pour me another, Hogan," he said. "And have one with me, it's pay day and Anne will faint from shock if I don't spend part of me check." He laughed and drained his glass.

"It's me, John," Timothy said, "it's Timothy."

Dougherty stared. The fat red face came into focus. Where the hell had Hogan gone to? And Father Scanlon? No matter now; his confession was made and he could relax. He nodded toward the bottle, impatient with Timothy, who stared helplessly and looked about to cluck like a mother hen.

Dougherty listened to the gurgling of the whiskey as it filled his glass. It seemed too loud for such a little bit of liquid. So much more like the gurgling of a brook as it flows over small rocks on a warm Sunday afternoon. A winding brook with a healthy young man and his two little daughters running beside it, screeching and laughing at nothing.

Timothy shook him from behind. "Time to go home, John, you've had enough." Dougherty pushed at the fat hands, asking, "Why aren't you behind the bar, Timothy? You belong behind the bar."

"Can't you see you've had too much, man?" the bartender shouted. "The girls will blame me. You don't look well, John; please go home."

238

Dougherty started to rise. He propped his arms on the bar and slowly lifted his weight off the stool. His heart skipped a beat and he coughed—a deep, slow, rumbling cough from the chest. He leaned far over to the nearest cuspidor, thinking, "It isn't the booze that's been making me dizzy." The shiny brass bowl moved from beneath his head. He twisted his neck to follow it, but the whole floor started to tilt, the yellow globe like a pendulum moving farther and wider with each stroke. He toppled off the stool, his head moving in an arc until it smashed against the foot rest.

The room filled with clouds of cigarette smoke that swirled around his head. The smoke drifted up through a circle of faces too hazy to identify. Terry O'Shea's voice came through the noise and smoke, urging, "Up Johnny boy, on yer feet. On yer feet and you'll beat him yet," but Dougherty's nose hurt so that it must surely be broken and Anne would later use the disapproving face while she bathed the crooked nose. If they would let him rest here on the sawdust, he would be fine. Let Burke grin and clench his dirty fists, what does it matter? Anne's gentle fingers would be his later and Burke forgotten while she comforted and kissed the bruised knuckles. The girls too would feel at his nose, asking, "Who hurt your nose, Daddy?" and he would laugh and slap their behinds gently, telling the little one to put on some bloomers and cover her backside. What would that hulk of a Burke know of this? Of a soft mattress moving in a darkened room where breezes filled the curtains and whispers stopped with lips and fingers. A man's family who only waited for him to come home and kiss them all, his three lovely ladies. But now he was being pushed to his feet, strong fingers pressing beneath his armpits. The crowd faded until only Fat Timothy was left, holding him up, their faces nearly touching.

"Are you all right, John? That's a nasty lump on yer forehead."

III

Dougherty swayed between Timothy's heavy arms. The rows of bottles in front of the mirror pitched toward Dougherty, then rolled away from him. His image danced behind the bottles. He rubbed his fingers over the lump on his forehead. The whiskey wasn't causing the dizziness, he thought; he was tired. A bed. To lie across the soft mattress and stare at the ceiling of the cool, familiar room where each piece of furniture knew him. Undisturbed. Old, dry skin able to relax between sheets that had been shared with Anne. To see her face and the faces of the children —so much clearer than the grown girls. To be a part of those faces—of the thin, bony arms that wrap around a man's neck and pull his head from the evening paper . . . My daddylove, who hurt your nose?

He pushed at Timothy's arms and staggered to the street. The voice behind him was a far-off buzz. His head throbbed in the glare of sunlight from the heated sidewalks. Long lines of telephone poles wavered and escaped him when he reached out for support. Only the gray, clapboard house remained still, until he climbed the wooden porch and then it reeled beneath him. The key found the lock. He fell forward through the door onto his hands and knees in the narrow hall. His arms reached up and circled the rungs of the banister, pulled the thin body erect, then up the stairs until he reached the bedroom, where only the white curtains moved, billowing across the bed.

He lay face down, breathing deeply of the warm air and listening to his heart beat. The bed seemed to vibrate from it; to groan from the fast, steady pounding. The movement of the mattress upset Dougherty; he pushed his body up to a sitting position, thinking, "I'd better have a look at the little ones. Anne will have a fit if I'm too stewed to look in on the girls." He rose from the bed and stumbled into the hall. Everything was too bright again; he could see only the strong, white light. He groped with his hands until he reached the girls' room; there the light dimmed and he could open his eyes fully. He looked around the room for the little ones. The girls' room was empty—the bed carefully made and no toys in sight. Dougherty saw them for a moment as grown-ups standing half a head taller than he, saying, "Oh papa, not again." He turned from them and looked to the bed. The little ones were there, covers held tight around their necks, giggling up at him. "Kiss us goodnight, daddy," they said, and Dougherty strode across the room, careful to avoid the doll carriage. He sat on the double bed and pinched at their noses. "Who's yer best boy-friend, tell me," he asked. They squeezed his thick hands. He bent to kiss them, but felt only the warm sheet against his face. The smell of soap and toothpaste vanished and he rose, confused for a moment, then ran for his bedroom. He eased himself onto the bed and lay on his back, relaxed; the room was cool and settled; heavy brown furniture that belonged where it was. The girls would be fine now that he had kissed them and smoothed their covers. In the morning he could sleep; Anne would see to that.

The old man dozed, breathing slower and letting his eyelids flutter so that he saw himself in the vanity mirror as a series of flashes—now here, now gone, hazy and colorless. The house is safe and the little ones dreaming. The bit of drinking means nothing if a man does what's needed in a house. Anne can shout now and then, but she knows what a man must do and what his needs are as well. The children safe and his confession well-made with a good penance—now he could rest. The reflection darkened, blurred . . . the furniture, too, receded. Only the bed seemed real now. His fingers pressed into the soft mattress, rubbed the sheets, then held them tightly. He clutched at the mattress. The bed was real. And the image of the tiny, sleeping faces in the next room.

7. Orange Blossoms
in the Dust

Roman Spring

BY OCTAVIA WALDO

UMBERTO PETRANGELO waited beneath a red and white striped awning in the Piazza Bologna—his blue gabardine coat patched black over his broad shoulders and chest from the March rain falling against him. Now and again he thrust his left arm upward to examine the watch on his wrist, and as if not trusting what it told him, he lowered his ear to it. Tick-tock-tick—through the tuft of gray-black hair imbedded there like steel wool plugged into a hole. Tick-tock-tick— until his brain was satisfied. It was four o'clock.

The rain fell like a cascade of pine needles over Rome. Rain —thirty days of it. It marked the interlude between winter and spring, and spring was late in coming. There was nothing to do about it but wait. There is nothing to do about most things that are late in Rome, whether it be an appointment, or a bus, or a promise. Or even hope.

Traffic swept swiftly on wheels through the piazza, splashing the rain from the streets upward as if attempting to send it back where it came from. Someone sang, "The rain will end tonight," to the tune of "I'll never smile again," and someone else chanted, "Spring is fickle, the bitch," and still another called, "God is making water over the pilgrims. Some baptism!"

Petrangelo laughed to himself. He was a man in his mid-fifties, short, with a ruddy look about him. In one large fist he carried a miniature bouquet of blue-purple violets, their little heads drenched with rain. He had held them upward all this time. "Eh, what does it matter?" Petrangelo laughed over them. "Wet or not, they bring good fortune." He gave them a sound shaking. Good fortune! A touch of it hurt no one, and judging from Signora Maxwell's last letter, she could do with more than a touch.

"Waiting for a loved one?" a woman laughed, pointing to the

bouquet as she passed by; and he called after her, "Eh!" His mouth wrinkled in an expression of whimsy. "People of my age are too old to wait for love. Either they have it, or they don't." He tipped his soggy hat after her; rain poured from its brim like milk from a pitcher.

This was not a good day for Ruth and Adam Maxwell to return to Rome, he thought. Adam hated rain. His mood was bound to reflect it.

"Excuse me," he said to a Roman standing next to him. "The bus coming up from Naples—is it late?"

"What do I know? I?" The man pointed all ten of his grubby squat fingers to the pit of his chest, and shrugged his shoulders and his brows to the sky. "Him!" He pointed one finger through the rain to a red, ripped sweater and patched blue jeans that hovered over the gutter, splashing large G.I. shoes into the river that curbed the sidewalk. "Ask him. He should know. He's here all the time." In and out the G.I. shoes splashed. Up and down nodded a very round head, balanced on the tender thread of a skinny neck. Back went the head. Eyes gazed at the sky as if in all this world of Rome they knew nothing more beautiful. Rain sluiced against this beaten frame of a man, poured into his mouth like water gushes from the mouth of a fountain. If he knew when the bus would come, he couldn't tell it. He had no tongue.

Petrangelo made a pained face. "Ass!" he said to the man next to him. "Ass! What kind of joke do you think you're playing?" Incensed, he walked across the street grooved with trolley tracks to the café in the center of a tiny green island, surrounded by rain water. He let himself inside the warm smell of steamed coffee and sweet chocolate. He could watch the bus stop through the glass doors of the café. He could see the piazza from there— the square as he knew it through Ruth Maxwell's drawings: the post office to one side standing a story high, proud and modern, flaunting its new lines before everyone like an adolescent. It was still too new a structure to mind the rain. Other buildings were not so fortunate, and like elderly ladies they tried to make up for their mottled vanity with a striped awning here and there. A bright light. A geranium, like a vermilion sun, glowing in a window.

246

He recognized the plane trees in the center of the square from one of Ruth's paintings—not bathed in sunlight, but badly in need of it. Their limbs, tired of begging to a sky that would not hear, had drooped over the flat roof of the café and over the empty benches, making an ineffective canopy for people to pass beneath. The old men in berets and sandals, reading newspapers in Ruth's drawings, had abandoned the square; and not even a shadow of a child playing hoop and ball haunted the rain. Petrangelo's eyes followed the sweep of the major *via* curving the piazza. He saw the seven smaller *vie* departing from it for separate points in perspective, like rival siblings leaving home. And he knew with an understanding based on a skilled and analyzing eye that from above, from the arched windows and balconies, from the roof tops, and higher still from where the rain began, the square looked like a huge spider that had lost a leg and could not move because of it.

Silently he appraised the square, his storeroom of a brain drawing from one remembered sketch and another and still another to make his waiting more meaningful. It was like meeting a childhood acquaintance after having heard every detail of his secret self from a friend in common. Yet Petrangelo had passed through this square countless times, accepting it as just another landmark in his life. He had taken it for granted; while Ruth had had to learn about it as she had had to learn Italian: slowly, cautiously, focusing her eye to the tones of faded color, as she had tuned her ear to the subtle nuances of speech.

But Ruth had added something to her drawings that in fact did not exist in the piazza—something of herself: a touch of surprise, a mood of loneliness, an unqualified fear. All of them, perhaps, and perhaps none of them, Petrangelo thought. All of them and more composed the clay that had formed her. There was no denying her gifts. She was young, of course; but her skills equaled and surpassed those of many of his older students at the *Accademia*. They surpassed Adam's too, but Adam had a whip inside him, and so far as Petrangelo could see, Ruth had only an ambition. A quiet ambition. In his thoughts he applauded her, and he remembered her smile—a hesitant brilliance, disarming because *that* no one could take for granted. If his own child had lived—but what was the use of thinking the impossible? The war had claimed his daughter and the war was a long while over and done. He didn't want to think of the war. Four years were enough time for a man to look back and recognize the ending of that nightmare. It was all he wanted to know of it now. "Period," he said aloud, and turning toward the bar, he ordered an *espresso*.

He tried to conjure up some image of Ruth Maxwell; but his was a common failing. The more he felt for a person, the less he could narrow his vision to one aspect, one face, one quick mental snapshot. The fault intruded into his work; it sent him pondering over endless studies in charcoal and plaster and iron, always goading him to delve deeper and deeper into a problem. In the end people and sculpture were essentially the same to him. He wanted to do right by both.

He drank his coffee.

With Adam Maxwell, however, Petrangelo had no problem. His mind dictated, "Adam Maxwell, age twenty-four, husband to Ruth. A boy who wants to go to the top. As if the world had a top!"

"Ah," Petrangelo put down his cup. He put Adam down too, in his mind, and tapped his spoon against his saucer for an encore of coffee. Principally, Petrangelo thought, Adam learned about life through books, and he learned about painting that way, too. "Well, life is not so simple," he'd told Adam once over a cognac. "One can't go about collecting and selecting from the printed page. There comes a time for the human being to involve himself in his work. Look," he said, holding up his wide hand with its five scarred fingers spread apart, "there are five major political parties in Italy today, not to mention all the smaller parties just beginning to hatch. There could easily be twenty-five times that number."

"We fought a war to get rid of a couple of them," Adam had said.

"You didn't fight it alone." Petrangelo's dark stare had questioned Adam closely, silently: the long muscular body hunched over the counter, the brooding face with its indelible shadow of a shave like a tattoo over his lower jaw. And a furrowed forehead that made Romans label him "a serious American."

"But you were never at war," Petrangelo had said.

"I was at school," Adam had said, swallowing his cognac with the urgency of a man killing pain with drink.

"You learned a lot about our war, I suppose?"

"We couldn't avoid it."

Petrangelo had nodded his head. "Living," he had said, "like studying, needs a little practice." He had tapped Adam's shoulder in a gesture of friendship, and had felt him shrink beneath his touch and icily move away. He had reminded Petrangelo of a man whose boyhood was confined to games of single prowess: to swimming, to weight-lifting, perhaps to tennis, where the threat of one man's physical contact with another was kept to a minimum.

"Tell me," Petrangelo said to the waiter behind the bar, "the bus from Naples—when does it get here?"

"When it feels like it," the waiter laughed. "These private lines are made to suit the moods of the bus drivers." He clucked his tongue, and Petrangelo resumed his vigilant post at the door. Few people stirred in the piazza. The doors to the post office, of heavy glass, attracted no one. As if by order of Senatus Populesque Romanum, people stayed away when it rained. The tiny awnings jutting out from shops and stores in stripes of colors looked like the abandoned entrances of circus tents. Nothing but increasing darkness and the never-changing descent of rain visited the square. March was capricious. March was all woman.

II

March.

Orange groves.

The smell of the wisteria.

A cobbled walk that goes up and up and at the peak undulates to a by-path of pine groves; and the smell of lemons; and the beating sun, everywhere.

This is what they left behind them for rain. Solid masses of rain, broken only by tall buildings and pulled-up collars and black umbrellas—silk and cotton, new and patched. From the street these fabric domes blocked the view of the sky. To people looking out past them from inside the bus, they blocked the view of the city.

All the way from Naples to Rome, Adam and Ruth Maxwell sat, side by side, not touching. In Ruth's mind and on her tongue there were many things to say, but these thoughts stayed with her in private conversation until she was not sure whether she had or hadn't said them aloud.

To her left, glazed Roman eyes stared at her, "undressed her," she thought. No use making a scene. She turned her face to Adam and to the steamed window where his head rested. Through finger streaks on the window pane she could see the rain. "Why did Turner like mist?"

"Who?"

"Turner. He liked mist. He'd have liked this."

"This isn't mist."

"I can pretend," she said.

He shook his head slowly, snickered a little. "Baby, you're bats," he said.

"That's me." Her oval face was a flush of embarrassment and giggles.

They could still joke a little. A laugh now and then; it broke the silence, if nothing else. But her laughter continued far too long. A nervous laughter—it told too much about her. Better stop, she warned herself.

"La gioventu!" sighed a generous mouth on a man's skin-pocked face. "La gioventu!" with a smile from the seat across the aisle.

"So I'm young," Ruth wanted to snap at him. It was damn hard to be twenty-one, damn hard with people taking advantage at every turn, and letting you know you were too young to know better, and even if you did know better, you hadn't fermented long enough in the bitter yeast of life to attract more than, "Wait a bit. Wait till you're on the aging side of life."

"You mean one has to metal some in one's own juices to get a proper perspective," she always felt like saying, and she could just hear the sour retort, "Youth! It has imagination, and a certain insight. But life isn't what you think."

What was the use? Her head was heavy with sleep. But sleep had been taking a vacation from her; as if she were a pariah, it visited her too infrequently, and then only out of unavoidable duty. But the man across the aisle had not been talking about her.

The sleeping children in the front seats had wakened, and now their mother hovered over them, changing their diapers.

"You like?" the man said to Ruth. "Babies. You like?"

"Yes, I like." She turned her head away. She wasn't looking for a Roman stud. But an old wound in Ruth's chest opened sharply, quickly, and closed. "Damn him, damn Romans, for seeing too much."

"Are we almost there?" she asked Adam with forced enthusiasm. She would try to be happy about this trip. They were, after all, returning home. Their home away from the States, and in the States they had no home. Home. Her own sheets—American percale—not Italian linen, and her own towels, terry cloth, warm. She was tired of linen, tired of ornate embroidery, tired of tastes Italian. She thought with pleasure of the baths she would take whenever she desired a bath, with no one to question, "Do you have skin disease? Too many baths, you know, are bad for you— they dry the skin." Even the gas tank on the wall over her bath, which she would have to light with a match, and which would grumble and groan while the water trickled through the tap, seemed an incredible luxury to her now. Yet she did not delude herself; there was nothing in Rome awaiting her that had not awaited her in Capri, in Naples, in Pescara, on the Riviera. With cruel accuracy, Ruth's mind uncovered the shelters of her make-believe life. With cruel accuracy, it reminded her that she had been making believe for one year and eight months. But she turned her attention away. "Are we almost there?"

"Almost, Ruthie," Adam said. The nickname fell from his dry lips like a yellowed and crackly loveletter falling from its hiding place in a book. And falling as it did, unexpected, she looked upon its return with hesitancy. Don't look back, her mind warned her. Don't lose this thread of the present—it's too tentative; but her thoughts forged ahead, away from hearing the futile admonishments to protect herself. Her eyes traced Adam's profile against the window glass—bronzed from Capri's sun, the pointed features shone like glazed terra cotta. It was an angular face given to softness around the jaws. Adam liked food; he liked good food; he liked it served with decorum. Likes leave their marks on a face, Ruth thought.

Adam's eyes were closed, but he wasn't sleeping, although he had rolled his scarf for a cushion and had propped it between his head and the window. His black hair, streaked red from the sun, was thick with tight waves.

The quickly dimming darkness of late afternoon cast its incisive shadows upon Adam, and Ruth saw his face in another time—not as it was now, but as it would be: drawn and robbed of the sun's glow, the long sideburns, white over his coarse skin. It was not the first time her eyes played this deceptive game. But today she knew a bewildering pain as she wondered if she would see this face she had conjured up; if, indeed, she would know it and love it. She reprimanded herself for the habit of drawing from the past and projecting into the future. Few artists, of course, would deny doing this in their work. But this was not work facing Ruth; it was flesh, human flesh, created out of life, not out of pigment and a limited imagination. Still, Ruth could not deny, it was the present that overwhelmed her. It was the present she had trouble holding on to, the present, far more than death and the after-life, that she could not face.

Adam's hands rested flat against the tweed flanks of his legs. Strong hands, with thumbs like a fifth finger on each, and paint filling the cuts and cracks of his skin. "I wish I weren't a coward," Ruth thought, slipping her right hand under his left. With palms meeting, the fingers found their own way to fold their touch together, and merge an obedience made of silence and an unwillingness to ransack their relationship. The lazy pattern of living had reinstated itself, had returned an assuagement made of compromises and complacency. It had made things safe again between them.

Outside, horns blasted. Children and men and priests on bicycles dispersed with splashes the rain gathered in pools in the street. Inside the bus, people could not hear the shouts from the outside.

The bus driver cursed loudly, intending his blasphemy for the policeman he had splashed a few seconds before. The rain was too much for him. It was too much for everyone. It was like this all the way from Naples, all the way through the Via Appia, where only the cypress trees, an occasional team of oxen, and the soggy straw huts broke the monotony of the monumental sound that roared down from the mountains and was swallowed up by the earth.

The bus come to a jolting stop. "Eh-eh," protested the people. "Do you think we are animals?" The bus driver made a gesture with his hand and forearm.

"*Maleducato scimo!* You poorly educated fool!" cried a woman. She carried two white live chickens in a covered basket.

The bus driver made another gesture, this one with a deliberately slow sweep of the hand under his chin to signify that nothing could interest him less.

The doors opened to the Piazza Bologna. The bus driver dismounted first into the rain. After him followed the woman with her high shrieking voice, scolding him to the accompaniment of fluttering white feathers and the irate cackle of hens. But the bus driver had ears only for the small voice that came from under an umbrella. It told him the results of the nation's lottery. He had eyes only for a mug of steaming liquid which someone handed him.

Inside the bus, people pushed to the exits. *"Eh-eh! Attenzione.* Keep your hands to yourself! My husband will kill you! What do you take me for, anyway?"

Ruth Maxwell wrapped the oilcloth coat around her and preceded her husband to the door. They had waited till last. Adam Maxwell rounded his body with the weight of bundles and bags and paint boxes, labeled with sunshine labels of Capri, and attentively followed Ruth. "Be careful, Ruthie," he said.

The repetition of her pet name in his mouth made her order her steps. Two delicate and precise steps down. She thought, "Delicate steps with a size nine shoe. American milk-fed hoofs. Italians never heard of such grotesque feet." And precise was hardly the word to describe her nature. Suddenly two disfigured hands touched her sleeve to assist her, and Ruth shuddered beneath a polite smile. "Hello," she said to the round head and the round open mouth in which no tongue lived. "Hello," while

253

memory told her that everyone called him *Lo Storto*, the crooked one. He held the door for her as he held it for everyone, and through this square aperture of bus, silently, he opened Rome to her face. She felt a shiver go through her as she stepped into the rain. She did not look back. She knew Adam was fumbling through his pockets for aluminum coins stamped with grapes and the lire sign to give to Lo Storto. Adam could be counted on to do a thing like that, just as he could be counted on never to give a lire to the church.

She saw Lo Storto's smile and the innocent admiration of his eyes. Admiration for Adam. A look of dignity through which one man accepts his lot and rises above it to equal any man—for who in Rome has not suffered?

The crowd was thick in the piazza. People kissing on both cheeks. Umbrellas bouncing like black parachutes. The cackling hens and the flying feathers. The endless welcome caught within a close embrace—within a whispered word. Welcome to the tune of laughter and tears and sobs like pain. Welcome. This time it was for her. "Eh, Ruth Maxwell. Eh, Ruth and Adam Maxwell!" She recognized the agile speed of Petrangelo's body, weaving his way toward her—the little bouquet of violets waving like a blue and purple tweed tassel in the air; and the months that had removed her from Rome suddenly closed with the warmth of his hands upon hers, while the tassel of Roman superstition passed from his touch into her gloved palms. "Violets. They bring good fortune," he laughed over his shoulder, while his hands tapped their welcome against Adam's upper arms.

"What's happened to spring?" Adam said.

"Oh, spring has been crawling through Rome like a beaten whore. But she'll settle down soon. These women, you know, are like babies, they have to be housebroken." He stopped to help Adam with his bags. "It looks as if you have had a productive trip," Petrangelo said.

"Not bad," Adam said. "Twenty canvases."

Petrangelo gave a little whistle. "Excuse me if that's a little."

"It's enough for a show."

The words took Petrangelo by surprise. He scanned Adam's

face in the rain. The black stare beneath Adam's thick brows and the preoccupied frown encised with white lines on his sun-kissed forehead told Petrangelo nothing. "Are you thinking of having a show? Is that it?" Petrangelo asked.

"Yes," Adam said.

"But are you ready? For a show?" Petrangelo said.

A taxi swished by and showered them with the street's filthy flood, and Ruth said, "Hell, all over my stockings," and Adam snapped his fingers after the cab, lifting his voice to hail it. He deflected from this mission for a brief second, just long enough to say to Petrangelo, "I am ready," and continued his finger-snapping and calling until the taxi stopped and retraced its course to them. But Adam's words had left their mark on Ruth's face. Clearly, she had heard them for the first time. Her eyes narrowed themselves as they always did when she expected words that would exclude her. It was as if she were guarding against possible pain by drawing them near-shut—as if no disturbance now could enter these blue slits and find the way to her heart. She held the violets to her nose and smelled the rain. But her eyes were narrowed still, although her face tried to smile, tried to accept the better side of things. "Poor baby," Petrangelo thought. "She must have been a hurt child."

They settled themselves inside the cab with their bundles stacked beneath a black oilcloth tent on the roof. And the cab took off. From both its sides enormous wings of water soared upward to touch the iron gates of lonely villas lining a labyrinth of empty, winding streets. In the dim light of late afternoon rain, colors glowed with their natural brilliance. Sepia and cerulean, thallium and viridian, orange and pink—there was no sun to unify them, no glare to disturb their true identity. The medlar tree held it own pure green sacred. The cypress, too, was green— a dense green, with shadows, tarnished umber; and the pine standing next to it was distinctly toned with blue.

Inside the cab, Petrangelo reached across Ruth to touch Adam's wrist. His touch was insistent, as it might have been were he communicating with someone very young or very old—as if this contact with the flesh would insure contact with the mind. He

said, "You really feel you have it now—a show—a complete statement of yourself?"

"Yes," Adam said.

"Have you negotiated for an exhibition?"

"I have a plan," Adam said, and the tone of his voice told
Petrangelo he did not wish to discuss it.

"Of course a show is the hope of every artist. It is what he
works toward," Petrangelo said with exuberance. "It calls for a
celebration. Let me offer you a drink." His eyes turned to Ruth
and back again to Adam. "I know a nice place nearby. We can put
down your bags first. We can keep the cab waiting—the driver
won't mind."

"No need to go out again," Adam said. "We'll have a drink at
home."

"It would give me pleasure to have you as my guest." But the
words were useless. Petrangelo knew that Adam was not a man
to take from anyone. *"El bene,"* Petrangelo might have said. It
was all in the nature of the beast; but his was a true Italian
nature, and the only way to insult it was to turn down his offer
of food and drink. He buried his hurt. "I would be pleased to
have you join me," he ventured again.

"Another time," Adam said, as he had said when they first met.

"Another time, sir," with polished politeness, addressing Petrangelo formally in the third person. It had been a welcomed
contrast to the prevalent *voi* and *tu* which the fascists had planted
in Italian mouths and which had lagged on the tongues of post-
war Rome. "If it will not inconvenience you, sir, my wife and I
are tired." It had been a pleasure hearing Italian spoken properly
in the mouth of an American.

"Of course," Petrangelo had said. "I'll show you to your apartment immediately. You understand it's apt to be modest."

"Professor Veloni warned us what to expect."

"Yes. He wrote me he would." The letter had burned in
Petrangelo's pocket. "Be kind to the boy," it had said. "Help him
find the best." But Romans rarely parted with the best. "It's
been a long long time since Professor Veloni was in Rome,"
Petrangelo had said. "The war has caved the very heart out of

256

modesty and has left her rather bare. I don't want you to be disappointed. My wife and I will help you in whatever way we can. Professor Veloni, you know, has been a good friend and we want to do our duty by him. You're quite sure I may not welcome you with an *espresso,* or perhaps you prefer an *aperitivo?*"

"Another time, sir."

Petrangelo sat back against the leather seat of the cab. For a moment he caught a glimpse of Adam as he had seen him then— a frightened young man. With an eagerness to be left alone. An eagerness to find his own way. It was an admirable trait, and Petrangelo had liked him for it. "You speak Italian very well," he had said.

"I should," Adam had said. "Four years with Professor Veloni."

"And your wife?"

"Not a word."

"But you will learn Italian," Petrangelo had said to Ruth in perfect English. 'I'll give you a dozen of weeks," and he had watched her smile for the first time.

"What has been happening here?" she asked him now.

"Well," he shrugged his shoulders and rubbed his palms together between his knees. "Life!" he laughed. "You can't stop it. Two nights ago the communists threw a hand grenade at the Christian Democrats' headquarters, and last night the Christian Democrats returned the hospitality. Tonight it's the communists turn, and if they take it, that'll mean the third sleepless night for the police." Petrangelo's face strained in the effort to recapture tidbits of news scattered about the corners of his mind that marked their leave from Rome—the daily occurrences that keep a whole world preoccupied with the beat of living and make one man's absence from the scene trivial. "There's the same fuss over the Marshall Plan. And there's at least one pilgrim to every Roman crowding the gates of the city. Romans are counting on Holy Year to stir up business." He spread his hands apart. "What more is there to tell? Our friends are busy with work," and he mentioned them in litany-like fashion. "Coorman is always at the foundry; he has sold nearly everything in his studio. Corraldo Lenghi is tearing out his hair over the *Biennale*, but he has plenty of hair. Not like me," he laughed. He thought he saw Adam's jaw tense with a tight grinding motion, but it was momentary; he could not be sure of it. He asked, "Have you sent to the *Biennale?*"

"No," Ruth said. She twirled the bouquet of violets like a pin wheel. "Neither one of us has sent."

"There's still time to submit a painting. Corraldo could let you have all the information," he said, while the cab turned into the Via Torlonia, and slowly made for the flooded curb, alongside of number nine. Across the way the cypress and pine formed a wall around the old Villa Torlonia—the old villa, as hidden from sight as its recent past was hidden from the present. A guide book would not have troubled to mention it.

"Ah, the Villa Torlonia," Petrangelo sighed. "But it's a school now, you know. For the English."

"For me, it will always be the place where Mussolini lived," Ruth said.

"They should burn it," Adam said, stepping out of the cab. He turned to offer Ruth his hand, which she took, and he drew her from the protection of worn leather into the awful rain. "They should burn it," Adam repeated, looking at the dense wall of evergreen.

Petrangelo struggled out of the cab and stood beside him. "There are so many pasts in Rome," he said. "If you put your mind to it, there would be no end to burning." Even number nine must have a past, he thought; but his back was turned to it. He could hear Ruth's heels click their way over puddles as she ran through the iron gate past the garden of medlar trees and ilex, into the glass lobby of number nine. She was home now, he thought; for better or worse, she was home. He turned toward the driver and argued about the fare. It was the Roman way of doing things, and even rain could not change that tradition.

The Bundle and the Reed

BY SYLVIA BORDAN

MRS. TROUT! the diminutive oily-skinned porter called to Kitty softly. Her startled eyes shifted. His face sagged in a smile. "That's your taxi, Mrs. Trout!" The foreign words rolled uneasily on his Spanish tongue. Kitty stored them away. It was the last time she would hear that name.

Below her on the wide, shallow steps that led up to the high-domed lobby of the Hotel Cortez in El Paso, the flat-faced Mexican driver with his pressed-in nose, his skin the color and grain of an old apple core, waited, feet astride, creased shirt flapping around the outside of his shabby trousers. One onyx eye squinted up at her from his tilted head. The other shone in the overhead light like the white of an egg. It had no pupil.

He turned silently. She followed his broad, heavy back. Their feet clapped down stone steps, past potted ferns into the golden September sunlight of the city which boasts sunshine three hundred and thirty days a year. A little square of green with palms, empty benches, and a dry semicircular granite fountain stretched before them. They crossed the road. Kitty's knuckles showed white over her handbag. She clambered into the battered brown taxi.

Two women in black, side by side, wearing hats, sat primly in the shadows of the rear seat beside her. The cab swerved south, whirring through the clean, modern business district with its broad streets, sparkling store windows displaying back-to-school checks and plaids, women's fall woolens in cocoa brown, forest green. Bond's. The Texas Mart. No one spoke.

Kitty's icy fingers, tense as fork prongs, clung to the slippery faded leatherette of the seat in front of her.

One by one the Anglo-Saxon faces of passers-by were replaced by Mexicans. Torsos shorter, squatter; skin duskier, hair black, glittering in the morning sun, already lent the streets a narrow, dingy appearance. The buildings began to shrivel; grew older, dirtier. They saw broken steps, stucco chipped and not repainted; women in flouncing bright cottons; rickety open fruit stalls under swarms of flies, surrounded by clusters of barefoot, sticky-fingered children; a vendor, his impassive face polished like an eggplant, long black hands dangling at his sides, trousers drooping, tied with string; flaking store signs in Spanish.

The yellow trolley on its lonely single track clattered by, its sign screaming, "Juarez!"

Hot and cold splinters tingled up Kitty's spine.

She wanted to reach her antennae out for these sad-eyed women. "Soon we'll be at the border," she smiled. Their faces emerged from the dimness.

The younger one's face at her right lit up with gratitude. "Yes. Do you think they'll ask us for identification?" She tossed her sand-colored hair. It flowed over her dark shoulders like golden syrup. "How long does the whole thing take?" Sifted through the dusty windowpane, sun motes, like yellow butterflies, fluttered over her soft straight nose, the curve of her smooth chin and throat. She was very pretty.

The older woman at the far window on the other side of the girl, slim in her black sheath, perched stiffly upright, a little forward and sideways on the front quarter of her seat. Her transparent fingers, like drifting leaves, moved over white gloves, over the tight black skirt that came exactly to her knees. In their high-heeled pumps, her legs, with knobs for knees, pressed close together, slanted to one side.

"Oh, they're happy to have Americans. They ask for nothing." The pouched eyes in her pointed face crinkled.

"Really?"

"It's an assembly line. You're out in twenty minutes." Her voice sounded hollow. Strained. A thread of perspiration glistened high on her forehead. She jerked her close-cropped pepper-and-salt head under its white pillbox toward them with a thin smile. "How long have you girls been in El Paso?" Her bright, haggard stare flitted from the girl's face to Kitty's and back again.

"Just got in!" smiled the girl. Her open mouth showed a scattering of widely spaced teeth. "On the divorcee jet!" She bounced a little in her seat. She wore no stockings and smelled of Arpege.

"From New York?"

"Brooklyn. I mean, that's where I lived when I was married." Her eyes, a transparent green flecked with yellow, seemed to twinkle. "Hotel St. George."

The car jolted over railroad tracks. Kitty's stomach seesawed. The damp dress shifted on her taut shoulders. The air grew thicker, more rancid. She could already see the green booths of the border guards. Beyond them, in the no man's land between the United States and Mexico, Old Mexico as it is called here, a row of crumbling, pastel adobe huts, uneven in height, slanted at dizzy angles. She stared into the sunny squalor.

"At the Hotel. . . ?" Kitty's eyes opened wide.

The girl nodded. "For more than a year and a half Lou refused to look for an apartment. Each Sunday he was too tired."

Kitty smiled at the vagaries of husbands. The woman clucked, shaking her head slowly in sympathy, her fingers curling over a tired, wet ball of a handkerchief. The chaste pearls around her tissue-paper neck shimmered.

The freckle-spattered girl stared uncertainly at the stolid neck of the driver in front of her.

"He wouldn't—" she breathed, gurgled, stopped, then lowered her voice to the barest whisper, "—he wouldn't go to bed with me either." She mouthed the word "bed." "Each time I brought up the subject he said, 'The question is: why is sex so important to you?'" The hissing syllables spilled from her lips, scattering mirth.

Bubbles of laughter broke through their sighs, fed upon themselves, bursting off fresh sparks like a rocket, lifting their tensions into the early morning breeze.

The ice in Kitty's shoulders melted to her tingling finger tips. Her hands loosed their grip, fell lax, limber in her lap. Impulsively she squeezed the girl's soft, warm palm.

This day she had dreaded for so many months. It might not be such a grim one, after all. And tomorrow. . . .

The Night of the Falling Star

BY BEATRICE F. CONRAD

EVEN as she slept, the comet called to her. And in her dreams she followed it, running down the tunneled night beyond the tree-black rim of the horizon. Always she pursued through wind-swept corridors of dark; and always, as her grasping hand reached out, the magic slipped forever past her straining fingers.

On this September evening Eloise Lurie deftly sponged a last few drops of water from the drain board of her kitchen sink. She was a small woman approaching middle age, gentle of manner and almost colorless, like wood that is bleached by the salt and sun. Conscious of her husband waiting for her on the back porch with binoculars in hand, she hurried to finish her work and turn off the glaring overhead light. "I won't be a minute, Michael," she called.

Childless for sixteen years of marriage, they were bound together more closely than if there had been a child. Buying the weekly groceries became a joint expedition; the placement of a new lamp required a conference. Their lives had intertwined into a comfortable dependency, like the gnarled wisteria on their front porch, still twisted around the frail support which long ago it had outgrown.

When Michael seemed to be smothering under the weight of his wife's constancy, she would bear his rebukes meekly and regretfully grant his evening or weekend of freedom; but she herself would never change. She loved this man as if he were her own creation. She envied the mother who had borne him. And in the tolerant darkness of their room, Eloise would draw him to herself, unashamed of the words that could not be spoken by day. "Come here to your mama, baby boy; come, precious, and Mama will love you to sleep." He was all the child she would ever have. There would be no son to grow as Michael had grown, heir to the boy he once had been. The judgment of her husband's doctor (*prognosis doubtful, adoption recommended*) had stripped the act of love of meaning: a treeless view, an empty cup. And as her years passed fruitlessly, Eloise pitied his wasted strength with all her abortive mother-love.

Eloise wiped her hands on the dish towel and hung it along the sink edge to dry. The moist cloth reminded her of her nephew's diapers—not really wet, but sufficiently damp to suggest the delightful necessity of picking Bobby up and changing him. She smiled, remembering the sleeping baby last Saturday night, his gossamer hair gleaming like spun gold beneath the small night light. He had worked his way to the top of the crib until the fluffy top of his head was flush against the blue padded bumper. His fists were loosely clenched at shoulder level. He seemed, after five months of life, still to seek in sleep his nine-months' embryonic pose. Eloise had pulled the baby down to the center of the crib and lightly traced with her forefinger the round perfection of his cool cheek. She longed desperately to hold him, to feel his weight and warmth, but she did not disturb his slumber. Now, reaching into the closet for a sweater to slip over her thin shoulders, she remembered the softness, the baby smell: curds, talcum, urine; and, remembering, her heart contracted with loneliness. Tucking in a faded wisp of brown hair, Eloise flicked off the harsh kitchen light and wordlessly sat down on the wooden step below her husband, resting her head contentedly against his knee.

As darkness fell the last three nights, they had watched together on the back porch for a new comet to appear. This day had been ripe summer with a first hint of the smoky crispness that autumn soon would bring. A few stars and a silver slip of moon commanded all the evening sky. The white frame house creaked in its old joints and settled down to summer night.

Michael focused his lenses on the northwestern horizon, scanning it with a lover's care. He was a tall, lean man, handsome in spite of his receding hairline. The hand that held a pair of three-power binoculars was tanned by the New England sun; the fingers were tapered and precise. Slowly he scanned the darkening horizon. There had been moments in the working day when, lost in smaller galaxies of molecule and atom, his thoughts had wandered to the comet waiting invisible in the sunbright sky. These last evenings, the laboratory's daily friction and routine had drained quietly away as he waited with Eloise for the comet—Arend-Rolland, sixty million miles away in the black emptiness of space. They waited in darkness: the man, the woman, the neighboring stars.

Suddenly Eloise felt her husband's body tighten. His voice was tense with elation. "There she is, Ellie, just where I knew she'd be!" His face was filled with awe. "My God, but it's beautiful," he said, and drank deeply of the wonder. "Take a look." He handed her the glasses. "Focus just above that tall pine tree, beyond Arcturus, the brightest star." The binoculars brought the top of the pine tree close. Eloise focused on the heavens above it, spanning with one incautious movement of her wrist millions of light years. And then, just beyond Arcturus, whose light had left its star before her birth, a stationary smear of white paused, mysterious in their familiar heavens. Through the binoculars Eloise could see its star-like head and an uneven two-pronged tail fanning upward in a milky haze.

"Take a good look, Ellie, because it will never come back again."

"Why not?"

"The orbit. Some comets have orbits so immense that if they ever return at all, it won't be for forty thousand years."

Slowly she handed back the binoculars, trying to comprehend a space and time that could go on so endlessly. "Is this comet as big as we are, Michael?"

"Oh, bigger, much bigger."

"Might it hit the earth? Could it destroy the world?"

"Uh-uh." Intent upon the starry sky, he did not sense her fear. Through the damp silence there came the chirp of a cricket in the lilac hedge.

"Michael, what makes you so sure it won't hit us?"

"You really want to know?" He grinned at her in the darkness. "Well, to put it in words of one syllable, the velocity of the comet

264

is equal to the gravitational pull of the sun; and so as it approaches the sun, the comet is thrust outward again. Okay?"

"Oh sure," she said, "that's easy as pie."

For several minutes they did not speak. Hands primly clasped upon her knees, Eloise sat on the steps like a docile, well mannered child until her husband put down the binoculars. "Listen," he said, "the show changes at the Strand tomorrow. You want to go? After we've seen the comet again, I mean."

She wet her lips with the tip of her tongue; her answer came in a rush of breath. "Oh, Mike, I'm awfully sorry. I told Lil I'd sit with Bobby."

"What do you mean you told your sister? How about telling *me?*"

"I'm so sorry." Her voice was a whisper, scarcely louder than the surflike rustle of the unseen leaves.

"The hell you're sorry. They use you like a floor mat and you don't know the difference. They're too damn cheap to pay a baby sitter."

Eloise replied hesitantly, softly, as if to fend off his rising anger. "They've got a lot of expenses with a new baby and all."

"If they couldn't afford a baby, they should have used some self-control and waited."

Her voice became harder, edged with sarcasm. "That's not for you to say."

"Why not? We've all got our weaknesses and your brother-in-law is a little muddle-headed. Listen, Ellie, you and your sister think that kid is the baby Jesus or something. But their neighbor's girl could sit with Bobby and fall asleep on the sofa just as efficiently as you do."

Eloise stood quietly at the foot of the steps. A cool leaf brushed against her bare ankle. Her heart drummed a staccato beat against the narrow cage of her chest. There was a bitterness here that was not of their making, wine turned to vinegar before their unwilling eyes. Her voice came toneless, level across the darkness. "I wouldn't expect *you* to know about such things, but a ten-year-old girl can't take proper care of an infant if it wakes up and cries in the night." Then her anger drained away as swiftly as it had appeared.

"Okay, okay," he muttered, putting the binoculars in their case. "Sit for them every night of the week if you want to. You lock up. I'm tired. I'm going to bed."

For an hour Eloise read the evening paper, listlessly turning the pages. Then, neglected by his master in their bedtime ritual, the dog began to whimper at the back door. Eloise let him out. "All right, Hansel, but make it a short one." The dachshund's tags jingled in the darkness as he sniffed and ran from favorite tree stump to forbidden bushes. Eloise waited on the tiny back porch, breathing deeply of the cool damp air, scanning the northern sky.

It was the season for falling stars. She studied Michael's comet, so faint to the naked eye. It touched the treetops now. Her imagination was kindled by this eerie visitor. Her mind reached out to the vastness that its orbit traced, the incomprehensible path through the starways of a universe infinite only to finite beings. "We are," Michael once had quoted to her, "poor helpless creatures on an undistinguished planet in an obscure corner of a small and fading universe." She felt a sudden chill that woolen sweaters could not warm. The dog was slow tonight. She could hear him sniffing and knew that he was burying his black nose in the wet grass where a rabbit or chipmunk had passed. Suddenly she gasped in wonder as a blazing meteor split the deep sky. It plunged earthward for a timeless instant like the shattered fragment of a dream. Shivering, she whispered to the listening night, "I am afraid." A breeze came up and the branches rustled their response. She whistled to the dog and he scampered obediently to her side. Then Eloise shut the door quickly and locked it, to close the crowding stars away.

Except for the yellow glow of a parlor lamp, the house was completely dark and quiet. The dog sniffed at his bowl and, finding only water, walked away in resignation. He scratched at the scatter rug beside a comfortless heating vent, turned around in a circle twice, and then curled up to sleep.

Eloise switched off the lamp and climbed the carpeted stairs in darkness. She had never completely outgrown her early fear of

the dark. Her childhood nights had been immense, like tremend-
ous black cats ready to pounce and smother. Even now when she
slept, she started to quivering wakefulness at the creak of a warped
board, the slam of a screen door. She mounted the stairs quickly,
ashamed of the panic that pressed at her heels. She hurried to the
shelter of the friendly quilt and fresh cool sheets, to the comfort
and strength of Michael's presence; but he was distant and secret
in sleep. "Michael?" He turned without waking and took her into
his arms. As Eloise closed her eyes, the meteor flashed before the
camera of her mind. Etched into her memory, it haunted her and
did not fall. Suddenly she could not bear her loneliness.

"Michael," she whispered, "wake up. I love you, dear. Do you
hear me, Michael?"

He grunted.

Their window was a frame for the starry night. She closed her
eyes and kissed his face and said his name again. "Michael," she
whispered, "talk to me." And she began to weep. "I love you so
much," she said. "I always will. Oh, Michael, we are so very small."

He awakened to her tears falling on his cheek. "Don't cry,
Ellie. Did you have a dream?"

"No—yes—it's *all* a dream."

"What's all a dream?"

"Oh, Michael, I shall love you always—I promise, forever—
when we are dust and the world is gone like a falling star in the
empty night. Oh, Michael, if we only can love hard enough it
will be for always. Say it darling, say we will."

"Ellie dear," his tone was apologetic," could you please move
your elbow out of my side?"

She moved her arm. *"Tell* me, Michael; *say* it. Say you'll love
me then."

"When?"

Her panic turned to anger. "You didn't hear a word I said!"

"Ellie, I've got to go to work tomorrow. You know how much
I care for you. I love you as much as one human being can love
another—here and now—and when it's over, that's the end."

Burying her face in the pillow, she continued to weep, soundlessly, desolate. He drew her to himself and kissed her salty lips
and bent his head to kiss her neck and breast.

267

"No!" She pressed him away, her hands hard against his cheek and forehead.

"Why? What have I done?"

"Nothing on purpose," she sobbed, "nothing really. But your kind of love, it's just not enough."

His perplexity became touched with irritation; his patience frayed at the edges. "Ellie, my kind of love had better be enough —it's all I've got to give. Now look, dear, you can stay in bed as late as you please, but I have to be up before seven."

She did not answer.

"Come to me," he said. "I'll hold you close and you'll fall asleep." He tugged at her shoulder. "Come on, now. You'll feel more cheerful in the morning."

Suddenly she pulled away from him, strong with despair and distaste. "I'll be all alone then like I'm all alone now. Even when you listen you don't understand. I'm lost in quicksand. I'm drowning, Michael, and you tell me I'll feel better in the morning. Nothing we do in this room has any meaning. Your kind of love—it doesn't mean a thing!"

She tossed back the quilt and jumped from the bed. Pulling on her robe, she thrust her feet into her slippers and ran blindly down the stairs, away from her husband's questioning, outstretched arms. An open pack of cigarettes lay on the kitchen counter and she lighted one. Then, as if drawn by a power she could not comprehend, Eloise unlatched the back door and went outside.

She could not sit down on the wooden steps because they were wet from the heavy dew. Her eyes seached the sky, but the comet had sunk below the horizon and the night was veiled with mist. The cricket still chirped insistently in the evening-shrouded lilac hedge. Then suddenly it was still. And seen from the hedge, from that small distance, Eloise was a shadow merely. The orange light of her cigarette glowed like some lost and uncharted star that waited to fall through the autumn night.

8. The Good Die First

Anemones

BY PETER KOTSOGEAN

ON A SUNNY Sunday afternoon, February 5, 1961, a paralyzed city digs itself from under a blanket of snow. New York City has had a seventeen-inch snowfall; coldest day of the year, two degrees below zero; most consecutive days below freezing since some time when grandmother must have been a small girl. The big city does not wear its winters well.

The corner of Eighth Street and Sixth Avenue, in Greenwich Village, is always busy, but today lines of people wait to slip, skid or carefully tread through narrow defiles that cut the snow banks which everywhere line the intersecting streets. Many prefer to walk on the street itself, swept clear by snow ploughs, and the slick ice churned and ground to bits under the tires and clanking chains of cars and buses.

Having bought my Sunday *Times,* I cross the street and trudge to a clearing on the corner, stomp my shoes, shaking the snow from them and, with difficult short steps interrupted by little skids over the ice patches, slosh up the street to home.

Warm moist air inside the shops condense against cold windows into a frost maze of ice crystals transforming my favorite window, that of the flower shop, into a sparkling garden of blurred pinks, yellows, purples, and massive greens. In the clear side window, I see a vase of anemones, a vase of memories; a promise I remember mother telling us children: "No, my darlings, it will never happen again. God promised the world so long as there is a rainbow there will never again be another great flood." It is a rainbow of anemones: reds, purples, whites. Their long barren stems lift bright heads above the tall vase, opened petals show black-buttoned eyes set in white circles and they wear lace collar ruffles in place of leaves as other flowers do.

"Hey! Out of the way."

These words disrupt a dream. Workers are clearing the sidewalks, they chip at the frozen mass and shove the fractured ice and compacted snow into the mounting banks. The street sings sounds of screeching shovels, scraping snow ploughs, chipping picks, but where the snow is soft they scoop and toss it like winnowing wheat into the wind. I stand against the candy store window, but my gaze is still on the flowers. Others appear; pink potted azaleas sit on the floor, purple African violets line the window ledge, yellow tulips wrapped in heavy brown paper await their new owners, large bunches of olive green and pagoda like eucalyptus leaves flash into mind their medicinal odors of long-forgotten cold remedies.

I open the door and carefully step on the row of dirtied newspapers stretched in a long line the length of the store.

"Good afternoon, sir. How much are the anemones?"

"Six dollars a dozen, sir."

"Oh!" I had expected three or at the most four dollars, but maybe I can get only half a dozen. "They are lovely. Where are they grown?"

"Yes, they are nice. We bring them in from the local greenhouses."

"Well, please give me half a dozen and mix the colors."

My impulse is to tell him why I want the anemones, but I had better not to a complete stranger. Perhaps I can remark about the cold, the snow, how anemones remind me of spring, how they remind me of a spring in Athens.

II

April in Mediterranean lands is one of nature's wonders, but April in 1949 was too soon after the war, and Greece was suffering from a bloody civil strife. This Sunday was Easter, the festival of resurrection. This Sunday I was reversing the significance of the day; I was ending two lives, my wife Mara, and my four-month-old daughter, Despina. A sudden disappearance and utter silence for several days of someone so close as a wife or child in a tragedy-ridden land should be sufficient to warn that only death could explain the mystery. But like the hope that springs eternal, the mind can resist even the thought of such a possibility, and while I had received an anonymous telephone call giving cryptic but precise instructions, still my mind refused to know what it could easily deduct.

Acharnon is a strange neighborhood to me, but that may be the reason they chose it. Ayios or Saint Pantalemon is a large church and has been under intermittent construction for many years, work on the exterior finish has not even begun, and in places long-weathered scaffolding dug its claws through ugly holes into the interior. I did not go inside; I had no desire to see what it was like. I sat at the small outdoor coffee shop only because I had been instructed to do so. As a matter of fact, I had no desire to do anything. The disappearance of my family and the mysterious telephone call reduced me to a state where I ceased to function except to obey and then only autonomically. Only as I sipped the sweet Turkish coffee awaiting the church clock to strike the hour, eleven Good Friday night, did the first rumblings of tragedy begin to stir.

On the high campanile, the clock struck its first gong. I tried to rise, but each time the dull metallic thud beat me down. I trembled, my tremblings were sychronized with the reverberations of the tolling bell. It stopped, I rose. A man crossed the street a block from me. I followed at his pace. He entered a side street. I reached the end of the block, crossed the street and entered a silent world of frightening darkness and awful expectancy.

At the end of the block he walked in silence on the sound-absorbing soil street. He turned a corner. I was left alone to walk through two whitewashed walls that seemed to converge, but at infinity. Only tiled roofs and large spreading fig trees lifted themselves over the level of the walls and prevented them from crushing in on me. I reached the corner, afraid to turn and look down the dark and quiet street, but my feet kept the momentum where my heart was afraid to go. The street was empty, but near the far corner stood a paper bag. My instructions were to follow a man until I came to a paper bag and there to hand through a hole in the gate fifty gold pounds, about two hundred and fifty dollars, and wait.

I put my hand through the hole, opened my upturned hand and waited to feel a bag of gold lifted from my palm. Gently the weight eased from my hand. My hand was empty, it hung in space detached from me, but it was grasping for a clue to my life. Does one ever know how long these little eternities last? This eternity lasted until the tinkle of metal coins in a quiet night began time again. Someone counted the gold pieces. Then two objects were placed in my hand. One was a piece of paper. The other? It felt like a dirty handkerchief whose mucous had dried and stiffened.

I could hear scuffling and running footsteps around a building, and fading into the night.

I clenched my fist tightly, withdrew my hand, dashed it into my pocket and retraced my steps. Up to the corner, down the horrifying walled street at the end of which a bare light bulb hung and spread apart the darkness. The same coffee house, the same table, the same chair, and I pulled from my pocket the tightly-clenched fist. I brought it close to my chest, and with the other hand shielded it from view of the hundreds of people who passed in and out of Ayios Pantalemon. All stared as I furtively opened my hand and peeked at what I held.

III

He opened the large sliding glass door to the refrigerated stand where a bewildering assortment of colors and shapes were their own best sales appeal. He selected the color variety; two each of red, purple, white and one odd-colored blossom. It was white streaked with red.

"I'll let you have seven." he said. He held the bouquet extended, as the water dripped from the stems in sharp and steady plops on the paper.

IV

Drips of melting wax fell in sharp and steady plops on the paper guard of my candle. The congregation sang the joyous hymn, and with a blessing from the priest the midnight service of the Greek Orthodox Easter mass ended. We turned, greeted friends and relatives. Christos Anestos: Christ Has Arisen. I greeted my aunt and uncle, avoided others and hurried from the church to miss the jamming crowd at the doorway. The night air softly touched my brow and mingled freshness with the odor of burning candles and rosemary-scented incense. I paused not a moment, not even to enjoy the relief of fresh air, but ran down the flight of stairs, jumped into the waiting carriage and drove to the church steps to gather in friends and relatives. They climbed into the carriage, my uncle, aunt, the three children, and two neighbors, each holding a burning candle in cupped hands in the hope of lighting the Easter candles at home from them. We departed for home, for Easter breakfast and sleep. My relative knew of my tragedy, and with a silence of love and understanding the usual joyous Easter ride home was broken only by the clop-clop of horse's hooves and by the grinding of the wheels over the graveled paths. Numerous lights radiated from the brilliantly lit church and like ours pierced the darkness to home.

My thoughts were far from Easter candles. I thought of Stavro at home waiting for my return. The large white pine box which we had made that day would be securely fastened in its crib and strapped to the packsaddle of our mule. The shovels, saddle bags filled with lunch, water jug, new linen sheets, and green fodder for Penelope would all have been expertly strapped, hooked, or hung from the saddle. Stavro would be sitting at the front steps. And in a few moments I and Stavro would be on the road leading to the ancient marble quarries on Mt. Penteli.

V

"Do you want the stems cut, sir?" My flower man placed the flowers on the counter and was unwinding the brown wrapping paper.

"No, thanks. Just wrap them in tissue paper, please." I can't stand the idea of wrapping these rainbow colors and hiding them from view even as I walk home. I will be able to glance down at my swaying arm and enjoy a streak of spring as I walk through the snow.

VI

The macadam road ended, and we picked our way in the dark-ness over the rock path that lifted us above the clusters of lights and long lines of lights still radiating from the churches. A trace of dawn pinked the sky, solid mass of blackness broke into hills with valleys, plains ran from below us and stopped suddenly at a sea, Marathon Bay. We watched the red from the east chase the pink through the sky. Only the braver stars stayed out, but even they lost their twinkle and hung helplessly in the sky. A single tall cypress shot boldly into the bluing sky, and a meek white-washed chapel clung to its roots. This was Ayios Louka, St. Luke, and here we took our rest.

On a marble seat against the chapel I sat while Stavro picked from the saddlebag a handful of green fodder and scattered it over the ground for the mule. Unwinding from the saddle hook a bright red saddlebag, he walked and crouched on the ground before me. Of the two Easter eggs he held in his hand, he offered me the choice of the colors. At first he avoided my glance, but when I picked the red-colored egg and challenged him to a duel of Easter eggs, I could see his eyes and they, too, had lost their twinkle like the stars that hung helplessly in the sky.

"Christos Anestos," he smiled. The edge of his blue egg plunged and shattered the shell of mine. A broken mass of red lay in my hand. Suddenly I clenched my fist; soft ooze of white and yellow squeezed through my fingers, and broken pieces of red shell fell from my hands.

Since Friday night, when I pushed my hand through the gate post with a bag of gold and received in its stead the handkerchief with the strange feel of dried mucous, and finally when I sat down at the coffee shop outside the church of Ayios Pantelemon, I was not reminded of the strange handkerchief. Or rather, I re-fused to be reminded. But this moment I opened both hands. In one the smashed red and oozing Easter egg, and in the other the handkerchief, blood-soaked and holding my wife's wedding ring and the baby's baptismal cross.

Stavro grabbed my fist between his two peasant hands, "Sig-nome, Kyrie," and kissed my hand, while from his eyes he let drop warm moist tears as if to soothe the pain of what the contents I held in my hand had caused.

VII

"That will be two and a half dollars and eight cents tax," he said as he handed the anemones to me. I withdrew a clenched fist from my pocket and handed to him the crumpled ten dollar bill. I watched his surprised expression as he unfolded the bill and stole a quick glance at me, but turned away embarrassed as our two glances met. He rang the cash register.

VIII

With his coat he wiped the crushed mass of egg from my hand and, hoping to please me, said, "I brought several candles for us to light in the chapel, Kyrie Koutsogianni." He rose and rushed to the mule to unwind another saddlebag, and reached across the mule's back to remove two large candles. He held out the two candles to me with a smile of pride, for I knew the sacrifice this poor man had made to buy these ornate offerings. But I couldn't go in the chapel to pray, I couldn't relive the agonies of my tragedy, for I had not the simple faith of Stavro.

"Thank you, Stavro, but I think I'll sit here and look out at the sea. That island must be Euboea and Turkey can only be about one hundred miles away. Wish I were going some place right now. Any place, so long as it is far, far away."

My remark was unkind and, judging from Stavro's sudden pained expression, I knew he felt its rebuff and detachment. But this was not the place or time to tell that I did not believe, that I could never pray, and that the only reason I went to church was not to offend my kind relatives. And besides, I doubted that Stavro could understand anyone disbelieving in God, in church. or in pursuit of one's sacramental duties.

"Light them for me, Stavro, and pray, pray for me."

"I will light them for you, Kyrie Koutsogianni. I will pray for you."

We had left Kiphissia, the summer city of Athens, on its one thousand foot perch at the base of this fabled marble mountain, Penteli, and had ascended on the opposite side away from Athens. From near the little chapel I looked into the moving sun, over the mountain of Euboea and out into the Aegean, where bronzed islands and rocks dotted the sea, while below lay the plain of Marathon, its famed battle site and the glistening white marble dam. The mountain slopes were bare of woods, all had been slashed during the war by a desperate people, and the thin soil cover washed away, leaving now only bare rock polished by time.

The sun glittered on the far sea, jumped the island of Euboea to glitter on the narrow strait, and up the mountain slope glittered from polished rock to polished rock and to shine on my face.

Inside the chapel I heard mumblings as Stavro must have lit the candles and begun the prayers. I moved my head back to hear better, but still only a low mumble was audible and the scratching of hobnails over the marble floors as he moved to pray from icon to icon; the Saviour, the Holy Virgin, the saints and their martyrdom; all cheap colored prints in gaudy gold frames or old relics whose paint long-since removed by revering touch and devout lips. A creak of a door, a snap of a latch, and I knew that Stavro had exhausted all the saints in heaven.

Walking toward me, he stooped to kiss my hand and to bless me, *Kyrie eleison*: God Have Mercy On Us, and made the sign of the cross.

What green sprigs of fodder Penelope left uneaten, Stavro fed by hand. He patted her nose and when she finished her meal he tapped her neck gently and picked up the reins. Thus we began the ascent to our goal, the ancient marble quarry. Stavro led the way, rein in hand; then came Penelope and, bringing up the rear and holding onto the tail of Penelope, I stumbled along the trail over the rocks.

Large for a Greek mule, but then Penelope wasn't Greek at all. My family in America bought Penelope through a relief organization, so she and the other large dark mules immigrated to Greece.

The trail steeply inclined, the sun rose high in the sky; I took off my coat and brushed the sweat from my brow. Penelope, too, felt the sun's warmth; perspiration beads ran from around the saddle strapping and the hair lost its smooth glossy sheen. She

278

tugged at her tail violently to rid herself of flies so that I let go my guiding tow and stumbled my way unaided.

With a lusty swing of my coat, I shooed the flies away from Penelope, but they buzzed a few inches from my whirling coat only to descend immediately on Penelope's rump. Several times I brushed away the flies but finally flung my coat over her rear, tucking the coat collar under the saddle and allowing her tail to swish freely through the rear slit of the coat. Perhaps the flies found their way under the coat to continue annoying the mule, but I could see it no longer was grateful for the diversion along the trail.

IX

"Your change and thank you very much. I hope you enjoy them."

"It certainly is cold." I stopped. My flower man talked to someone else.

"Yes, ma'm, what can I do for you?"

"I'm Mrs. Chrisholm."

"Yes, Mrs. Chrisholm, the flowers are all ready."

To linger in the store was useless. The slim chance to tell him why I bought anemones vanished with the entrance of the new customer and left me no choice but to leave. I wanted him to know my buying anemones differed from others who purchased for decorative purposes.

I stepped out into city street. The air was crisp and clear, and for a rare moment in this big city, I enjoyed a deep breath of air.

Plop! A dull thud as a cluster of snow fell from an overhanging accumulation. Passers-by darted to avoid the falling snow.

X

Plop! Plop! The dull thud of the mule's flat shoes as she walked on level ground and on soft soil. We had arrived at our destination, an ancient marble quarry where centuries of cutting had incised the slopes and where ages of dust and soil could accumulate into a floor of soil mantel.

Relief of level ground and the strange sight of an abandoned quarry made me forget the reasons for which we had come so far.

Twisted squares and rectangles tangled with tall bore holes. Numerous small caves tunneled into the rocks, sharp angular forms jutted irregularly along the cutting face, and blocks cut on all sides waited only the final cleaving. Long before I had come into this life, others must have stood near this same spot to contemplate the view and speculate that from here, perhaps, the marble for the Parthenon had been quarried.

Higher above I could see the peak of the mountain and the crest of the spur over which we would soon cross. I knew that once the crest was crossed, I could look down on Athens and see, rising from its center, the Acropolis with its Parthenon. The moment to contemplate the site was over; we had not come to admire the ancient quarry.

Stavro unlooped the ropes securing the coffin to the crib, letting one end fall to the ground, and braced the coffin on his back to ease it to the ground.

The sight and sound of a coffin falling to the earth ended what little diversion my mind could seek to escape the unpleasant task ahead.

"My God! We're here. What a strange place. The whole idea is preposterous. Why am I here? I'm an American in a strange country. Mother! I don't belong here. I want to be home where I should be, where I never should have left. A hill! A steep hill. Run down a steep hill. He's going to drop the coffin. Stavro! Stavro!"

I ran in panic toward him. I had no idea to help; only to run and shout. Stavro looked up from his humped position under the coffin in amazement at my yells.

"I'll help," I said, recovering from fright and panic. The two of us eased the wooden box to earth.

I walked a few steps away and waited helplessly while Stavro brought the shovels and stood directly in front of me. His eyes searched my face for a clue of the right thing to say. What good are words at moments like these when even their sound cuts bitter? No, this moment was for silence and sympathy.

Instead of the fear and panic of a moment ago, my heart ached for the pitifully poor man who stood in front of me. My eyes followed the deep wrinkle starting from one ear and branching into numerous lines to disappear under the stubby gray beard. Years of wind had worked to carve the deep lines, and years of sun had shone to darken the fair skin which showed around the edges of his coarse woolen underwear. Instead of a suit he wore a kaleidoscope of colored cloth cut in the shape of a suit. If there were a single piece of the original suit, it could not be disting uished from the patches of every color and texture: browns, reds, greens, squares, stripes, or herringbones; and there were patches on patches.

Poor Stavro Frankos, he had fled the island of Chios during the war after his wife and large family had starved to death. How he survived even he could not say.

Frankos is a common name on Chios. The people say they are the descendants of the crusading Franks who ruled the island centuries ago. Judging from his blue eyes and few remaining blond hairs, I could believe the story.

My uncle offered him a place to live and food in exchange for tending the garden and for numerous chores which his willing and learned hands did, to my uncle's admiration.

"Stavro, I like you very much. I don't know how I can ever repay you for your kindness in coming with me here. I would rather have you with me now than anyone else in the world." I meant what I said for his simple and strong faith gave me a courage I doubt I could have attained in any other way. I reached to his hand, pressed it tightly, and took the shovel. We stood in silence but we both looked for signs of a fresh burial.

No longer did the awaiting task terrorize me, and even if my flagging spirits collapsed to send me at any moment rushing head-long down the slope in frantic terror, Stavro's presence prevented it. I thought the events of the past few days had drained every emotion from my body, but I underestimated the capacity of the human heart, and in the next moment I was to know something of its vastness.

We walked a few paces and, around a sharp facing of the jutting rock and in an alcove, it was. A bed of anemones, brilliant little wild flowers in reds, purples, and whites. The warm sun had opened their petals, and thousands of black-buttoned eyes in white circles smiled at us. Even where the brick-red earth of the recently dug grave had been turned over, their stems bent, but they turned back to smile. We stood with tears running down our cheeks, but we smiled.

Hundreds of blossoms made a bed in the sweet-smelling pine box, and on the bed of anemones we laid the two bodies. I brushed the soil from around their faces, and the morbid vision vanished in the bed of bright anemones.

With my hands I scooped two clumps of red soil, and with water from our jug worked the soft ooze into strength to preserve the blossoms I encased. They were white anemones streaked with red, the outsanding blossoms of the whole field. Into their hand each, I placed the small ball of soil and flower.

Reaching into my pocket, I drew out the blood soaked handkerchief and took the ring and the cross. On my wife's finger I placed the wedding band and around the child's neck hung the gold cross. I walked back to the spot where I had scooped the blossoms, buried the handkerchief, and patted the earth over it. We nailed the lid, and fresh pine scent rose to sweeten the air and to ease our task.

We would leave in a moment, cross the ridge, and make for Moni Penteli, Monastery of Penteli, where we would find an attended chapel for the night. I also knew that when we crossed the ridge, waiting eyes would be searching us out. I would leave another bag of gold behind the marble wayside shrine as we would leave the monastery.

XI

"I'm sorry, pardon me." Mrs. Chrisholm had opened the door and was leaving the store.

The sidewalk home narrowed between the buildings and the snow bank. The bright sun melted the snow on the eaves above. Drops of water fell in a cascade along the path and pattered small holes in the snow. In a single file the people walk, and where two meet they stop and carefully edge past.

The larger store entrances are oases of dryness and secure footing. This is the bookshop. A child talks excitedly to her mother and points at a particularly appealing book in bright colors, *Monkeys of the World*.

"Have you ever seen a monkey?" I asked.

"Of course, lots of times," she replied, annoyed that I could have doubted for a moment.

"Would you like this pretty bouquet of flowers?"

Her face lost its haughty pose, her mouth opened slightly, and she turned in question to her mother.

"All right dear, you may take them. But thank the man for the pretty flowers."

She blushed, shyly accepted the anemones, and gave me an inaudible, "Thank you."

"Would you do me a favor?" I asked.

She nodded her head in assent, but still hung her head and wore a cute pout on her lips.

"Would you give me that one flower, the white one with the red streaks?"

"Uhu." She suddenly perked up and eagerly picked the red and white blossom and handed it to me.

I walked up to the corner, stumbled into the deep snow of the side street, and made the first footprints to mar the whiteness of the snow, which everywhere changed the city into another place.

Winter's dress, a summer's dream.

Stranger at the Wake

BY HELEN TENNEY

O N THAT JULY afternoon the heat clung to New York streets like a moist, feverish embrace. It was our twentieth anniversary, Joe's and mine. We were both astounded that our sometimes tenuous, always tumultuous marriage had achieved this permanence. And so, immersed in the eminence of the day and cheered by its sunny kindness, I forgot to look back over my shoulder at the specter I had been staring down for nineteen years. The specter darted in and snatched, convulsively, triumphantly. So it was that I Marian Reilly, born Marian Goldstein, was on my way to my first wake, the day after the twentieth anniversary that never was celebrated.

Third Avenue in Brooklyn is a quiet old street, rather dreary, with little stores with old fashioned lighting, stores that sell plumbing supplies, Syrian and Italian groceries, newspapers, and candies, or offer such services as shoes repairs, bicycles rented and repaired, guaranteed repairs on televisions and radios. In the late Sunday dusk of July 27th, 1958, even the cars and almost empty buses whirred along rapidly, almost noiselessly, along the forlorn, forgotten thoroughfare.

The trim red-brick house with the white colonial doorway on the corner of Eighty-First Street was, by contrast, cheerful and bright until one noticed the bronze plaque that read McLaughlin's Funeral Home.

I entered the house, my sister-in-law, Margaret, whom we called Bud, holding my arm, and the others behind us. The small foyer led to the office on one side, and directly before us was a large black bulletin board, the unbelievable legend spelled out in neat white letters: Joseph P. Reilly, Room A.

As I crossed the threshold of the room, I wanted to break loose, run back through the dimly-lit, thickly-carpeted corridor, away from the musky mingled odor of disinfectant and dead flowers, the much fainter scent of fresh roses and gardenias.

It was a very large room. Along the cream-colored walls stood rows of empty wooden chairs. The electric lights shone on the long parquet floor before us, a floor newly waxed. It seemed like a ballroom before the musicians enter—the waiting chairs, the unscuffed floor. From far off, as from another room, like this, perhaps, I heard a murmur, an undistinguishable monotone of words run together like a string of small beads. I could not understand a word, but I knew what it was, a prayer for the dead. I looked across the long interminable room. There on the dais stood the black coffin I had selected for Joe only the day before. Mr. McLaughlin had said, "I know it's hard, but it's got to be done. Here's the catalogue. This is a very popular number in the medium-price range." There it was, guarded at each end by two candle-shaped lamps casting a soft amber glow across the white satin of the open coffin. Back of the coffin, baskets of flowers, white carnations, roses, lilies, gladioli. I was surprised. I had not thought about flowers, and I was grateful to the friends who had remembered Joe.

Now I was looking down into the coffin. I saw a large waxen face, a whitish-gray clothing-store dummy. I looked away. This was not Joe. The figure in the coffin could not be the man who had died with my arms around him. I looked again. Yes, he had iron-gray hair, a high forehead. But surely his nose had never jutted out like that. The face in the coffin was expressionless, yet very stern; the thin lips, that I had last seen twisted in pain, were now full, a straight line across his face. Joe, alive, could set his chin and look harsh, determined, aloof, but there was always a little wavering light in his blue eyes, and the corners of his lips would tremble just a trifle, so that I knew I could make him smile in a minute if I wanted to. The man in the coffin might have been a bank president pictured in a small inset on the business page of *The Times;* or a pillar of the church. But he wasn't my Joe. I looked longingly down for something that would let me see Joe again. Even the heavy eyebrows we used to kid about, saying he looked like John L. Lewis, no longer looked heavy. I touched his hand. It was very cold, and his face was the face of a stranger. I was a stranger here, too. I said to Bud, "Tell me what to do. I've never been to a wake before."

Burial

EXCERPT FROM A NOVEL BY CHAYYM ZELDIS

DAYLIGHT like troubled water. A sunless October dawn. Between the windrow of dark cypresses bordering the citrus groves, Lazar and Lennie saw below them a small wedge of earth clear of trees except for sapling pines scattered among the gravestones. They had seen this cemetery many times from the road where they now stood: this would be the first time since they had come to the kibbutz that they would visit it. They stood silently, waiting—the mountains opposite them in unsure distance and towering over all, and the cypresses dividing the groves looking like men wading chest-high across a green river.

The sky was unchanged gray as the men from the kibbutz came into the cemetery to dig. Unhurriedly they took up positions and began. The flat bottoms of their shovels rose and fell. They had brought picks along too, but they did not need them. The earth they had selected for the graves was soft and almost stoneless. A few inches under its crust it was damp from the water of the irrigation sprinklers in the bordering groves.

Lazar and Lennie—touching her face now with her finger tips as if it were a strange object to her—watched from the road as the shovels swung up—dull silver in the daylight that was strangely akin to them in color—and dissociated themselves from the dirt they had bitten out and scooped high. Crumbling, the dirt fell to the sides, its occasional red clots breaking with soft hissing sound. Then the shovels dropped, and under the pressure of heavy shoes, bit again. Soon the diggers were hidden to their knees in the deepening holes.

The men took turns digging. They smoked and talked in low tones during their intervals of rest. Three graves were being dug. One of them was for Fyvel, the friend who had come to Israel with Lazar and Lennie. It was nearly noon when all three holes lay gaping, with high mounds of earth whose red the daylight scarcely varnished tumbled beside them. The diggers put down their shovels at last and turned away. A white grub squirmed on the ground and one of them stepped on it accidentally.

Lazar and Lennie had remained in their place all through the digging. Only when they saw that the settlers were beginning to assemble did they leave the road and make their way down a slope to the cemetery. They stood over to one side, near a windrow, and Lennie took Lazar's hand. The mountains were out of sight. Gray bone of the sky hung over their heads.

Settlers continued to arrive—on foot and in vehicles from the surrounding settlements. Many of them were from across the valley and further. Some came directly from the fields in clothes that were dark with sweat. Mules and horses, carts and wagons and jeeps crowded the road from which Lazar and Lennie had watched through the morning: the pale yellow road-dust was still unsettled in the air. From the groves, unseen crows cawed without stop.

After some time, Avram, the work-manager of the kibbutz, walked over to the graves. He spoke briefly. One of those killed in the Arab attack last night had been a friend of his more than thirty years. They had come from Russia together and come to the valley together. The second was a youth of seventeen who had come from Poland. The third was Fyvel. One mortar shell had killed all three.

Avram looked shrunken—even frail. His small body seemed to have lost the stature that had made it, in spite of its size, formidable. The hand that had received a shrapnel wound during the attack was in a sling. He stood in sandals and gray shirt and worn pants, staring at the settlers and at the solid motionless walls of cypress green. The crows cawed fiercely, making it difficult at times to hear what he was saying. Every now and then a mule brayed and blotted out his words altogether. His head dropped. His feet stirred. It took a little time for the settlers to realize that he had finished speaking. By the windrow, Lennie held Lazar's hand tightly. She moved closer to him.

"It's only the moment that has to be gotten through," she whispered, "because—because the past is already done with and we may never have a future. It's only *this moment* . . . this moment and no more . . ."

Lazar said nothing He squeezed her hand still more tightly.

"Lazar, tell me—I won't be sick now, will I—*will I, Lazar?*"

"No, you won't be sick. You'll get through it."

"Promise?"

"I promise."

Through an opening in the windrow opposite them, a wagon drove in with the three coffins. They were of unplaned wood and were amazingly white, somehow the very brightest objects to be seen anywhere about. There was something obscurely obscene about their color and cleanness and even rectangular shapes. The two red mules drawing the wagon halted and twitched their long ears and glanced about suspiciously. The left one snorted and tossed his head.

The diggers went over to the wagon. Other men from the crowd were ready with ropes. Avram called the name of each of the dead as his box was lowered into a hole. It took very little time to get the coffins out of sight. On the wagon one moment, they were gone the next.

Both mules pawed the earth. The left one sniffed at a pine branch on the ground, raising its dry brown spines. The grave-diggers returned to the pits and again wielded their shovels. Earth flew quickly, rapping gently at first on wood and then collapsing soundlessly on itself. One of the diggers took off his shirt. Strange October noon—sunless, humid, staggering under the weight of a bitter heat which had no visible source.

Naked flesh glistened, and the earth, falling ever more rapidly —as if it were glad to return—glistened too. There were a few very old men in the crowd who now edged forward, almost to the line of the diggers. They were all of them wizened, all of them with sparse hair and stringy beards and all with faces so tight over the bones that it looked as if some penurious hand had gathered in and was still gathering in the skin. Slowly, as if drugged, as if somehow they hated to part with the words, they began the prayer for the dead. Their dull eyes rolled with the effort of their words, and their thin voices strained and cracked but carried surprisingly over the cemetery. Before their moving lips and trembling hands, the shovels moved like pistons. One bare back shone coppery, like a warrior's shield. The dirt rained red. The old men mouthed a toothless sorrow that seemed to have already included them as well. One woman sobbed out loud—she was the only one. Avram stood mute, head down. The snorting mules were lead away.

"So," hissed Lennie, *"so it's back to God's smelting furnace!—"*

Her entire body shook. Lazar put an arm around her. The withdrawing wagon startled the crows and they lifted in sudden shrieking flight and scattered over the cemetery. They wheeled and cawed and settled heavily again in the cypresses and in the orange trees. The last spadesful of earth fell. The three graves were covered over.

In a terrified whisper, Lennie said: "Which grave is Fyvel's? I didn't see!"

"I . . . I didn't either," said Lazar.

"Were you watching the crows?"

"I—think so."

Lazar looked at her:

"They'll put up a stone," he said, "and we'll know."

"Ah, yes . . ."

She leaned against him and closed her eyes and then opened them:

"We'll have to write his folks."

"Yes, we'll have to," said Lazar.

"What can we say?"

"We'll say something."

"There's nothing . . . *nothing.*"

"We'll invent something."

The digger with bared torso threw down his spade. It struck a rock and rang. The crowd of settlers seemed to awaken with the sound. It began to disperse. On the road, motors flared into motion. One mule brayed and others took their cue. The yellow dust swirled up. The settlers melted away. At one end of the red cemetery earth—between two twisted, white-trunked pines—the fresh, soft swells of untrampled dirt lay: below, behind. Only the few old men stayed, not finished with the words of prayer that were as blind as their own faces. Beyond the cemetery, beyond the groves, the mountains rose faceless into the neutral sky— indifferent under time as they were under light. Between their spurs were bone-white shelves of rock. From the moving vehicles on the road of the kibbutz, the dust curled in dark yellow rings.

Lazar and Lennie were among the last to leave the cemetery. Holding her arm tightly above the elbow, he said:

"God, how I wish it were tonight already! Death . . . is never farther away than when we make love!"

"I wish it were tonight without a thought of death!"

They walked along the windrow without paying attention to

where they were going. Lazar's mouth moved with curious stiffness:

"Violence," he said, "as silent a sphinx as is nature itself."

"But we have each other, haven't we, my darling?"

"Yes, we have," he said.

They looked at each other. They had passed through a gap in the cypresses and entered a lemon grove, almost without realizing it. They halted where they were. Motionless shade was thick sediment under the lemon trees. The smell of leaves and trunks and mingled earth was almost bitter, and the light between the rows jaded and thin, and the moldering leafage underfoot saffron and soft as rancid butter. Two tiny birds with sapphire breasts scissored by over their heads. They heard the wings flicking in and out of the foliage. And then silence returned.

"Safe," whispered Lennie, pressing to him, "oh, God, *if we only could be safe!*"

She began to weep.

"What's the matter, darling?"

She shook her head.

"Everywhere, *everywhere*," she said through her weeping.

"What—what is it?"

"I—I don't *know*—I don't know myself—"

"Tell me."

"Only," she said, burying her face in his shoulder, "—*only that there is so little in this world that is not menace.*"

"I'm between you—and the menace," he said.

She shook her head.

"That's menace too!" she cried out, drawing her head back. "There's no escape from it, none at all!"

"It's not true, darling."

"Nothing's true!"

He drew her head in close again and stroked her hair and said, "I love you, Lennie—that's true."

She turned up her face and they kissed and held each other under the poised unmoving glossy leaves against whose blue-green shapes her hair looked like a visor that had been hammered out of soft thick gold. Their bodies pressed together and thrust savagely against each other.

"Tell me again that you love me," she said hoarsely.

"*I love you, Lennie.*"

"Say, '*that's true,*' like you said it before."

"It's true, Lennie."

"*But tell it to me with all of you,*" she muttered through her set teeth.

Moaning, half-sobbing, she clutched at him and clung to him and tore at his clothes and made him sink to the earth of the lemon grove with her.

"Not tonight," she gasped, "*—now!—*"

"Now."

"*Forever.*"

"Yes."

"*We'll never get up from here.*"

"Never."

The sapphire birds flashed by again, this time over their writhing legs. In a short while, both of them were still. Something crackled in the dry twigs. Her cheek on warm, damp earth, Lennie saw a turtle moving along. Its shell glowed deeply, like amber. A crow cawed.

"I could sleep," she murmured. Then she said, "I *wasn't* sick, was I?"

"No."

"Do you know why?"

"Why?"

"Because you promised me I wouldn't be! Remember?"

"I remember."

She placed her hands on his cheeks and gently turned his head: "See the turtle?"

"Where?"

"Oh, he's disappeared! But listen to him."

They both heard the grave stirring of leaves and twigs. She put her legs together. They were white and smooth as the flesh of a tree from which the bark has been stripped. He put his hand over them.

"You make the best blanket," she whispered.

"I'm glad."

"Lazar."

"Yes?"

"I—I'll be pregnant now, won't I?"

"You could get pregnant, of course. I—we didn't—"

"But I *will be,* won't I?"

He saw her eyes.

"Yes, you will."

"Promise me—"

"I promise you."

They lay quietly in each other's arms. The turtle continued to crawl. A praying-mantis was poised frozen on a branch. The earth seemed to grow warmer and they could not help drowsing. A long way off—across the valley, perhaps—sheep bells tinkled. The clear little sounds broke over them as softly as ash. Then utter stillness returned. Lennie stirred. Suddenly she opened her eyes and said:

"Lazar, I heard it just then."

"Heard what?"

"The life within me."

He sat up and bent over and kissed her parted lips:

"I heard it just then," he said, "the life within *me."*

Sunday Mourning

BY HELEN HUDSON

MR. HAWLEY, the undertaker, was a big man with a tweed jacket and a seat in the New Hampshire legislature. He thought of himself as a public benefactor, serving both the living and the dead, and it hurt him to know that he got no thanks from either. People were uncomfortable around him, feeling that he always wanted something—their votes or their trade. And he knew they considered it entirely fitting that he should have had no children. Death and taxes being sure things, Mr. Hawley had, so to speak, cornered the market. But it made him a lonely man. He wandered through the state Capitol with a lugubrious air, and his voice in the funeral parlor seemed to solicit votes from the dead.

Now, seated behind his desk in the Hawley Memorial, he stuffed the tobacco down inside the bowl of his pipe with a competent thumb and went on reading aloud from the form in front of him. The couple on the couch sat quietly with enough space between them for a wet dog. As soon as they got the news, they had driven up from New York in a dirty black station wagon with a great scoop of a dent in the left fender. They did not look at each other but kept their eyes on a long, sly sunbeam that stopped suddenly in front of Mr. Hawley's desk. It was a Sunday afternoon and the small office was hushed, folded into the double silence of time and place.

"Disposition of the body?" Mr. Hawley read in his booming voice.

"Cremation," Mr. Lewis said and looked, at last, at his wife. She was a small scrawny woman with a round little mouth shaped to hold a straw, as though she took life in tiny sips.

"Yes," she said. She had a sudden vision of a New Hampshire hillside stroked by the sun, ribbed by the roots of ancient trees with a stone to mark what she had lost. Otherwise there would be nothing, no trace—no more than a sunbeam at dusk. "Yes, cremation," she said.

"Very sensible," Mr. Hawley said. "After all, the body is just a house. Felt that way when my father was taken. His body was just the house he lived in. Not much use when he was gone." Mr. Hawley always tried to give his customers what they wanted. Just as he tried to find out what his constituents favored. The trouble was that some people wouldn't say. They let him stand on the doorstep when he was canvassing with the door open just enough to keep him from getting in or going away. And at the funeral parlor they looked at him with hatred.

But the couple on the couch hardly looked at him at all. Queer pair, they sat there stiff as strangers with nothing to say to him or each other. The woman was skinny and white as a peeled stick, the kind who wore loose belts and last year's hemlines, for all she came from New York; the kind who sat through the service with her gloves on and her eyes dry and complained about the bill later. The man was better, solid, with the sound of coins in his pocket and a pen sticking out of his jacket. Yet they had stuck their kid in Mrs. Peabody's "Home" and wanted it buried the minute it died. Dainty little thing she was, too—light hair and long, thick lashes that turned up at the ends. All except the mouth. He felt badly about the mouth.

Mr. Hawley wrote "Cremation," leaned back in his swivel chair, and lifted a match to his pipe. "'Course, you'll have to have a casket just the same," he said. "That's state law. But a child's casket's only seventy-five dollars. Pretty little thing. White with silver handles. I'll show it to you later."

Mrs. Lewis was clutching the edge of the couch. A white casket with silver handles, she thought. Not a soft bed with a pink quilt but four sides and a lid that closes. To be shipped like a shoe in a box from this world to the next.

"'Course," Mr. Hawley was saying, "we don't have the facilities in a little town like this. We can have it done for you in Boston or Worcester. We usually send to Worcester. It's closer and cheaper."

"Worcester's all right," Mr. Lewis said.

"Yes," Mrs. Lewis said. She had never been to Worcester but she remembered Boston where the narrow, winding streets led back to the past; where cows still grazed on the Commons once a year and the Charles stretched a silver tongue to the sea. Worcester she imagined as a brown industrial town, noisy with the manufacture of bottles and buttons. "Yes, Worcester," she said.

"All righty." Mr. Hawley filled it in on the form. "Perfectly simple. We have a truck going out in the morning. Now there's just the matter of the ashes. We can ship them anywhere you say, along with a nice little urn."

Mrs. Lewis had her head down and her shoulders were twitching. He hurried on as though talking would cover the sight. But Mr. Lewis got up and said he thought they would like to have them scattered over the hillside. He gestured toward the window where they could see the sun, swollen and red, above the horizon. "Near where she lived," he said.

"Fine. Fine," Mr. Hawley said. "We'll have the driver . . ." and he bent to record the final item on the form, the disposition

294

of the ashes of Polly Lewis, aged two years and three months who died in convulsions at the Peabody Home for Handicapped Children at two o'clock in the morning on November 7, 1960.

Now came the hard part. Mr. Hawley hoped they wouldn't make a fuss. He totaled it up and handed it to Mr. Lewis, saying quickly that of course there was the usual discount if paid on receipt in full. But Mr. Lewis was already reaching for his pen and checkbook. He glanced over the bill, not even stopping to ask about the $1.47 (postage for ashes from Worcester, Mass., to Keene, N. H.).

"Well, now," Mr. Hawley said, "would you like to see her? I can bring her right up. Won't take but a minute and she looks real pretty. Pink party dress Mrs. Peabody at the Home bought, and white shoes and all. Only thing is—well, the mouth wouldn't close all the way. You know. But she's a real little beauty." He jumped up and hurried down the stairs.

The couple in the office remained exactly as they were; Mr. Lewis standing at the desk, staring out the window, still holding the pen in his fist; Mrs. Lewis clutching the edge of the couch as though she were in danger of being tossed off. It was so still she could almost hear the dust settling inside the sunbeam.

Finally she raised her head and looked at her husband. "I can't, Will," she said. "I just can't."

He walked over and put his hand on her shoulder. "Okay," he said gently. "You don't have to."

And then Mr. Hawley was at the door saying, "All ready, folks. Just come this way." He looked changed, somehow, standing there smiling at them, with his jacket buttoned and his hair smooth. Like an M.C. who knows that the next act will stop the show. But his smile faded when Mr. Lewis told him that his wife wasn't quite up to it, and his voice lost volume. "Sure. Sure. Just as you say. Takes people differently."

Mrs. Lewis, sitting on the couch, staring at the floor, heard their footsteps in the hall, heard Mr. Hawley say, "Too bad about the mouth though . . ." She jumped up suddenly and walked to the desk. She could not bear to look out the window at the dignity of the naked trees and the stripped hills rising boldly to the sky; at the order and decorum that lay outside Mr. Hawley's office.

Instead, she forced herself to examine, with great care, the items on Mr. Hawley's desk; the pen and ink set with the Kiwanis Club inscription; the insurance company calendar, the ashtray with the silvery ash and the burnt and broken match sticks. She could feel the red eye of the sun glaring at her over the rim of the hill. She picked up a small Bible only to find it was a cigarette case with one stale cigarette leaking bits of dried tobacco. She closed the lid and walked slowly back to the couch.

"It's all right, darling," Mr. Lewis said, coming in to stand beside her. "She looks fine. Just fine." He nodded at her several times.

And then they were saying goodbye to Mr. Hawley. He wondered whether they wouldn't like a spot of something, even if it was Sunday. He had it right there in the office. But the Lewises thanked him and said they had to get home that night. He felt their hostility in the quick touch of their palms. And then they were gone and Mr. Hawley stood at the window and watched them drive off in their dirty black station wagon that looked so much like a hearse, except for the dirt, their stiff profiles fitting into each other, making an angular pattern against the bleeding sky.

But further along the road where Mr. Hawley could not see, at the railroad crossing where the gates were down, the car stopped and the pattern broke. Mrs. Lewis bent her head and sobbed and Mr. Lewis put his arms around her and let her cry into his jacket. They sat that way for a long time, long after the train had passed and the sound of its whistle had died and the gates were up.

Mr. Hawley, at the window, thought of their stiff profiles and that moment at the casket with only Mr. Lewis standing there, staring silently, his face blank as though he were looking into an empty drawer. Mr. Hawley remembered how hard he had worked that morning to get everything ready for them on such short notice with no help since it was Sunday. He had done it all alone, leaving the warm pocket of his Sunday bed early with his wife still spread beneath the blankets, dreaming her Sunday morning dream of pancakes on a tray and dinner at the Old Colonial. Mr. Hawley had gone downstairs, through the chill, thick air of the house, tightly closed against the winter night, with the coffee pot still silent on the stove; out into the new morning, breaking a path through the cold; down into the basement to spend hours on his feet bent over a small, still form. As he worked, putting the mask of sleep over the face of death, he felt a vague excitement, as though he were, indeed, reviving her, as though the eyes he had closed so carefully might open again and see him, without reproach: a kindly man who knew his trade and did it well. He had made her beautiful and Mrs. Lewis had not even looked. Her own mother and she had not even looked. Mr. Hawley sighed and closed the drapes.

He walked slowly to the next room where the casket stood before a backdrop of silk curtains, its lid still raised. Mr. Hawley looked down into it. The child, delicate, faintly tinted, lay like a flower in the white, satin-lined box. As he stared at her in the faded light, Mr. Hawley realized that now, somehow, even the mouth looked peaceful, as though it had relaxed and closed with only a slight parting of the lips. She was perfect. He let the lid down gently and lifted her in his arms. Ignoring the silver handles, he carried her, pressed against his chest, down the stairs.

Beat of Time

BY PAUL BARTLETT

IGNACIO PUENTES waited for his audience to grow quiet, pained by their mild applause. Whether due to the rain or poor publicity, the Copenhagen welcome was disappointing, especially since this was the first appearance of the Mexican Symphony Orchestra. As lights dimmed, gloom, almost vaporlike, settled over the audience. Rain swirled against the auditorium roof. Behind Ignacio, muffled coughs reminded him of prowling village goats . . . back in Mexico, far back in time. He caught the eyes of his concertmaster and sent him a twisted smile; then, the discipline of a lifetime controlling him, he lifted his baton, leaning forward, balancing carefully.

Forty years ago, in little Oblatos, he had begun, fingering the chipped blue fringed piano, the heat everywhere, the cliffs outside. The cliffs—green and rolling—were in the sweep of his arm as he conducted, folds and swells bulging in his memory, an aqueduct bridging them, seventeenth century *cantera,* pink, smothered by those green cliffs, locked there, connecting old and new.

That period of his life was forever abrasive—deep in beginnings. His teacher had been half-gourd, half-tortilla, a thing twisted into a frenzy of personal apprehension and musical genius. She had told him, as she hissed over his keyboard, cedar-framed photos on the wall behind her, the story of the broken baton, the Spanish maestro who believed he could go on conducting until his baton could take it no more, and so it had been one evening in Barcelona, the Beethoven ringing out, then, both of them crumbling.

Now, as Puentes flicked his baton, he found it more buoyant than air, utterly transparent. Through it, he took in his orchestra, men, women, music, all inseparable in his brain, dark notes and dark clothes mixing: he was still recalling that Spanish tale and yet his mind, crucified to the music, was driving in spike after spike of sound, piercing with the lance of the oboe the ears of his listeners: this was his "Symphonia Indio," composed in Oblatos, jotted among mountains, written in ships, jets, salons, quiet hotel rooms and noisy malecons. This was himself, out of tortilla and gourd: and his baton snatched up a rattle of seeds, the rustle of *viejos,* the clatter of death: the teacher of those valley days, dead for many years, lived in the percussion, the creep of it, the frustration of its ascendency: the cliffs came out of their *pastora* to jig across the Copenhagen stage, hesitating among the violins where the concert master drew his bow like a sedative. There were sedations from this point: the sleep of pines, the volcano-rabbit padding its crop-eared way among needles and grass: icy winds subtracting romantic impulses that were semi-autobiographical. Aztec tone and Toltec tone mumbled, but they were not the crux of this symphony. The soul of it, the depth of it, was the suffering that had gone into his art, the trials he alone knew, his loneliness and frustration, criticism and condemnation: they were the cellos and violas, years of beginning in the harp, his leaving the conservatory in the flutes, leaving himself, stumbling, climbing cliffs, slipping back: the horns were his world of romance when Chula had been so close, had travelled with him, Chula of the dark, dark hair, dark face and steely eyes, whose arms were warm, his Khatchaturian, his Villa Lobos, his Debussy: love? It was Chula, the ripple of her laughter, the flash of her grins, Chula—who tore up the adverse clippings, who stole for him, wept for him: then that day, in the *cordillera,* she had died for him, at that rarefied height, after a stroll, a talk under deodars, after plans for tomorrow, after acknowledgments of success: death, he heard it perch on the tip of his baton.

Ignacio shook himself and bent sidewise: he was lanky, pottery-faced, long-nosed, dark-eyed, forty-eight, gray: the gray seemed to leap out of his head, seemed to walk along his hairy hands: the elegance of his suit seemed to tear away from him: the light that liquored overhead, like dried tequila, shook as he shook: the music, watching him, the musicians, listening to him and watching him, bowed: there were grave notes from the horns, the brass sliding into dominance.

He sounded her name in his inner ear, the sacred ear some men have: his Chula, Isabel Consuelo Monteverde, alma, vida, nació en la ciudad de San Luis Potosi: then the whip of time struck and he heard the grumble of those who had battled his progress, who had defied his dedication to Mexico and things Mexican: he heard Aztec assault Toltec drum, pyramided by antiquity; he heard bass notes scuff under foot, telling him, guiding his baton.

The baton became a streak of blue, flame blue, and he saw it ripple across the harp that held, for spliced seconds, the Chirrugueresque membrane of yesterday: in that happy membrane, he and Chula strolled through the old park, the old cypress stiff in the fog, the fog cold on their clasped hands: she was talking about their son and what would happen to him, such fine things: that old colonial fountain stood on the left and as they circled it, noticing how the water had eaten away the cantera, making notches, children dashed off, spinning hoops: Mexico, mejíco, mexique—the words stole over his baton.

I'm forty-eight, he thought, I'm strong: I made this orchestra of men and women from jacales, out of tough minds, skull adobes, hardened into form. I whipped them into shape, and kept them there. I raised money for them. Battle after battle, toward victory. I fought to keep Felipe out of jail: I fought to have Ernesto with me.

Ernesto, softer, softer with your clarinet, let the ripeness and wisdom of your years creep into your tones.

And last night, Manuel sat up with me, late, looking at my album, seeing Chula's face, seeing the faces of a million miles of travel, the million wearinesses, the spume of those years.

Talk baton, talk to them, tell them how strong we are, how important; let us be glorious, let us pour out the pulque of our souls . . . show Copenhagen!

They tell me, those critics, that I have fumbled Liszt and mutilated Chopin—they tell me I have gone too far.

So, tonight, tonight, let's tell them that Ignacio Puentes is good, let's tell them that music is the greatest art. We'll show them this hall was made for sound: we'll put it across the ceiling and underneath the seats; we'll hang it on the grilles of memory.

Hunger, who feels hunger greater than the hunger for sound?

Gourmet of sound, reach out, tap with the slightness of your wood, eat with your ash the little notes that fall, spin them back again, back to Oblatos and the green, back to the house and the quiet tiles, the red tiles that mama loved to shine, the tiles of sitting, spinning my top, walking, falling between cliffs, getting up.

What is music but getting up and going on and on?

As he reached the culmination of his symphony, as the final movement drifted into the cadenza for violins, Ignacio heard the snap of wood and realized, as he looked at his baton, that he had hit the stand. The splintered wood flashed, and in the bright light, he came to a standstill. Pausing, hand on rack, the music dying, the auditorium soundless, gray hair over his forehead, he saw, in his surging mind, the slopes drenched in green, his teacher beside the fringed piano. Then, turning, bending a little, he walked painfully off-stage, one hand against his chest, the other grasping his baton.

9. Symmetry in Fire and Ice

Stand by Me, Kate

AN EXCERPT FROM A PLAY BY WILLIAM ALFRED

Act I   Scene II

Ten o'clock the same night. The parlor of Matthew Stanton's flat on the second floor of his house in Fifth Place. The set is on two levels, the lower level containing the kitchen of the Haggerty flat, which is blacked out. To stage-right there is a steep, narrow staircase. Enter *Matthew Stanton,* from stage-right, carrying a bottle of champagne, and his hat and topcoat. He pauses a moment at the bottom of the stairs. He is a handsome, auburn-haired man, dressed in a very good four-buttoned suit of expensive serge. He bounds up the stairs to his flat, and through the door. He flings his hat and coat on a chair, hides the bottle of champagne beyond the sofa, notices the door is open, and shuts it.

STANTON

Katie?   Katie!   Where the devil are you?

KATHLEEN

In here in bed.

(Kathleen's voice comes from behind the door.)

STANTON   Come on out in the parlor.

(Enter *Kathleen Stanton* closing the door behind her. She is tall and slim and fully dressed in a broadcloth suit, the blackness of which brings out her auburn coloring, and an uncanny resemblance to her husband. She brushes her full red hair, dressed in a pompadour, back with both her hands.)

KATHLEEN

I had a bit of headache and lay down.

Surely, Matt, it's not past closing, is it?

I wish you wouldn't take those stairs so fast:

They're wicked; you could catch your foot and fall.

Why, Mattie darling, what's the matter with you?
You're grey as wasps' nests.

STANTON   I'm to be the Mayor.
They caught Quinn with his red fist in the till,
The Party of Reform, I mean, and we
'Are going to beat their game with restitution
And self-reform.' Say something, can't you, Kate!
    (Kathleen sits down heavily, and puts her hand to her
    temple.)

KATHLEEN
Oh, Mattie, Mattie.

STANTON   Jesus!   Are you crying?
I've what I wanted since I landed here
Twelve years ago, and she breaks into tears.

KATHLEEN
It's that I'm—

STANTON   What?   You're what?

KATHLEEN   Afraid.

STANTON   Kathleen,
Now please don't let's go into that again.

KATHLEEN
Would you have me tell you lies?

STANTON   I'd have you brave.
    (Kathleen rises angrily and strides toward the door to the
    bedroom.)
Where are you going, Kate? To have a sulk?
Wait now, I'll fix a sugar-treat for you,
Unless, of course, you'd rather suck your thumb,
Brooding in your room—

KATHLEEN   I have the name;
As well to have the game!

STANTON   It's riddles, is it?

KATHLEEN
Riddles be damned, you think me idiotic;
I might as well fulfill your good opinion—
    (Matthew walks toward her.)
Come near me and I'll smash your face for you.
    (Matthew embraces her.)

304

STANTON

You're terrible fierce you are.   I wet me pants.

KATHLEEN

You clown, you'll spring my hairpins.   Mattie, stop.

STANTON

Are these the hands are going to smash my face?
They're weak as white silk fans. . . .   I'm sorry, Kate;
You made me mad.   And you know why?

KATHLEEN   I do.
You're as afraid as I.

STANTON   I am.   I am.
You know me like the lashes of your eye—

KATHLEEN

That's more than you know me, for if you did,
You'd see what these three years have done to me—
Now it's my turn to ask you where you're going!

STANTON

I begged you not to bring that up again.
What can I do?

KATHLEEN   You can call Father Coyne,
And ask him to apply for dispensation,
And we can be remarried secretly.

STANTON

Now?

KATHLEEN   Yes, Matt, now.   Before it is too late.
We aren't married.

STANTON   What was that in London,
The drunkard's pledge I took?

KATHLEEN   We're Catholics, Matt.
Since when can Catholics make a valid marriage
In a city hall?   You have to tell the priest—

STANTON

Shall I tell him now?   Do you take me for a fool
To throw away the Mayor's chair for that?

KATHLEEN

I haven't been to Mass for three years, Matt,
Or made my Easter-duty.   If I died,
I'd go to hell—

STANTON   I think the woman's crazy.

KATHLEEN

Don't you believe in God?

STANTON   Of course, I do;
And more, my dear, than you think that He
Would crush you as a man will crush a fly
Because of some mere technical mistake.

KATHLEEN

Mere technical mistake?   It's that now, is it?

STANTON

That's all it ever was?

KATHLEEN   A mere mistake?
A perjured marriage, three years fornication,
And now presumption—no wonder I am barren.
     (Pause. Kathleen takes a cigarette out of a box on the table,
     fits it into an ebony holder, and lights it, as if Stanton were
     not there.)

STANTON

I wish you wouldn't smoke them cigarettes.
Hightoned though it may be in France and England,
It's a whore's habit here.

KATHLEEN   '*Those* cigarettes.'
Don't try to hurt me, Matt.   You know you can,
As I know I can you.

STANTON   What do you want!

KATHLEEN

I want to be your wife without disgrace.
I want my honor back. I want to live
Without the need to lie.   I want you to keep faith.

STANTON

Not now.   Not now!

KATHLEEN   You've said that for three years.
What is it you're afraid of?

STANTON   Losing out.
You do not know these people as I do.
They turn upon the ones they make most of.
They would on me, if given half a chance.

306

KATHLEEN

    Matt, losing out? What profit for a man
    To gain the world and lose his soul?

STANTON   His soul!

    That's Sunday School! That's convent folderol,
    Like making half-grown girls bathe in their drawers
    To put the shame of their own beauty in them,
    And break their lives to bear the Church's bit.
    We are not priests and nuns, but men and women;
    The world religions give up is our world,
    The only world we have.   We have to win it
    To do the bit of good we all must do,
    And how are we to win the world, unless
    We keep the tricky rules its games are run by?
    Our faith is no mere monastery faith;
    It runs as fast as feeling to embrace
    Whatever good it sees. And if the good
    Is overgrown with bad, it still believes
    God sets no traps, the bad will be cut down,
    And the good push through its flowering to fruit.
    Forget your convent school. Remember, Katie,
    What the old women in the drowned boreens
    Would say when cloudbursts beat their fields to slime,
    And the potatoes blackened on their stalks
    Like flesh gone proud. 'Bad times is right,' they'd say,
    'But God is good: Apples will grow again!'
        (Pause.)
    What sin have we committed?   Marriage, Kate?
    Is that a sin?

KATHLEEN   It is with us.

STANTON   Because

    You feel it so. It isn't. It's prudence.
    What if they should deny us dispensation?

KATHLEEN

    Could we be worse off than we are?

STANTON   Kathleen!

KATHLEEN

    Could we be worse off than we are I said.

STANTON

Could we! We could! You don't know poverty;
You don't know what it is to do without,
Not fine clothes only, nor a handsome house,
But men's respect. I do. I have been poor.
'Mattie, will you run down to the corner,
And buy me some cigars?' or 'Mattie, get
This gentleman a cab.' Twelve years I served
Ned Quinn and Agnes Hogan, day by day,
Buying my freedom like a Roman slave.
Will you ask me to put liberty at stake
To ease your scrupulous conscience. If you do,
You're not the woman that I took you for
When I married you. Have you no courage, Kate?—

KATHLEEN

Will you lecture me on courage? Do you dare?
When every time I walk those stairs to the street
I walk to what I feel is an enemy camp.
I was not raised like you; and no offence,
Please, Mattie, no offence. I miss my home.
Whore's habit it may be to smoke, as you say,
But it brings back the talk we used to have
About old friends, new books, the Lord knows what,
On our first floor on Baggot Street in Dublin
With the last sunlight glancing off the tea,
And the shrewd people smelling of the cold
Laughing for the sake of laughter. Matt,
This following, you think so much about
You made a perjured marriage to preserve it,
I never knew the likes of them to talk to,
Person to person. They were cooks and maids,
Or peasants in the country houses, Matt,
All they can find to talk of, servants' talk,
Serfs' talk, eternal tearing down.
Don't tell me I don't know what poverty is.
What bankruptcy is worse than banishment.
They say the sense of exile is the worst
Of all the pains that harrow poor, damned souls.
It is that sense I live with every day.

308

WILLIAM ALFRED

STANTON

Are you the only exile of us all?
You slept your crossing through in a rosewood berth
With the swells a hundred feet below your portholes;
And ate off china on a linen cloth
With the air around you fresh as the first of May.
I slept six deep in a bunk short as a coffin
Between a poisoned pup of a seasick boy
And a slaughtered pig of a snorer from Kildare
Who wrestled elephants the wild nights through
And sweated sour milk.   I wolfed my meals,
Green water, and salt beef, and wooden biscuits,
On my hunkers like an ape, in a fourfoot aisle
As choked as the one door of a burning school.
I crossed in mid-December: seven weeks
Of driving rain that kept the hatches battened
In a hold so low of beam a man my height
Could never lift his head.   And I couldn't wash.
Water was low; the place was like an icehouse;
And girls were thick as fieldmice in a haystack
In the bunk across. I would have died of shame
When I stood in the landing shed of this 'promised land,'
As naked as the day I first saw light,
Defiled with my own waste like a dying cat,
And a lousy red beard on me like a tinker's,
While a bitch of a doctor with his nails too long
Dared tell me: 'In Amurrica, we bathe!'
And the others laughed to jolly him along.
I'd have died with shame, had I sailed here to die.
I swallowed pride and rage, and made a vow
The time would come when I could spit both out
In the face of the likes of him. I made a vow
I'd fight my way to power if it killed me,
Not only for myself, but for our kind,
For the men behind me laughing out of fear
At their own shame as well as mine, for the women
Behind the board partition, frightened dumb
With worry they'd be sent back home to starve
Because they'd dirty feet.   I was born again.

It came to me as brutal as the light
That makes us flinch the day the midwife takes
Our wet heels in her fist and punches breath
Into our dangling carcasses: Get power!
Without it there can be no decency,
No virtue and no grace.   I have kept my vow;
The Mayor's chair is mine but for the running.
Will you have me lose it for your convent scruples?
    (Pause.)

KATHLEEN

You never told me that, about your landing.

STANTON

There's many things I never told you, Kate.
I was afraid you'd hold me cheap.

KATHLEEN   Oh, Mattie,
Don't you know me yet?—

STANTON   Stand by me,
Stand by me, Kate.   As sure as God's my judge,
The minute I get into City Hall
The first thing I will do is call the priest
And ask him to make peace with God for us.
Stand by me, Kate.

KATHLEEN   I will, though it costs my life.
    (Stanton kisses her.)

STANTON

God stand between us and all harm.   There now!
I've wiped those words from your lips.   Ah, where's my mind!
I've brought champagne, and it's as warm as tears.
But get the glasses.
    (Kathleen gets two glasses from a dresser, and sets them on
    the table.   Mattie opens the bottle with a pop and fills
    them.   They lift the glasses to each other.)
             Let the past be damned,
The dead bury the dead, the future's ours.

Curtain

Radio Weather Report: Korean Battlefield

(For Lt. Billy Hall, Killed in Action)

BY MARION MONTGOMERY

"The sun came out this morning after weeks of rain." **CBS**

"The sun came out this morning after weeks of rain"—
Already, jets scream silver through the sky;
The sucking sea of mud will dry
And tanks and men move forward once again.

The season is at harvest; jagged seed of steel,
Unplanted, rust upon the rusting earth
While the life-giving sun gives birth
To hope, and all the anxious seedmen feel

How strangely planting and the harvest are but one:
The sky now clear, the sun-red driven seed
May find more fruitful earth to feed
Its moment-yielding harvest to the sun.

Young Girl:
A Stroll before Her Wedding

BY MARION MONTGOMERY

The pale wisteria petals flutter along the ground
    and are blue butterflies.
The three mysteriously mortal leaves of the elm move
    on the gravel walk with yellow wings.
Mimosa blossoms are cocoons that hide the incarnate
    grub of desire.

Even the trees are wings, moving the earth toward
    a flower of cloud.

Final Performance

BY ELIZABETH BARTLETT

A spinner in the green years, I trudge the snowdeep woods
To find the Rima trees where I was warm in silk through
Those first winters. Then, the unwinding thread,
From which I swung by two spare arms and legs,
Hung in the air like a gay trapeze, each vine
Humming to the brace and pull and reel of child's
Spider ways, an upside down dancer with her feet
In the clouds, and the heart in her mouth a feast.
A beginner in the green years, my thick wool thumbs push back
The broken twig, the empty nest, the closed gray flaps
To summer's Ringling tent. Embarrassed, I lift
A rose still red and moist and soft. Again I twist
Its thin stem toward the light, and dare the sky
To seize my heels and trick time's crafty eyes,
While I repair the web, then climb to one last height
Before I leap—to catch the hands of night.

Bowling Green, Manhattan

BY ROBERT WINNER

The windows flame at noon—
Dreams bent inward, towers
From another age—
The loose elegance of dainty castles,
    In the thin cracks of sky—
Look up! Columbus knew
Clouds, light-edged by the sun,
Stretched in their blue lanes
Returning over the Atlantic
Migrants—slowly circling—
In Spain's sun—visions remembered
Whispering on the lap of ocean,
The sea's face, blue-feathered,
Lions in the fern dark, steps
At the ends of first streets.

Appendix I:
Art in a Small Compass

Images and Harmony

"Art begins," wrote Tolstoi, "with the wee bit." Often the young writer will strike off a single magic sentence, an image, a page of images, a line of poetry, that would enrich even a great novel, like the image of Petya's last moment in War and Peace. *Perhaps the young writer cannot trace the spark of the sudden creative blaze that illuminated his thought and set fire to his words. Yet there must be a conscious mastery of the craft, beginning with the "wee bit," the luminous phrase and the architecture of the sentence, before the writer can hope to direct and conserve the stream of his creative energy, or sustain the magic touch of his first tiny creation. As Milton knew the epic similes of Homer, touching them with a unique Miltonic strain, so the young writer must relearn the classical arrangement of images, enriching the classic techniques with the unmistakable impress of a new creative personality. The classic skills of description and narration are after all only a recognition of the reader's need for an orderly arrangement of ideas, images, scenes: the spring before the lilac, the gloomy walls before the gray face, the frame of man before his countenance. In a hundred places Dickens uses a blending element to set a mood of place or person and give his images an emotional consistency: the sun's glare, smoke, mud, rain, moonlight. A writer neglects this classic resource at his peril. First he must master it, then give the resource of the masters a new grace or poignancy of effect. Each writer, it is true, is his own structure. But why should the author's own way of meeting the reader's needs not encompass the rich resources of his great predecessors? "If you do not have a talent," said Flaubert to Maupassant, "you must build one." One way to build a talent is consciously to attempt the theories and techniques of the great stylists from Homer to Conrad.*

It is a delusion difficult to dispel that some genetic magic separates the amateur from the professional writer. The real difference is that the professional writer is able to achieve with relative regularity those effects that the amateur achieves, consciously or not, only at rare moments. The sketches that follow represent genuine creative achievement in the "wee bit," an achievement preceded by years or months of labor to blend the classic skills with the author's unique way of looking at life.

317

Where Is My Father?

BY LILY PORITZ

I SAW HIM only that morning, my father, when I brought in from the garden the new September roses, the dewdrops shimmering like tears on their petals, and placed them in the vase beside his bed. He lay asleep as I climbed onto the black leather stool and drew up the canvas shade, heavily drenched in sickness, allowing a soft ray of Cape Town sun to shadow the yellow crust on his face. And the lifeless blue eyes of my father opened to the light.

"Daddy? Can I massage you now?"

He looked down at me, with eyes determined not to close, and his dried mouth stretched in a tired smile.

"My child!"

I had seen him only that morning, as I strengthened his unused limbs, gently rubbing the palm of my hand into them, moistened and invigorated by eau de cologne. How proud he had been as he stretched forth his wrinkled hand to reach my own, his head lifting from the pillow, upright as the weight of my hand fell away. And the words of my mother last night rang true: God had come—father was well!

He had awakened suddenly at sundown the night before. He had awakened hungry, and we heard his voice asking for food. He drew himself upwards on the bed, unflinchingly, and parted his dry mouth to the thin liquid my mother nursed to coolness and fed him with a child's spoon. He had asked for more and still more until the household came alive and we all surrounded him, my brothers and sisters, in withheld wonder. "Bring down Leah and Jean and Harry and Joseph!" my father proclaimed as the warm broth colored him. "Bring them all to our house, and we will celebrate."

Just the night before we had a houseful of people, just the

318

night before we heard him laughing, laughing as he had not laughed for more than three years. And the yellowness—the deathly mustard veil—was gone from his face. His skin took on a luminous glow, the blue eyes radiant in rebirth. He was a child now, proudly recalling the names of his children on each of his fingers. And we came around him, my sisters and brothers, and rose onto his thick rumpled bed, permeated by the stuffy smell of sickness.

Our shrill voices, broken in collision, hammered on about school and teachers as though with the moment's passing our words would go in vain. And we told him about our marks and report cards and that the next day was the last day of school.

"Last year you brought your teachers presents," he said. "This year it will be the same."

He could not take us to select the candies this year, but his trembling hand persisted as it wavered, weak and childlike, on the sheet of paper addressed to the confectioners.

I can see my father smiling as he wrote the note, aloof to the trembling fingers.

I took the box up on the platform and presented it to my teacher. Her smile was sweet as honeysuckles; her delicate white hands unfastened the silver-speckled wrapping.

"It's beautiful," she sighed, as she bent over the polished mahogany box, her hands caressing the mauve velvet. "Who selected this beautiful present?"

"My father."

"Tell your father I shall keep my most precious jewels in it and treasure it always."

I ran home through the fields, the wind laughing in my ears, dancing, suspended in a cloud of love. I breathed the sweet smell of green grass after the rainfall, the sweeping trees encircling me like a mass of embroidery. "Daddy! Daddy, listen what my teacher said!"

A long car stood in front of our house. Two men in festive dark suits were coming down the stairs, softly joking. Breathless, I met them at the gate and stood gazing up at them.

"My father? Where is my father?"

A hand caressed my hair, and the two men swept by me and descended into the long, shiny limousine. I raced up the stairs.

The shutters in our house were barred, the windows shut. I tore at the front door, and it swung open wildly. The mirrors were turned—darkness met me. "Mommy! Daddy!" I ran through the house—everywhere! Everywhere but into the dark room of sickness. "Mommy! Daddy!"

But I reached the end of the silent house and turned and walked slowly back to my father's room. And there I saw them— my mother, my brothers and sisters—their faces cast in stone, silenced, their eyes unmoving from the stiff white sheet.

My Father

BY MILDRED MEYER KING

AS SOME MEN are creative with words, or paints, or music, so my father was with food, and he was as temperamental as any other artist. He was very quiet, shy; he blushed easily. He was headstrong and independent, impulsive, erratic, subject to cloudbursts of rage and lightning streaks of exuberance and sheer joy. His movements were quick, his actions nervous, his ears as keen as a fox's. He cursed like a longshoreman, was a fighter when goaded, but beneath his gruffness lay kindnesss. How he loved to heap gargantuan portions on a hungry man's plate and watch him eat—a penniless as well as a paying customer.

He moved from restaurant to restaurant in Queens at varying intervals, and so we gypsied from town to town—from Ridgewood to Woodside to Hollis to Richmond Hill to Bellerose and then back to Richmond Hill. In each I remember a green enamel and steel hood hovering over the stainless steel steamtables; a large griddle sizzling with bacon, eggs, or hamburgers; two larger ovens containing succulent roasts; huge pots of soup and potatoes sitting on the stoves, smaller ones simmering stew or goulash; an enormous white refrigerator; smaller steel refrigerators; a glass showcase filled with pies, pastries, a large pan of bread pudding, and rice pudding topped with two golden inches of custard rich with a dozen eggs and two quarts of milk. About fourteen could be seated at the marble counter and there were usually seven tables, each seating four to six people.

I remember my father most vividly standing in the restaurant by his cutting board near the ovens. By afternoon his white apron was stained with blood, gravy, and grease after much cutting, cooking, and serving. His cigar was always accumulating inches of cold ash at the edge of the counter; his drinking mug was always filled with either coffee or seltzer water or whiskey. He consumed between a pint and a quart of whiskey a day, with intermittent dry spells, and worked eighteen hours a day.

My father had a fine, intelligent face, a high forehead and cheekbones, and aquiline nose, and sensitive, generous lips. He had gray dreamer's eyes and medium brown hair. He was stocky, about five foot five, with strong shoulders, arms, and hands. Though his temples had grayed, he looked much younger than his years, and even in 1956, when death tiptoed in, he looked more like forty-one than fifty-one.

I never knew what silent hopes nestled in his eyes, what lonely dreams tormented him, what anguished restlessness assailed his spirit. Except for occasional reminiscences of the Baltic Sea and the beloved Danzig he left at age nineteen, he shared little with anyone. On Sundays he would take long, solitary walks, or bus rides, or go to Rockaway or Long Beach and gaze at the water. Sometimes I accompanied him. And I wondered if the ocean, and the ships he had sailed on, harbored his secrets.

I didn't confide in my father, either. Yet between us there was a very special love, a mute, wordless understanding. Although affection embarrassed him, I often crossed his barrier of reticence with teasing kisses and rufflings of his hair or foolish tickles. I could feel his love, could see it in his eyes, and I knew he could feel my love for him.

I remember a Sunday afternoon so gray in my memory I can give it no reason. The moments it holds are permanently drenched with pain. It was a day in 1954 or early 1955 when I was still living in Richmond Hill with my parents. Perhaps it was the day my father started to die.

He had just come upstairs from the restaurant, where he had been puttering around. I heard him mutter a greeting to my mother as he passed the kitchen. He was wearing his white trousers and shirt and dirty black shoes. He looked tired but sober as he walked into my room and sat down on the bed. I stood in front of the dressing table combing my hair.

"What's the matter, Pop?" I asked the question casually—it was my mode with him. I saw his reflection in the mirror, his body limp, his head bowed, his shoulders bent, his hands drooped futilely over his knees, and it clutched at my heart. I put down the comb, walked over to him, and kissed his hair.

"What's wrong, Pop?" I said. He looked up at me and uttered my name. His eyes were filled with tears.

"What's wrong?" I pleaded. I had never seen him cry.

"I don't know," he said. "I don't know," and the tears stained his face. "It's everything."

"What is it?" I repeated inanely, and he shook his head.

I kissed his big, rough, gentle hands, his sweet cheeks, his hair, and pulled his head to my bosom and cried with him. There was nothing to say.

The Door Clicked Shut

BY ARLYNE KRUM

THE DOOR clicked shut. Naked, I lay between the sheets, shivering suddenly from the slightly open window which looked out onto a snow-shrouded Harlem. A tug whistle tolled mournfully.

Shadows flickered on the ceiling, gray and blurred by my tears, which trickled slowly down my cheeks until the salt drops burned my lips. Pushing the sheets away, I got out of the bed and hopped to the window, the linoleum cold to the soles of my feet. I stretched up to close the window, and was enveloped in a keen breeze which nipped my body. Away from the window, I could see my reflection in the oversized window pane. Hugging my arms about my self, more to conceal my nakedness than to warm me, I looked out at the uneven rectangles of light. I pulled the twisted cord that hung next to the window and the blind slats fell, moved for a moment, and lay still.

My eyes were dry now as I glanced about the sparsely furnished room. Of the two desks in the room, his was the cluttered one, piled high with medical journals, samples, books, and ragged scraps of paper. The ugly white oak furniture, shellacked to a high gloss, intensified the antiseptic quality of the room. The beds were covered with blue denim that had obviously been laundered too often. Two red vinyl desk chairs and two bookcases completed the furnishings of the Spartan-like room.

I had stopped shivering, and as I walked over to the desk, I played a game on the brown and green squares; right foot on the brown square, left foot on the green square. As I sat down, the plastic of the chair felt cold to my skin. My fingers played along the glass-topped desk, sticking and stopping in the sliding. Light from the bronze snake lamp gleamed on my hands as I fingered the papers that he had touched, trying to get closer to him by touching things that he had touched. Cumbersome, oversized texts crowded his bookshelves. Poised on the highest of the three shelves was one of the felt monkeys we had won at Palisades Park last August. The bright crimson was the brightest touch in the room.

Above the porcelain sink, in a far corner of the room, was the sole mirror. Dragging toward it, I reached for a glass. I turned the faucet, and cool water flowed into the glass. I drank deeply and splashed my flushed face with water. Only then did I look into the mirror. A face ugly with puffiness regarded me, and so I turned away.

I sank into the bed and covered myself.

The door opened softly.

Montauk Herman

BY ALBERT G. CRAZ

TWO GUINA HENS yawking through the tall grass beside the dirt road warned little Georgie he was getting close to Herman's shack. Around him stretched the marsh grass and flatlands cut with creeks and inlets just back of the ocean near Shinnecock Canal. On the roadway ahead, sun mirage swam like water, glistening under the white July sun which rolled in the naked sky. Animals kind of piled up after the hens: white and black bell-clanking goats, iron-throated dogs, and pigs with swaying pink bellies running along the dusty road ruts.

Closer to Herman's clapboard shack, a flock of gray geese moved like Paris taxis toward the yawning shade of the doorless garage. There were white chickens. And as the shack reared up from the grass, there was Herman. He always knew when someone was coming and would emerge from his house with a flourish. The loose screen door slapping dust behind him, its rotted screen coiling and uncoiling, and Herman himself squealing. He spoke in agonizing screams, as though he were falling always from some great height and emitting his death agonies. As he completed sentences, the pitch would always rise.

"Georgieee!"

"Hi, Herman." Georgie couldn't help grinning at the stubby man, even though he was around fifty.

"Gonna get some ducks?"

"Of course." But this was really their own private joke. Georgie always brought his BB gun and usually walked the marsh and creeks trying to jump a sleeping mallard or black. It was just for fun; a ten-year-old with a BB gun imitating the marvelous scenes of *Field and Stream*.

"Wanna eat with me?"

"Well, gee, I don't know, Herman."

"Killed a milk-fed calf last weeek!"

Georgie always worried about eating with Herman because of the canaries. Herman had a million canaries flying loose in the house and they sometimes flew informal bombing missions over the kitchen table and God knows where else. Yet Herman was an excellent cook, and there was never any nonsense about eating vegetables and other stuff. Just good beef, cooked rare; bread thick with butter, catsup and ice-cold milk. But the canaries kept little Georgie always on guard, as though he were ready to receive a surprise blow on the head.

Herman didn't help much either. Screaming away as he talked and serving the food with black crescent fingernails. His yellow teeth showed black edges when he smiled, and his breath close up was garlicky. Herman was dirty. His house was dirty. He was everything Georgie's mother was against. His shirt collar rim was smooth with grease. His skin pores were flecked black. On his suspender strap rounding his shoulder was a direct hit from one of the canaries. His heavy rubber boots gritted over the floor as he moved from the filthy bombed-out stove to the bedaubed and cluttered sink.

"Milk-fed calf?" Georgie asked.

"Fed it a gallon of milk everyday for ten months! Good stay-eeeks!"

"Well, okay, Herman. I'll be back in an hour or so."

"Be careful, Georgieee!" And with a bang of the screen, laughing in screams, into the house he'd go.

II

Georgie never knew how Herman made any money. Not that he needed much with his garden and the animals. For variety, blue-claw crabs and clams could be picked from the creeks and bay. And of course Herman had his junk. Almost as if it had always been there and Herman's shack had pushed up through it, were the stacks of oars, beach umbrella frames, beach chair frames, oil drums, clam rakes, paint cans and fishnet scraps which Herman steadily salvaged from the marsh. Occasionally someone would buy a rusted clam rake or a beach chair frame.

Then, too, Herman had a way with animals. His reputation for curing sick dogs and adjusting the organs of cats was legend. Georgie remembered once seeing a woman stop her Buick by Herman's shack and get out with a very young tiger cat in her arms.

"Sure I fix heeem!" Herman had screamed at the lady. Then he disappeared into his shack which in a moment filled with the screams of the cat and Herman both. Then out bursts Herman, laughing in wheezes, wiping a drop of blood from his pocketknife to his pants leg.

"One dollar pleeeze!" Which the amazed lady quickly paid as she clutched her still more amazed cat, and jumped into the Buick.

"Fixing" what seemed to be a perfectly all right cat puzzled little Georgie, but when he asked Herman about it Herman just laughed and screeched until the tears rolled and washed in white streaks down his unshaven face. When he'd gotten back a little control, he'd scream, "Feeex!" point at Georgie, and stumble around laughing and holding his small pot belly, the tears coming all over again.

III

Georgie only saw Herman really quiet and serious once. It had been the summer before when he had just gotten the BB gun. He was lying up on Herman's flat tar roof waiting to see what would fly over. He had taken pot shots at sea gulls hanging high in the sky just below the gray overcast. Nothing had happened. Once he thought he heard the slap of the BB in the feathers of a gull, but the bird just dipped in flight for a second and then kept right on going. Georgie knew there was a law against shooting gulls, but he really didn't think there was much chance of killing one.

But one gull came quite low. Its white wings bent and scalloped like a bread knife. Georgie couldn't miss, and the great white bird came down, but not in a tumbling, feathery heap. Its wings stayed stiff and extended, so it spiraled down, almost like a toy glider after it hits a wire or tree and the wings are crooked and it spirals in lazy swinging circles to the street.

It landed in the tall grass beside Herman's house. It was alive. When Georgie approached, the bird's golden eyes stared, and in the eyes were coiled surprise, fear, and helplessness. It didn't move. Yet the eyes were enough to keep Georgie scared. Georgie heard Herman moving toward him in the grass and when he turned to look he saw Herman's eyes for the first time with the laughing out of them. Instead they seemed filled with cold, dirty ashes.

"Go ahead, kill it! Kill it! A harmless bird; you can't eat it! It keeps the marsh clean. Kill it!" Then he picked up an old rake handle from the grass and handed it to Georgie.

The harsh squeaking of Herman had frightened Georgie more than the bird, and he felt like he had broken glass churning in his stomach. But he knew Herman was right, and he had to now finish what he really never wanted to begin.

After Georgie had dug the hole, spilled the black dirt over the pure white feathers, and packed the dirt down with the flat bottom of the shovel, he found Herman next to the garage, milking the black goat. He said he was sorry to the humped shoulders and bent neck as the milk hissed in steady squirts against the metal pail. And all Herman said was, "You eat chicken soup with meee?" And then he winked, jumped up screaming his crazy laugh as he thumped into the house slamming the useless screen door.

Ryker Alley

BY MAURICE POSNER

I THREW my barracks bag over my shoulder and, mounting the El steps, looked back over Ryker Alley. In the October afternoon shadows, I saw for the last time the Manhattan tenement ravine that I had called home. It twisted its narrow, winding way as if noise and soot, and the ant-activity of thousands of people, had cut a gorge between the overhanging gray-brown buildings. On the cobble-stoned street fell the patterned shadow of the overhead railway ties. Above me loomed the vaulted stone towers of the Brooklyn Bridge, its thin tracery of gray steel webbing the sky, the roadway in a swift arch soaring over the East River to the banks of Brooklyn. From rust-red escapes hung white bedsheets, billowing in the wind, and in their roundness looked like fungus clinging to a cliff side. As far as I could see, pushcarts lined the gutters. Vendors hawked their wares of pink calico and blue jeans, of plum blue grapes and brown-speckled bananas, and of brined herring and scaly carp on a bed of chopped ice. In the afternoon breeze wafted the salt, sewered smell of the East River. From below, I heard the honking of yellow, checkered taxicabs, the double-clutching grind of Mack trucks, their drivers cursing and bullying a path through the strangulated traffic; and from above, the anger of the subway trains. Across the street two young men in shiny gabardines and brown felt hats, their long black locks curling devoutly at their ears, entered a basement synagogue. Through the door which swung brokenly from one hinge, before the flickering candle flames of a seven-branched candelabrum, I briefly glimpsed gray-bearded men wrapped in striped, fringed prayer-shawls, rocking in prayer. Next to the El stairs, from behind a broken wood fence, seeped the smell of urine, acid and stinging. Through the fence I saw the empty lot where once stood the tenement in which I was born, now filled with undrained puddles of water, shining with the green glisten of broken bottles, and where frightened yellow cats foraged among the rusty tin cans. On a brown, moldering brick wall hung a tattered poster urging a vote for Fiorello H. La Guardia.

Through the August Night

BY CHARLES EDWARD BRYAN

I SQUIRM deeper into my seat as the bus races through the rain-soaked August night, its lights bouncing from the filmed highway and jutting into the mist drifting from the black Jersey swamps. I'm leaving behind a part of myself, a part that

I'll never get back again. The asphalt ribbon is broken by the flaring neon mosaic of passing roadhouses and drive-ins, and as these patterns of light flash past me, I wonder if that's all a man is: a series of sections scattered through the world with only memories to pull the threads together. Threads. Threads twining through time; threads of love, truth and aloneness; the threads of one's self—wrapped by the elusive thread of dreams.

This is the last run from Washington to New York; the bus is almost empty. A few passengers occupy the red-covered seats; their heads roll against the chair-backs and nod with the lurching of the darkened bus. My leg jostles the seabag propped alongside me, leaving a smudge on my starched uniform. I move my hand slowly toward my knee, then stop and lean back in the seat. Why should I bother? Who's going to chew me out? I've got my discharge from the Navy; there's no need to worry about a clean uniform any more—no need at all—I'm free. I'm going home. I should be happy—that's for sure.

But free for what?

A tired melancholy fills me as I rest my head on the cool window glass.

Before the Last Exam

BY NORMA COHEN

I CAN SEE the teardrops of snow dancing down through the space which hovers outside the window of my room. The roof top on the house opposite me is coated with a patchy film of white. Two broken fingers of ice hang from the edge, each tremorously alive with its glass glitter.

I sit on the edge of my bed and sink my head into the cup of my hands. Choked by the stale air, life has become mute between these walls. Shelves of books and stacks of papers. Stacks of papers and shelves of books. The mind crawls, quivers, and contracts, the heart of it enclosed and lost within—like that of a dead blossom.

Once, in the springtime, I walked past a garden in which there was a morning glory tree so full of blue and white blossoms that the branches leaned over the fence to let the unwanted ones fall to the indifferent concrete. I stopped, scooped one of the fallen white blossoms into my hand, and slipped it into the pocket of my skirt to carry home with me. Later, when I took it out and held it in my hand, I fingered the dry petals, wondering why they slept. I went into the kitchen and filled one of our chipped teacups with water. I placed the flower on top and watched it float there. But it did not even stir. It just lay there, looking as though it were crying into the water.

Mother came home and put her bundles of potatoes and onions in the bin under the window. When she stood up and saw the flower floating on the water, she remained motionless for a moment. Then she shook her head so hard that wisps of silvery hair fluffed out into the air like the cotton candy you see on paper stalks at carnivals. I remembered what she had said to me one night before my father came home from work, about the two of them being different than they used to be, that the two of them were getting old, that it was time I started being practical and making plans for the future. She plucked the flower from the water and tossed it through the open window. I ran to the sill and leaned out, watching the way the breeze sent it zigzagging between the clotheslines down to the green-yellow cement of the alleyway. I remember thinking that the floor, the breeze, and all the universe were laughing at me. I ran into my room, turned some jazz music on my radio, and made it play so loud I couldn't think about anything any more.

But, watching the snow today, I remembered. And now I fear that, in my weariness when the petals of my mind have closed and I can neither take my school exams nor think of getting a job, I too shall be blown down by a laughing breeze.

Snowstorm

BY REX ASHLOCK

A BLANKET of snow about a foot thick covered Manhattan after the storm that marked the last days of 1960. The last weekend of the year had been filled with the violent squall, winds that tore at the city with a rage that frightened the populace into retreat and blew snow in every direction along the Atlantic Coast before finally passing on out to sea in the middle of the night.

By Monday afternoon the hibernating city had barely begun to stir itself. Madison Square spread out silent and brilliant, a level valley of whiteness among the towers of the city, only a faint gray cobweb pattern of pathways etching the square and sidewalks adjoining it. The white calligraphy of the snow-frosted trees danced across the square, and the green bronze sculptures were nearly covered as though with dustcloths in a closed-up house. Along Broadway, Madison, and Twenty-Third Streets, the five- and ten-foot-high heaps of snow that had been plowed up to the sides muffled the sounds of the buses and trucks that moved slowly through the oatmeal-colored slush on the pavement.

Crossing Madison Avenue at Twenty-Third Street to enter the square, the first impression made by the landscape was its loss of definition. The boundaries of the square seemed almost obliterated. Ripple drifts flowed up and down over the accustomed forms of sidewalks and curbings and iron fences and benches, softening and melting them into a single white gentle surface. The narrow meandering pathways created by pedestrians made the new definition.

Only statues and trees stood above the white covering and against each of these a drift of snow like a frozen wave of surf. The charred-looking green-bronze statues, each wearing a tuft of

snow atop its head and shoulders, retained their military or ora-
torical poses, holding bronze sabers or bronze books and wearing
bronze capes, looking as unreal as when pigeons sat on their heads
in summer.

Now the pigeons fluttered like oversize snowflakes round a
diminutive figure near the pond in the center of the square. Snow
filled the cement circle of the pond like a cream pie, and near the
benches that faced the pond stood a gnomelike figure in the winter
clothing of a child: red scarf around her head, red mittens, pink
wooly coat, plaid slacks stuffed into red rubber boots. Waving
her arms at the center of the flurry of pigeons, she seemed to be
directing an airborne orchestra. She bent down and filled both
hands with bread crumbs from a paper sack at her feet and threw
the crumbs up into the bright hard light, and the pigeons flew up
in a flurry each time like old newspapers caught in a whirlwind.
They whirred around and around her, eating from her hands and
settling at her feet in a tight mass, pecking at the ground until
she repeated the action, and they all blew up into the air around
her again. As one came closer one heard the whirring of the birds'
wings and their choked guttural sounds as they lighted at her feet;
and one saw that she was not a child; her old crumpled yellow
paper face revealed no emotions as she threw crumbs to the birds.

On the other side of the circle of the pond, two tramps talked
with great seriousness. The silence absorbed their voices, giving
their actions the appearance of a pantomime. One sat on a bench
with his legs crossed and arms folded across his chest as though
it were a warm spring day; the bench was covered with several
inches of snow in which he was sitting, and his swinging foot
swept up a little puff of dry snow with each swing. The other man
stood talking, gesturing with large slow motions as though under
water, his red face distorted with expressions of drunken earnest-
ness. His unbuttoned tattered topcoat hung from his shoulders
unevenly, with a bottle in a side pocket, and swung with his ex-
aggerated ceremonial gestures like a ritual garment. His open-
necked shirt revealed a silvery curl of hair on a red chest and neck.
With each broad gesture made by the standing man, the seated
man nodded his head deeply in assent. They moved so in accord

with each other that they could have been puppets on the same string performing a slow silent ritual.

The great clock in the tower by the square cleared its throat and chimed four o'clock in deep bongs, the only clear sound to be heard. A susurrus drifted up from the traffic around the square: muffled metallic clicking of tire-chains against fenders, and the squishing slur of wheels moving slowly on the slushy pavement. The pigeons fluttered and the tramps gestured; as though seen from behind a plate-glass window: soundless.

Gray

BY EMILY GRECO

DIRTY SNOW piled against city curbs; shadows on the water touched with dirty green beneath an East River bridge; silver strands of metal stretching, curving downwards and upwards sustaining the bridge; the flickering of automobile tops as the sunless February day makes them like mirrors in their flight across the bridge's yellow-gray ways; the white blue-tinged gray of pigeons' opened tails, as in mass-flight they soar four stories high, with their darker-purple to blacker-gray outspread wings and thrusting, pointed heads; the air-gray sound of their fanning wings in the iron-gray sky, in the February sky. The aluminum gray of a crumpled typewriter cover, with black peeping from its curved folds. Gray showing through the outer rim of lipsticked mouths in the dust-gathering gray wind. Gray is light like hair almost wholly white, or lacquered like black hair turning white. Gray is the underside of an African violet leaf, and of many coins. Gray is the color of darkening hope and ebbing life. Dark gray is the color of rushing death. It is the rustiness of a squirrel's coat, warm coals of his tail.

An Empty Barrel

BY ISABELLE M. WEINBERG

MY EGO IS a large empty barrel with a hole in the bottom, in which sounds echo hollowly. Tell me that I'm clever. Tell me that I am good-looking. Tell me that I am your best friend, that knowing me has been a great pleasure in your life, almost a necessity. Tell me that my children are well-adjusted and happy children, that I have been good to them and that they will remember me with love, not hate. Tell me that my husband loves me and still is glad that he married me and that I am a good wife. Help fill the barrel, slowly, upward, upward. Tell me that I can write. Tell me that I am a person, not just nothing. Tell me that you care whether I live or die. Fill the barrel, *please.* And when it is filled, if you are silent, I shall be happy for one moment, one moment of eternity. And then it will slowly leak out of the bottom, drop by drop, leveling downward until the whole barrel is empty and hollow again and I am nothing. Then please, tell me again, say it all over again, tell me until you are crooked and gnarled and I am gray. Help me to fill that barrel again. Give me one more moment of fullness again and again and again. For unless you tell me that I am good, that I am somebody, that I count, that you care, I am an empty barrel.

Night Scene

BY MILDRED MEYER KING

ACROSS PARK AVENUE, in the quiet November night, I see the Seagram Building. Lit windows shine like gleaming dominoes, lend a shadowy luster to the tall, bronze sheath. Behind wide glass frames on the ground floor, hidden lamps illumine a sand-colored structure resembling the walls of an Egyptian tomb. Eight fountains, wreaths spraying silvery water, sit symmetrically on either corner of the diamond-dusted pavement. To one side, two trees, long-stemmed chalices, sway in soft concert with the wind. They raise their filigree branches, whisper their hosannas to the heavens. The midnight-blue sky, an infinite feathery quilt, blankets everything. Only the full moon glows, pale and ethereal, mid the trees' fragile limbs.

Corridors

BY JEANNE PFEIFFER

YOUNG VOICES sound and resound in the funnel-like corridor of the hospital on Welfare Island. Like a flock of birds, with song and cheer and twitterings, the Girl Scouts have descended, on an October afternoon, upon the inmates. Now gathering near one of the high, wide windows, for their annual Community Sing—led by a buxom yellow-haired girl, they went out across the corridor.

Out of the silence of their empty afternoons they come, the old and the young, in their washed-out dresses, the browns and grays that had faded on them for years. Back and forth, like figures in slow motion, they are rolled in their wheelchairs or are hobbling along the thickly linoleumed floor in uneven cautious little trots. Walking patients help others.

This is their outing, their hour-off from long and quiet wards. From a distance a voice, the strange, high-pitched voice of an Indian girl now joins in the chorus. Applause comes. Not always from their hands; in a warm murmur perhaps; in a face glazed with attention; mouths parted with pleasure and smiling. And there was something that continued uncaring on its own. Someone in a white head-scarf is leaning forward eating an orange; a fat girl with her arm round her friend whispering into her ear; a foot wriggling in the aisle to the rhythm of the tune. I looked around for Rosa. She belonged in another ward. Every day in her pink knitted sweater she would push her wheelchair along the long corridor—as if on a secret errand. Suddenly she stops, swings her chair from side to side, then a little to the left so to be closer to the young woman in the white dress who sits there erect and motionless for hours. A tilt of the head and Lillian's eyes dart recognition.

Without looking up, she lifts one of the lifeless hands clamped around the board that is attached to Lillian''s wheelchair. Beautiful, weightless hands. Elegantly aloof with their long, tapering fingers, the purplish enamelled fingernails and the faintest rosiness running underneath their paleness. Gently, without a word, Rosa draws the yielding hand toward her, pulling, easing each finger, then slowly spreading them around the board—one by one, relaxed now with the change of grip.

Their faces draw closer. Across a bridge of silence, love could only signal with their earnest eyes. Rosa turns away. Quietly as she came, she leaves as if it all had happened in the stillness of her heart, and not known to anyone.

Tea's Ready

BY TERESA O'CONNOR

LONDON'S BLEAK December night crouched outside our kitchen while my parents washed the dinner dishes. As the big oak table folded back into the paneled wall, my sister and I raced to the sitting room. We paused outside the towering, heavy door. From under the crack, firelight flickered and the crackling sound reached us and made me feel warm.

I ran in first; the shivering light made flitting and darting shadows on the warm, toast-colored walls, hid in the scrolled nooks of my father's chair, and gleamed on the smooth parquet floor. My little sister's blue eyes reflected the copper-colored light as she made shadows on the wall. I saw my own shadow, big and black and towering over me, sliding over the walls. It grew, mushroomlike, as I moved closer to the fire. I wanted my sister to be afraid and cry. The fire smelled like crisp burning leaves and warmed me like the hot-water bottle Mother tucked in the bottom of my bed every night.

My young mother, angular and short, walked in with a tray of hot tea. Her auburn hair and brown eyes, her rosy cheeks and thin pink lips, made her look like the autumn leaves on the mantelpiece. She set the white and orange cups on the round Indian brass table in front of the fireplace, and the cups shone in the shining table, wavering, like reflections on rippling water.

"The tea's ready," my mother called, and my father strode in. He leaned over the fire and warmed his long, calloused fingers. His blond hair splashed into his blue eyes, and he tossed his head back abruptly to keep it out.

I pulled the box-shaped stool my father had made in front of the fire and lifted up the brocaded, flowered top to take out some coal for the fading flames. I sat on the floor, my back against the stool, and warmed my feet. I'd keep them there as long as I could before it got too hot—like seeing how long I could hold a lighted match. My father sat in his big brown leather chair, with my sister on his lap, and read "Aladdin and the Magic Lamp" to us. As he read, he would pause to drink some tea, and the spoon tinkled against the saucer.

My eyelids fell shut and I snapped them open; I couldn't leave the glowing, copper life of the fire. But the night closed in, and my head fell back on the stool. I heard the muffled sound of teacups clinking, the clock on the mantelpiece chiming, the mellow, fluid voice of my father talking of the genie and magic. I felt the breathing of the fire on my feet, heard its sizzling gasps. And far, far away, the wind rattled against the windows. Then sleep whispered through the room and my arm fell to my side.

Homecoming

BY FRANCES DYLLER

D ARKNESS CLINGS to my palate; and in my nostrils, the
cloying musk of blackest night. The night is the pounding
of oceans in my ears and walls crumbling in silence in the
blackness behind my eyes. The night is my brother's death—the
death of my little one—my favorite—battering my senses, sizzling
against my flesh, gagging me with dry fuzz. I am creeping home
to my mother's womb, and I am afraid.

My footsteps are soundless. I am a ghost in a vacuum—a speck
of dust in a vast, toppling balloon. It is August outside, but here
it is bleakest December. My brother is under the ground, and I
shall die if it snows on him.

*His face was round and always dirty, with cheeks like vinyl,
and almost no chin at all. His hair was soft and brown, always
on his forehead, down almost to the shaggy brows that ran into
one another. And his eyes—deep brown, glowing almond eyes
dance, like flames, into my memory, and burn me.*

*He would stroke my face with pudgy fingers. He would clasp
his arms behind my knees and grunt, trying to lift me. He would
clasp his arms around my waist in a bear hug, and I would cry
that he was breaking my ribs.*

The balloon lurches, spinning my feet to the pavement. Here
is the tenement which spat me out. It is ready to swallow me again.
I bite my lip and taste the blood of my existence. I step over the
threshold.

The lobby is dim and it is grey like the inside of my agony. It
is part of me; it moves with me; it is as if I have never left it.

The lobby has not changed; it has not grown up or grown old.
Cupid stands on his pedestal in mottled bronze, reaching for an

338

arrow. His belly is fat; his navel protrudes. He has appeared ready to topple over on himself for these twenty years.

I run toward the stairs; my heels click the tiled floor. I skip; they double-click. My little one is dead and I am skipping. I am the embodiment of evil. I am the embodiment of darkness. My throat is parched.

One . . . two . . . three . . . The steps are dirty white marble: I recognize the dirt. It never changes.

Eleven . . . twelve . . . I have never climbed these steps without counting them. There used to be forty.

My legs throb. I feel as though I am trudging on foam rubber. I walk more slowly. Thirty-two . . . thirty-three . . . It is inexorable I will be there soon. I will look into their faces. I will see their torment and it will strengthen or destroy me.

II

These are my family, and they are sitting shiva. I am shivering in the doorway. They will notice me in a moment.

The living room is large and square with a high ceiling and green panelled walls. In one corner, the corner that has always been empty, stand baskets of fruit and candies covered with garish orange cellophane.

The sofa is a memory from my childhood. It is faded and frayed and the dirty tan cushions sag. Once, when I was young and immortal, it was re-covered, and I would sit on the floor for hours and look at it, for it was the most beautiful sofa in the whole world.

On the end-table burns the eight-day candle, yellow wax in a tall glass, a Star of David pasted on the side. Its flame jumps and dances a nervous ritual. The top of the glass is black with carbon.

The mirrors are covered with the tired sheets of a long marriage. It is somber here. I am growing tired. I could almost sleep.

My father sits on a hardwood stool in the corner—away from the rest. His head and his shoulders are bowed, and he is an old man. His face is dotted with black and gray stubble; his cheeks are gaunt. He rocks slowly back and forth, his arms scissored across his chest, embracing himself.

In a cluster sit my mother, my two sisters, and my only brother. (I have but one brother now. How strange! How terrifying!)

They look alike, these four. Their puffy, red-rimmed eyes, set in deep hollows, burn into one another. My sister holds my mother's hand in her lap and strokes it. The hand is small and round with loose flesh and knotted blue veins, twitching. I shall take this hand to my lips and I will hold it there.

There is a hush. They see me. They are coming toward me, and their eyes are not surprised that I have come.

My mother holds out to me a black ribbon like they are wearing over their hearts.

There is a stillness in the center of me, spreading outward. My tears flow warm, and my vision is growing dim. My face is covered with kisses.

I have come and I will comfort you. I am strong and I know your torment and it is my torment and I will urge it gently from your hearts.

I am sleepy now and I am warm.

The Lesson

BY ROSE WOLFSON

THE WOMAN at the white enamel sink scraped the silvery fish with short, hard strokes of a wide black-handled knife. Now and then she paused to listen, or turned to look at the blue electric clock above the high white refrigerator in the center alcove of the big, airy kitchen. Her steel-gray eyes were small, fringed by thick black eyelashes that contrasted sharply with amber-blond hair, worn in a tight bun.

Between the woman and the refrigerator stood a large round table, covered with a white tablecloth, hand scalloped in blue at the edges. Two bronze candlesticks, polished mirror-bright, glowed like an altar centerpiece on the table. Six straight-backed chairs surrounded the table, and a seventh stood off in a corner under a white wall cabinet. Diagonally across from the sink, a closed door led to a backyard garden. Through the glistening half-window of the door, she could see the drying russet remnants of summer plants and a fading, thorny bower on which a few thin clusters of tiny red roses still clung.

The woman turned back to her scraping, her thin, small mouth pressed into a narrow pink line. She was not really tall, yet she looked tall, with a fine slender neck and erect posture that gave her an air of distinction even in the coarse white apron that protected her paisley dress. Her figure, mature with much child-bearing, was broad; yet here, too, the long curves and firm roundness lent an illusion of height.

With a final jerk, the woman plopped the carp onto the wooden board on top of the enamel drain, and dried her hands on a damp, frayed towel on a three-pronged rack above the sink. On the topmost prong hung a fresh blue scalloped towel. She looked at the clock again. Three thirty. Thin muffled voices and squeaking sounds like a door on dry hinges reached the woman.

With tightening lips she moved away from the sink and peered down the long dark hall that led to the street door. But the sounds subsided and others came, unmistakable: the *tillop, tillop* of horse's hooves and the husky call of a vendor, "Vege-tables! Vege-tables!" That would be Goodman, the woman thought. No matter how many times the police told him he wasn't allowed to peddle on 140th Street, every afternoon he was here. Sometimes she felt like calling the police herself. What was the use of moving to a better neighborhood and paying so much money if you had a market here too? Soon there would be corner tramps and loafers like on Brook Avenue and everywhere in the Bronx. She frowned, her nostrils widening.

It was no good asking Saul to speak to Goodman, to warn him. "Listen Annie," Saul had said, "he has to make a living, too." That's how it is when you have a husband who's always crying over somebody else's trouble, she concluded, then asked herself silently, "And who cries for us when our house is burning?" Just as though it wasn't enough to try and raise five children.

As she walked back to the sink, she darted a glance at the clock again. Three thirty-five. She stood undecided, looking from the fresh salt-smelling fish to a thick coil of hard rope intended for

341

the new clothesline in the yard. It lay on the nearby window sill. The early autumn sun, moving westward, slanted through the iron bars at the window, and traced a shadowy frame for the rope. The outside door slammed, a loud metallic crash, and light footsteps sounded down the hall. Sure of herself now, the woman grasped the knife and returned to the fish.

"'lo." A short, blond boy of fifteen, with red-rimmed blue eyes, a small sloping nose and lantern jaw came into the kitchen. He carried three books held tightly together with a stained hemp strap. Except for his dust-covered oxfords, he was neatly dressed in gray mackinaw and blue kickerbockers.

The woman did not turn. Methodically she pried the point of the knife into the carp's neck and started slitting its belly. "Vere vas you 'til now?"

"In school." The boy waited, his gaze on his mother's back.

"You got homework?" She went on slitting the fish. A ripple of uneasiness passed over his face, and he hesitated, blinking his red-rimmed eyes.

"Yeh, but it's Friday so I don't have to do it right away." He shifted his weight from one foot to the other, still watching his mother's back. When she was silent, he turned quickly toward the hall.

"Liar!" She turned now, her hand trembling and still holding the knife. "I asked you vere you vas." The boy stood glued to the threshold. "Answer me!"

"I—I told you," he said, avoiding her eyes.

"Don't lie to me," she cried, shaking the knife at him, then suddenly aware of what she was holding, threw it into the sink, with a clatter. "I vant to know vere you vas all the time. Do you hear?"

"I don't know what you're talking about," the boy said in a low voice, one side of his long face twitching.

"Liar!" she said again, fumbling in her apron pocket. "I vas in school today. They told me. One month you vasn't there. Three cards already they sent. This one you didn't find." She held out a post card with typewritten lines on it. "One month! One month, you rotten little stinker, you ate breakfast and got lunch and made out you vent to school. I vant to know vere you vas all this time.

Vat you done. Talk." The boy said nothing. Her hands clenched in tight fists, she took a few steps toward him.

"In the park," he said hastily.

"Vere in the park?"

"Just in the park. We walked around."

"Ve? Vith who did you go?"

"Just—some boys from the school—you don't know them." He looked down at the floor.

"Du—" she started in Jewish, then checked herself. "You're lying," she went on in English, "you vas vith that gangster Curly and his good-for-nohting brother, vasn't you?" She was shouting now, and when the boy was silent, she screamed, "Come here!" He looked up then, his face twitching. "You're gonna tell me the truth if I break every bone in your rotten body. Do you hear?"

They faced each other across the room, the boy still near the doorway. He cleared his throat, "I told you the truth. I was in the park with boys from school."

A surge of blood turned her face a mottled red. Springing toward the window, she seized the coil of rope and dashed towards the boy, whipping the ends through the air. He backed off, but she caught him across the thick padding of the mackinaw.

"I'll kill you before you'll be a bum and a crook like them," she screamed, whirling the rope again. This time she brought it down across his legs. Gasping with pain, he let go his books, jumping aside to avoid her. But she followed him, again and again flailing his legs until he seemed to dance a broken jig. "Fifteen years ve vorked for you—to send you to school—to give you something to eat—your father carries a pack on his back and cleans toilets so you can learn, curse you, and you make this shame for us. Better you should be dead. With no one else ve got trouble, only you. You don"t vant to go to school? Then go to hell." She stopped to catch her breath. The boy, white and trembling, was crying silently, a stream of tears running down his cheeks. For a moment there was only the sound of the woman's sucking breath and the boy's uneven breathing. "Now you listen to me," she said more quietly, "if you don't vant to be honest and decent, if you're gonna go vith those gangsters, I'll send you up the river. Rot there." The boy stared at her, beads of sweat forming under his hair. "And I'm telling you this, until you're tventy-one, I got the say over you, and until you're tventy-one, I say you'll go to school. Do you understand?" She shook the coiled rope at him, the ends dangling like a severed noose.

The street door gave its metallic clang, and a young girl's voice called, "Hey Simmy, you're gonna catch it, mom—" A slim, dark-haired girl, in a red coat, taller but younger than her brother, appeared in the doorway. Her large hazel gaze went from the boy's pale, streaked face to the woman's flushed one, then to the rope in her hand. The girl's eyes widened, and she caught her lower lip between her teeth. Suddenly the boy bent down to get his books which had scattered in the fall, his head low. Without a word, the girl crouched to help him.

The woman looked as though she was about to say something, then abruptly turned away from the boy and girl bent over together.

Biographical Notes

WILLIAM ALFRED was born in New York City on August 16, 1922, the son of a bricklayer. He grew up in upper Manhattan and Brooklyn, attending St. Anne's Academy, Holy Innocents' School, and St. Francis Preparatory School. In 1940 he entered Brooklyn College, where he received training in poetry under the gifted and brilliant teacher, James Meagher. Inducted into the Army in January, 1943, Mr. Alfred served in Dutch East New Guinea and the Philippines. After his discharge from the Army in 1946, Mr. Alfred returned to Brooklyn College, where he received his B.A. in 1948. He received his M.A. from Harvard in 1949 and his Ph.D. in 1954. He is now associate professor of English at Harvard. In 1954 Mr. Alfred's verse drama, *Agamemnon*, which he had written while studying under Archibald MacLeish, was published by Knopf. Mr. Alfred's poems have appeared in *American Poet, Atlantic, Commonweal, New Voices 2*. His first long poem, *The Annunciation Rosary*, was published in 1948. Mr. Alfred's most recent verse drama *Hogan's Goat*, from which "Stand by Me, Kate" (hitherto unpublished) is taken, is his first extended treatment of a modern secular theme.

REX ASHLOCK was born August 23, 1918, in Spokane, Washington. He attended the North Central High School in Spokane, University of Washington, 1937-38, California School of Fine Arts, 1940-43, and University of California (Fine Arts), 1951, 1954, and 1956. He has two children, Margaret, eighteen, and Peter, fourteen. A painter and teacher of painting for many years, Mr. Ashlock has only recently turned to writing. In recent years Faulkner, Durrell, Camus, and Hesse have been most influential in his thinking about literature as visualization. "The Snowstorm" is his first published professional sketch.

ELIZABETH BARTLETT was born July 20, 1911, in New York City, where she attended Evander Childs High School and Teachers College, receiving her B.S. in 1931. During her teaching experience in New Jersey, New York, Texas (Southern Methodist University), and California (where she is now assistant professor of English at San Jose College), Mrs. Bartlett began to write poetry and stories which found gradual acceptance. Over two hundred of Mrs. Bartlett's poems have appeared in journals and anthologies, among them *Harper's, Saturday Review, The New York Times, New Mexico Quarterly, Yale Literary Magazine, New Story, New Voices 2*. Poetry to Mrs. Bartlett "creates new connections between the personal and the physical worlds, thus extending our view of both worlds and intensifying our sentient response to them."

PAUL BARTLETT was born in Moberly, Missouri, in July 1909, attended Ithaca High School, Oberlin College, University of Arizona, and various art schools in Mexico, where he lived and worked for many years. Mr. Bartlett began to write because he sought to be an innovator; for him "innovation is synonymous with mental freedom." The artist, Mr. Bartlett finds, is inhibited at every turn by the

345

necessity of earning a living: "Economic pressure is the bludgeon of all creativity." From the beginning Mr. Bartlett has combined painting and writing. His writing reflects his intense preoccupation with the imagery of color and all sensory response. Mr. Bartlett's first novel, *When the Owl Cries,* was published by Macmillan in 1959, and received high praise from the critics. His stories have appeared, among other journals, in *Accent, Arizona Quarterly, Kenyon Review,* and *Southwest Review.*

SYLVIA BORDAN was born in Canada and attended high school in Montreal. In 1950 she received her B.A. from Sir George Williams College. Afterward she became an elementary school teacher in New York City, where she wrote an article under a pseudonym about her experiences. "The Bundle and the Reed" is her first published sketch in the field of creative writing.

CHARLES EDWARD BRYAN was born June 28, 1936, in Saratoga, New York. He attended St. Michael's High School in Brooklyn, and was graduated from Brooklyn College in 1961. From age nineteen to twenty-one Mr. Bryan served in the United States Navy. He is now employed as editorial assistant in *Time.* "Through the August Night" is Mr. Bryan's first published professional writing. "A moment in literature," he writes, must be one "of vision, of confrontation, of truth, of wonder."

JOHN BURRESS was born December 31, 1911, in Halls, Tennessee; a part of his boyhood was spent in the small town of Senath, Tennessee. When the family moved north, Mr. Burress attended high school in Braddock, Pennsylvania. After two years in the Coast Guard, and marriage to Janet Young in 1941, Mr. Burress settled in New York City, where he attended the New School and devoted himself to finishing his novel, *Little Mule,* which was received with unanimous acclaim by the critics when it was published in 1952. Three other novels since that time have been similarly well received: *Apple on a Pear Tree, The Missouri Traveler,* and *Bugle in the Wilderness.* The selection in this volume is from an unpublished novel on which Mr. Burress is now working. The theme of the novel grew from the author's question to himself, "What would happen if a normal mind found itself trapped in a monster's body?" Now living in New Jersey, Mr. Burress commutes daily to New York to his work as a buyer of display materials for the J. C. Penny Company.

NORMA COHEN was born August 23, 1937, in Brooklyn. She attended Tilden High School, Brooklyn College, and the New School. Her desire to write has been intense and continuous from childhood. Authors who have been most influential in her development have been Rilke, Scharmel, Thoreau, Picard, Romain Rolland. "Before the Last Exam" is Miss Cohen's first published professional sketch.

BEATRICE F. CONRAD was born in Philadelphia. She attended Forest Hills High School and Hunter College. A high school English teacher, Mrs. Conrad is the mother of twins, Allan and Susan, age nine. Her poems and stories have been previously published in various anthologies, including *New Voices 4,* edited by Dr. Charles Glicksberg.

ALBERT G. CRAZ was born in New York City on June 26, 1926. He attended Brooklyn Technical High School and received his A.B. degree from Middlebury in

1950; his M.A. degree from Breadload Summer School of English in 1955. An English teacher in Sleepy Hollow High School, North Tarrytown, New York, Mr. Craz has been writing for many years. The authors most influential in his development as writer and critic have been Chaucer, Hemingway, Faulkner, and Conrad. "All people are significant," writes Mr. Craz, "if only to themselves. In each is a marvelous mixture of the strange with the valid." "Montauk Herman" is Mr. Craz' first published professional sketch.

EUGENE N. DOHERTY was born October 28, 1922, in Hammond, Indiana. He attended Thomas Jefferson High School, Elizabeth, New Jersey, and earned his B.A. at Rutgers University in 1953. An amputee veteran of World War II, Mr. Doherty served in the Marine Corps from August, 1943, to June, 1946, in South Pacific and China. Mr. Doherty lives in Somerville, New Jersey, and teaches English in the Valley Road School, Princeton. "Proud Words" is his first published sketch.

MARGARET DRURY was born July 16, 1908, in Montclair, New Jersey. After graduation from high school in Montclair, she attended Parsons Art School in New York. Now living in Princeton, Mrs. Drury and her husband John have two daughters, Susan, twenty-three, and Glennis, nineteen. In recent years, Mrs. Drury has found inspiration to write in the classes of Dr. Charles Glicksberg and Caroline Gordon. They taught her "not to think up plots" but to develop the ideas "ready and waiting inside me." Among the authors who have most influenced her, Mrs. Drury mentions Nancy Hale, and particularly her earlier stories.

FRANCES DYLLER was born October 31, 1938, in Brooklyn. She attended Erasmus Hall High School and received the B.A. degree from Brooklyn College. Now married to Jerry Dyller, a talented engineer, and living in Brooklyn, Mrs. Dyller is the mother of a son Barry, age two. "Homecoming" is her first published professional sketch.

JACK FIELDS was born in Philadelphia, September 9, 1916. As a child he lived in over fifteen foster homes in and around Philadelphia. He attended the Simon Gratz High School in New York. In 1950 he received the B.A. and M.A. degree from New York University. An English teacher in Great Neck High School, Mr. Field is married and has two daughters. A combat veteran of World War II (Southwest Pacific), Mr. Fields served as editor of *Yank* while he was in the Philippines, and contributed articles to *Salute* magazine with which he worked as editor after the war.

EMILY GRECO was born in the Bronx, the daughter of a designer who had migrated from Italy. As a child she attended elementary schools in the Bronx and Bensonhurst, later graduating from Bay Ridge High School. Working as a secretary, Miss Greco took evening courses at City College, New York University, and the New School. In 1949 she studied at the University of Florence in Italy. Miss Greco's writing appeared previously in *American Vanguard, 1952.*

BARBARA ANN GREVER was born in New York on January 14, 1928. She attended Forest Hills High School and later Beloit College, the Sorbonne, University per Straniseri (Perugia), the New School, Columbia. The writers who have had most influence on Miss Grever's creative development have been Sigrid Undset, Jean Giono, Jacques Cousseau. Mr. Lurton Blassingame has been a highly perceptive critic of her work. Though Miss Grever's father, Otto Lambert Grever, a noted poster artist, died when she was seven, she remembers him vividly, and his "art spirit" has had a profound influence on her career.

GWYNNETH FAIRE GROBIN was born December 1, 1933, in New York City. She attended Walton High School, Brooklyn College, New York University, and the New School. The writers who have influenced Miss Grobin in greatest degree are Proust, Faulkner, and Malcolm Lowry. Miss Grobin is married to Mr. Robert Weiss, attorney. "The Seed of a Giant" is her first published story.

HELEN HUDSON was born in New York City and now lives in Connecticut. She received her undergraduate degree from Bryn Mawr, her doctorate from Columbia. Stories by Dr. Hudson are to appear this fall and winter in *Sewanee Review* and *Stories for the Sixties.*

MILDRED MESURAC JEFFREY was born November 19, 1913, in Brooklyn. She attended Richmond Hill High School and was graduated A.B. from Hunter College in 1935 and M.A. from Adelphi College in 1935. She has also done graduate work at City College, Teachers College, University of Colorado, and the New School. Wife, mother, and instructor in English (Hofstra College), Mrs. Jeffrey has two children: Charles, eighteen, and Kathleen, thirteen. Mrs. Jeffrey has been working intermittently many years on a novel in which the heroine of "Persephone Lost" is the main character.

KENNETH JENKINS was born in Elizabeth, New Jersey. He attended Thomas Jefferson High School and was graduated B.A. from Columbia College in 1952 and M.A. from Teachers College in 1953. A teacher at Southside High School, Rockville Centre, and formerly a newspaper reporter, Mr. Jenkins is married to the former Elizabeth Hunte and is the father of five children: Roland, ten; Rod, seven; Howard, four; Rebecca, two; and Leah, two months (as we go to press). Mr. Jenkins writes: "Despite the most intimate relationships, people live isolated, separate lives touching at only scattered points the lives of others. This relationship between people, as well as the turbulent interior life of the individual, provides the writer with his greatest intensity."

ALVIN JOHNSON was born in Homer, Nebraska, December 18, 1874. He was graduated A.B. from University of Nebraska in 1897 and A.M. in 1898. In 1902 he received his doctorate from Columbia. Dr. Johnson served as tutor of Greek in the University of Nebraska and later as professor of economics at the same university. He also taught economics at University of Chicago, Stanford University, Cornell, and Columbia. From 1917 to 1923 he was associate editor of *The New Republic;* and from 1928 to 1934 associate editor of *Encyclopedia of the Social Sciences.* Dr. Johnson was director of the New School from 1922 to 1946, and since that time has served as president emeritus. In the 1930's Dr. Johnson led a movement to rescue persecuted scholars from Europe, a rescue financed by the Rockefeller Foundation and out of which grew the University in Exile. Besides many scholarly books and articles, Dr. Johnson has written two novels, *The Professor and the Petticoat,* 1914, and *Spring Storm,* 1936; an autobiography, *Pioneer's Progress,* 1952; and a volume of short stories, *The Battle of the Wild Turkey and Other Tales,* 1961. Dr. Johnson is the father of five daughters and two sons, all of whom have had distinguished careers. Dr. Johnson comes often to the New School from his apartment in Manhattan or his home in Nyack, where he has a large garden in which he renews his youth each spring.

DORA JEAN JOHNSON was born in Greenville, South Carolina, August 24, 1934. She attended Parker High School in Greenville, and was graduated B.S. from Winthrop College in 1957. Miss Johnson now works in New York City as an educational therapist with mentally ill children. The authors most influential in her development as a writer have been Carson McCullers and Thomas Wolfe. She has been previously published in *Lyric* magazine. Miss Johnson writes: "Life is at best a separate, sad, and brief blossom sustained at times only by the common root of pain, pleasure, suffering, and uncertainty which bind all men to this earth and to one another. Those who are hungry find no food between the covers of a book. All men are at some point in time voiceless. It is the duty of the writer to live with and work at the preservation of the human spirit."

ISMITH KHAN was born in Trinidad, British West Indies, in which city he attended Queen's Royal College. After migrating to the United States, he attended Michigan State University and was later graduated A.B. from the New School in 1955. Formerly a newspaper reporter, Mr. Khan now gives his full time to writing fiction. The authors most influential in his development have been Thomas Mann, Thomas Wolfe, and John Steinbeck. Mr. Khan's stories have appeared in the *Trinidad Guardian, New Voices 2, New Voices 3, Short Story,* and *Colorado Quarterly.* His novel, *The Jumbie Bird,* was published in England in 1961.

MILDRED MEYER KING was born in New York, March 15, 1930. She attended Jamaica High School, New York University, and the New School. In her development the most influential writers have been Stendhal, Huxley, and Durrell. Mrs. King's sketches in this volume are her first published professional work. She writes: "To me the most important step in writing is to break down the wall of secrecy which prevents one from expressing himself fully. . . . Though I kept chipping away at this wall, fear kept it from cracking and crumbling. Now, after about a year of inner struggle, I find I'm breaking through."

CLAUDE F. KOCH was born in Philadelphia, November 28, 1918. He attended Northeast Catholic High School and was graduated B.S. from La Salle College in 1940. He has done graduate work at Niagara University, University of Pennsylvania, and University of Florida, from which he received the M.A. in 1956. Mr. Koch served in the United States Marine Corps from 1941 to 1946, mainly in the south and central Pacific. He was company officer and is now a retired major in the Corps. An associate professor at La Salle College, Mr. Koch is the busy father of six children: Michael, fifteen; Christopher, fourteen; Stephen, thirteen; Gerard, twelve; Mark, eleven; and Mary Jo, ten. The writers most influential in shaping his style and creative outlook have been William Butler Yeats and Willa Cather. Among contemporaries, he is most indebted to Andrew Lytle and "young men like Hatton Burke who worked with him at the University of Florida in 1955-56. . . . I write to understand in a shapely manner, and (as Dante wrote) 'joy is a whip to the top.'" Mr. Koch has completed two novels, *Island Interlude,* under a Dodd Mead fellowship; and *Light in Silence,* under a *Sewanee Review* fellowship.

PETER KOTSOGEAN was born in Bellingham, Washington, August 10, 1916. He attended Whatcom High School in Bellingham, the U.S. Naval Academy, University of Washington (B.A., 1942), and Columbia University (M.A., 1949). During World War II Mr. Kotsogean served with the United States Navy. He has lived in Egypt, Japan, and Greece for extended periods of time. The most important authors in his development have been Dostoievski and Thomas Mann. Now living in New York after long stays abroad, Mr. Kotsogean gives his full time to writing and has completed one novel. "Anemones" is his first published professional story.

ARLYNE KRUM was born in New York, June 19, 1936. She attended William Cullen Bryant High School, Vassar College, New York University (B.A.), and the New School. Miss Krum now teaches English in a junior high school in Astoria. "The Door Clicked Shut" is her first published professional sketch.

RAE MAGAZINE was born in Poland. Upon migrating to America she attended Brooklyn College and the New School. The authors most influential in shaping her style have been Thomas Hardy, Katherine Mansfield, Dostoievski, Thomas Wolfe, and Joseph Conrad. Wife of Dr. Joseph Magazine, Mrs. Magazine is the mother of two children, David, nineteen, and Sara Beth, fifteen. An excerpt from Mrs. Magazine's novel appeared in *New Voices 4*, edited by Dr. Charles Glicksberg.

ANN McGOVERN was born May 25, 1930, in New York City. She attended Julia Richman High School and the University of New Mexico. Mrs. McGovern has one son, Peter, age twelve. She works as assistant editor of the Arrow Book Club for the *Scholastic*. Mrs. McGovern is the author of a number of children's books, but "Wonder Is Not Precisely Knowing" is her first professional story for older readers.

SHEILA M. McMAHON was born in Southampton, May 28, 1937. She attended Southampton High School, St. Vincent's Hospital School of Nursing (R.N.), St. John's University, and the New School. Wife of Kevin Guidera, a teacher of mathematics, Mrs. McMahon is the mother of two children, Kerin, age three, and Regan, age one. Encouragement from high school teachers of writing and Mrs. McMahon's work as a nurse (she still works part time as an R.N. in pediatrics) have stimulated her desire to achieve professional competence. "The day came, about a year ago, that the thought of what could have been did not comfort me, and I gathered the courage to find out whether or not I could write anything of note." Written in Dr. Glicksberg's class, "The First Stars Were Shining" is Mrs. McMahon's first published sketch.

MARION MONTGOMERY was born April 16, 1925, in Thomaston, Georgia. He attended the Robert E. Lee Institute in Thomaston, the University of Georgia (A.B., M.A.) and the State University of Iowa. Mr. Montgomery is now assistant professor of English at the University of Georgia. In World War II Mr. Montgomery served in the army, 1943-1946. Mr. Montgomery's first novel, *The Wandering of Desire*, was published by Harper in 1962; his first volume of poems, *Dry Lightning*, was published in 1960. His poems and stories have also been published widely in quarterly journals and anthologies, among them *New Mexico Quarterly, New World Writing,* and *Modern Age.*

H. L. NEWBOLD was born in High Point, North Carolina, November 3, 1921. He attended high school in Richmond and Newport News, Virginia. Dr. Newbold received his B.S. and M.D. from Duke University. He also attended William and Mary College, University of Chicago, Northwestern University, University of Illinois, University of Minnesota, and the Sorbonne. In 1946-47, Dr. Newbold served as first lieutenant in the Marine Corps. While practicing psychiatry in Chicago, Dr. Newbold turned to creative writing; later, he went to Paris, and there gave his whole time to fiction. After writing and publishing some eight novels under a pen name, Dr. Newbold wrote a novel of deeper purpose in *One-Third of an Inch of French Bread,* published by Thomas Y. Crowell under his own name in 1960. Dr. Newbold is now combining writing with the practice of psychiatry, and is living again in North Carolina.

TERESA O'CONNOR was born June 17, 1943, in London. When her family migrated to America, she attended Erasmus Hall High School and later enrolled at Brooklyn College. Her favorite authors are Dylan Thomas and Gerard Manley Hopkins. "Tea's Ready" is her first published professional writing.

VINCENT PATRICK was born in New York City, January 19, 1935. He attended high school in New York and was graduated from New York University with a B.S. in mechanical engineering in June, 1961. Mr. Patrick now works in San Jose, California, as a design engineer on automatic machinery. He is married and has two sons, Glen and Richard. He was previously published in *New Voices 4,* edited by Dr. Charles Glicksberg.

JEANNE PFEIFFER was born in Vienna, Austria, in 1894. A widow, Mrs. Pfeiffer is the mother of two sons: John, author of *The Human Brain* and other notable books; and Andrew, designer of surgical instruments. For many years Mrs. Pfeiffer coached her own group of actors and actresses, the Federation Players. The authors most influential in shaping her style have been Gogol, Stendhal, Conrad, Forster, Rilke, the Goncourt brothers, and Dostoievski. Mrs. Pfeiffer writes: "I really started writing about eight years ago. In a state of worry and anxiety I had to fasten onto something. The intensity of writing became for me a fighting weapon: rebuild, retrieve, recover."

LILY PORITZ was born in Cape Town, South Africa. Miss Poritz attended Durfee High School, Fall River, Massachusetts, was graduated from the Fay School, Boston, and later studied at the American Academy of Dramatic Arts and the New School. Her first play, *My Star of Hope,* was performed at the New School in 1959, and her second play, *The Proud Lady,* received honorable mention in the National Collegiate Playwriting Contest sponsored by Samuel French. Miss Poritz now works in the editorial department of the Macmillan Company, book publishers.

MAURICE POSNER was born in Wilkes-Barre, Pennsylvania, August 3, 1913. He attended Groton High School, Yonkers, and was graduated B.A. from New York University in 1939. In World War II Mr. Posner served five years as captain of ordinance. He and Mrs. Posner now live in New York City, where he works as a structural draftsman. Mr. Posner's first published story, "The Feast of the Passing Over," in the writing of which he had the criticism of Dr. Ernest Wright, appeared in 1953 in *New Voices: American Writing Today*. Of his creative aim Mr. Posner writes: "I should like to reveal the contrariety behind apparent harmony, to point out the disparity between our cultural values as professed and as practiced, to disclose the underthrust of violence and self-seeking beneath all the forms of our institutional life. Through wit, satire, and wrath, we can repudiate the educative factors of our life, and perhaps begin anew."

RAMONA ROBINSON was born July 11, 1927, in Maywood, California. She attended high school in Huntington Park, California, and attended the University of California at Los Angeles, 1944-1946, as a music major. Wife of Mr. David Goldman, Miss Robinson has worked as singer in churches and synagogues, as actress in summer stock and on Broadway in "Pajama Game," and as an editorial secretary. "Carousel" is her first published sketch.

AMANDA ROWE was born in Massachusetts, April 30, 1931. She was graduated from Boston University in 1953 and received the M.A. in education from Yale University in 1954. In 1955 she attended summer school at Oxford University. Now a high school English teacher in Arlington, Virginia, Miss Rowe is working on a novel of which "Where No Sea Runs" is the first chapter. The present selection is Miss Rowe's first published professional writing.

JULIET TOUBIN SAUNDERS was born in New York in August, 1922. She attended Walton High School and was graduated B.A. from New York University. Mrs. Saunders took various courses also at Tufts, Columbia University, and Boston University. Wife of Jason Saunders, professor of philosophy, Mrs. Saunders is the mother of two children, Rachel, six, and Mitchell, eleven. She has been twice listed by Martha Foley among distinctive writers of American short stories. Her stories have been published in *Matrix, Carolina Quarterly, University of Kansas City Review,* and *New Voices.*

WILLIAM M. SHEPPARD was born in Coulsdon, Surrey, England, February 12, 1928. He attended Malvern College in Worcestershire and was graduated from the Royal Military Academy Sandhurst in August, 1948, where he was commissioned second lieutenant in the Royal Artillery. Mr. Sheppard served five years in the British Army. The writers most influential in shaping his style have been Steinbeck and Dickens. Though Mr. Sheppard has written articles for his regimental maga-zine, and a documentary on cancer called "The Mystery of the Human Cell," produced in San Francisco in 1948, "The Evening Paper" is his first published writing of creative merit. Mr. Sheppard has worked as an actor, singer, pianist, producer of television programs.

FRANCES SILVERBERG was born in Baltimore, Maryland, October 29, 1916. She attended Julia Richman High School and New York University. Mrs. Silverberg is married and has a son, Barry Seligman, age twenty-five. "Rebecca by Any Other Name" is Mrs. Silverberg's first published sketch of professional merit.

HOLLIS SUMMERS was born in Eminence, Kentucky, June 21, 1916. He attended Madisonville High School in Kentucky and was graduated A.B. from Georgetown College in 1937. He received the M.A. from Bread Loaf School of English in 1943 and his doctorate from State University of Iowa in 1949. Serving now as professor of English at Ohio University, Dr. Summers is married to Laura Vimont Clark and is the father of two sons, Hollis, seventeen, and David, thirteen. Dr. Summers is author of three novels, *City Limit* (1948; Bantam Books edition, 1949); *Brighten the Corner* (1957); *The Weather of February* (1957). In 1954 Dr. Summers edited *Kentucky Story, A Collection of Short Stories,* for the University of Kentucky Press. In 1950 Dr. Summers edited, with Edward Whan, *Literature: An Introduction.* He has written two volumes of poetry, *The Walks Near Athens* (Harper, 1959) and *Someone Else* (Lippincott, 1962). Dr. Summers is also the author of numerous short stories published in anthologies and quarterly journals, including *New World Writing, Accent, New Voices 2, Sewanee Review, Midland, Colorado Quarterly, Prairie Schooner, Chicago Review.* His poems have been published in many literary quarterlies and magazines, such as *The Saturday Review, American Scholar,* and *Antioch Review.* Dr. Summers is indebted for the shaping of his style mainly to the poets of the seventeenth and twentieth centuries.

HELEN TENNEY was born October 24, 1910, in New York. She attended Newtown High School, Hunter College (evening), and Columbia University Extension. A widow, Mrs. Tenney is the mother of two sons, Robert, age twenty, now a junior at Fordham University; and James, age sixteen, now a senior at Fort Hamilton High School. Literary influences on Mrs. Tenney have been diverse: Dickens and Thackeray, Sagan, Salinger, Steinbeck, and Faulkner. "Stranger at a Wake" is Mrs. Tenney's first published sketch.

SALLY THOMPSON was born April 21, 1921, in Dallas, Texas. She attended high school in Tucson and Phoenix, Arizona, and Coatesville, Pennsylvania. Mrs. Thompson was graduated B.A. from University of Pennsylvania in 1943. Wife of Henry LaRue Thompson, Jr., Mrs. Thompson is the mother of two children, Ted, fourteen, and Susan, eleven. Among contemporary writers, Mrs. Thompson is most indebted to Flannery O'Connor, Carson McCullers, and J. D. Salinger. Mrs. Thompson's first novel, *The Keener Love,* was published by McDowell, Obolensky in 1960, and in England by Anthony Gibbs and Phillips in 1962. "The writer by nature," says Mrs. Thompson, "is torn between observation and an aversion to judge. Engaged in watching from the outside, he is yet compelled by a paradoxical compassion to feel deeply over what he sees inside."

OCTAVIA WALDO was born in Philadelphia, where she attended Overbrook High School and was graduated from Temple University. Later she received a Fulbright Fellowship and attended the Academy of Fine Arts in Rome. Married to Dr. Norman Locke, Miss Waldo is artist and teacher as well as writer. Miss Waldo's work has appeared earlier in *New Voices 4,* edited by Dr. Charles Glicksberg. Her first novel, *A Cup of the Sun,* was published by Harcourt, Brace in 1961.

EDWARD WALLANT was born October 19, 1926, in New Haven, Connecticut, the son of a soldier and salesman. After elementary and high school years at New Haven, Mr. Wallant attended the University of Connecticut, Pratt Institute, and the New School. In World War II Mr. Wallant served as gunner's mate on a destroyer. His present job is that of a commercial artist. "Talent," writes Mr. Wallant, "is to a large extent awareness, the sensitivity and receptivity to the world of man and nature." Mr. Wallant's distinguished first novel, *The Human Season* (Harcourt, Brace, 1960), was received with unanimous praise by the critics. His second novel, *The Pawnbroker* (Harcourt, Brace, 1961), served to place Mr. Wallant among the most superbly gifted writers of his generation. [Mr. Wallant died as this book was going to press, thus depriving America of an outstanding literary talent.]

ISABELLE MOHEL WEINBERG was born August 16, 1929, in Ellenville, New York. She attended high school in Ellenville, Miami Beach, Florida, and Indianapolis, Indiana. Mrs. Weinberg was graduated A.B. from Indiana University in 1950. For briefer periods she later attended the University of California at Los Angeles, University of Pennsylvania, Adelphi College, and the New School. Married to Dr. Hyman Weinberg, she is the mother of three children: Robert, age nine; Andrew, age seven; and David, age two. Mrs. Weinberg's stories were published in her university magazine, *Folio*. "An Empty Barrel," however, is her first published sketch of professional significance. "There is a moment," writes Mrs. Weinberg, "after writing about oneself and hearing a critic's impressions, when one feels discovered and understood beyond his own consciousness. At this moment loneliness is gone. That is why I try to write."

SALLY WEINRAUB was born March 29, 1924, in Manchester, England. She attended Withington Girls' School in Manchester. Married to Martin Weinraub, she is the mother of three children: Jacqueline, age twenty; David, age four; and Jennifer, age three. "Knifed with a Black Shadow" is Mrs. Weinraub's first published professional writing. In her judgment, the aim of the artist should be to portray "the flames burning in the apparently frozen, the sad weight of loss of innocence, faces that radiate simultaneously love and hate."

ROBERT WINNER was born February 3, 1930, in New York City. He was graduated from the Bronx High School of Science and in 1952 received the B.A. from Sarah Lawrence College. A composer of music, Mr. Winner has given fruitful study to the relationships of music to poetry and diction to painting. "Bowling Green, Manhattan" is one of his first poems of professional merit.

ROSE WOLFSON was born in New York, June 13, 1908. She attended Theodore Roosevelt High School and was graduated from New York University with the degree of B.S. In 1930 she received an M.A. from New York University, in 1948 the degree of Ph. D. Now a practicing psychologist, Dr. Wolfson is the author of various professional articles and book reviews of books on psychology. "The Lesson" is her first published work in creative writing.

CHAYYM ZELDIS was born in Buffalo, New York, October 7, 1927. He attended Central High School in Detroit, the University of Michigan, and later the New School. In his late teens Mr. Zeldis migrated to Israel, where he lived for many years with his wife, Malcah; his two children, David, ten, and Yona, five, were both born in Israel. Stories and poems by Mr. Zeldis have appeared in *Commentary, Accent, New Voices 4, Midstream, A Treasury of Jewish Poetry*. His first novel, *Streams in the Wilderness*, was published by Thomas Yoseloff in 1962.

354